# PROTEINS

## Their
## Chemistry and Politics

*AARON M. ALTSCHUL*

CHAPMAN AND HALL

LONDON

Copyright ©1965 by Basic Books, Inc.
*Manufactured in the United States of America*
DESIGNED BY VINCENT TORRE

CHAPMAN and HALL LTD.

*11 New Fetter Lane*

LONDON E. C. 4

*To Ruth's parents and mine*
*and to Uncle Nic*

# Foreword

THE IMPORTANCE OF nutrition, food science, and technology to national development is increasingly recognized by governments of developing countries. There now exists widespread evidence that malnutrition, particularly protein deprivation, early in life may produce, in addition to problems in public health, physical and mental stunting cumulatively detrimental to the over-all productivity and vigor of populations. Inadequate levels of protein in the diets of preschool children, beginning with weaning, are recognized as a major cause of high infant mortality. It is for these reasons that UNICEF — the United Nations agency whose special concern is the health and welfare of infants, children, and mothers of the world — welcomes the appearance of this timely and challenging discussion by Dr. Altschul of the nature of proteins and their significance in building a stronger rising generation.

UNICEF has always devoted considerable attention to providing milk to children, first from external sources and then to the processing and expanded use of indigenous milk supplies. In collaboration with FAO, assistance has been given toward construction and operation of some two hundred milk plants in various parts of the world. Nevertheless, in a number of countries, particularly those in the tropics, it will be impossible to meet the protein needs of the increasing numbers of infants and children by this

vii

traditional means alone. For this reason, UN agencies are assisting programs to provide low-cost, processed, protein-enriched foods capable of meeting in an economical manner the nutritional needs of children in low-income urban groups. The value and potential of local protein resources, particularly protein concentrates from oilseeds and fish, is receiving increasing recognition, not only by nutritionists, but by all who have become informed on this important subject.

There is a need for progress in the general areas of food science and engineering to solve problems which presently delay the rapid development of new protein-rich foods. It is in the dissemination of knowledge about new sources of protein that this book will provide a very valuable contribution.

MAURICE PATE
Executive Director
UNICEF

*United Nations*
*August 1964*

# Preface

THIS BOOK deals with diverse subjects which have in common the word "protein," yet it is not intended as a catalogue of the many ways of using this word. It deals with two important and related issues—the role of proteins in the human diet, and the problem of world protein supply. It provides an introduction for those who seek a view of the developments and frontiers in the chemistry and biochemistry of proteins.

Proteins are essential ingredients of all living things. One could choose to traverse all of biochemistry by following the consequences of protein chemistry and metabolism. Speculations on the origin of life start with attempts to explain the beginnings of proteins. The word protein is the key to exciting moments in science: enzymes—insulin—the alpha helix—protein evolution.

Proteins are a food. Much is known about the role of proteins in nutrition. Less is known about subtle relationships between diet and health, and the place, if any, of proteins in this picture. Yet there is a greater awareness among the general public that within this relationship might lie the opportunity to prolong life, improve health, and reduce the prevalence of ailments such as cancer and coronary heart disease. Such a situation can easily degenerate into food faddism and even chicanery. I do not pretend to offer simple answers; I seek merely to present the fundamentals of proteins in foods and the issues as they seem to be developing.

Less obvious is the connection between proteins and politics until it is recognized that protein is a foodstuff in short supply; unless we learn to provide sufficient protein for the present, there is little hope for feeding the anticipated thousands of millions of the future. Who can conceive of political stability in the face of hunger?

Those readers who have a special interest either in the role of proteins in the diet or in protein supply may wish to proceed directly to these sections. For them, the earlier sections of the book will provide background and clarification of obscure points. I would remind such readers that one cannot deal adequately with these aspects of proteins which affect the well being of people without somehow being aware of what proteins are.

I am indebted to my friends and associates for help in formulating concepts and for critical review and discussion; to my daughter Judy for editorial assistance; to my daughter Sandra and her husband Frank for cheering me on; and to my wife Ruth for infinite patience and sympathy during a job that took too long to finish.

New Orleans
July 1964

AARON M. ALTSCHUL

# Contents

CONTENTS                                              xii

# PROTEINS

# I

# INTRODUCTION

# CHAPTER 1

# Introducing Proteins

FROM THE very beginning of time, man recognized the need of an animal substance in his diet; without this he could not grow, stay well, or flourish. This may account in part for the important place of livestock and for the poverty of civilizations with little of animal substances in their diets. An early classification of foods might have been into those having an "animal principle" and those with a "vegetable principle," based on their source. These two classes behaved differently under conditions suitable for decomposition: the former putrified, and the latter fermented. It was only late in the eighteenth and the beginning of the nineteenth centuries that investigators discovered this so-called "animal substance" also in plants. Beccari in 1728 recognized an "animal principle" in plant products; he separated wheat into an "animal" part which is now known as gluten and a "plant" part which is starch. Eventually opinion began to settle on a class of substances which had the properties of this so-called animal material in common. These were named *proteins* ($\pi\rho\omega\tau\epsilon\iota\sigma$—preeminent—most important) by Mulder in 1838; they were found to be distributed universally in all living matter.

3

## Proteins as Food

Proteins[1] are a food just as are fats and carbohydrates, vitamins and minerals; yet there is something special and unique about proteins. We can understand this better by classifying the various types of foods. For example, we may classify foods according to the amount eaten—large amount daily or trace quantities; we may consider a particular food as an energy food, or we may be interested in special nutrients. Of course, the classification will depend in part on who eats the food—it will differ in particulars from species to species. For simple-stomached mammals, the answer will roughly be the same.

Most of the food eaten daily consists of carbohydrates, fats, and proteins. No other food material approaches any one of these in the quantity eaten; their total is exceeded only by the daily intake of water. This, then, is one property of proteins as food: proteins are a major foodstuff.

Some foods are primarily sources of energy (measured as calories). They furnish fuel for the normal physiological processes; they are used as eaten, and the excess is converted into storage forms of energy for later mobilization. Such is the principal fate of carbohydrates and fats; that portion which is not utilized for energy is converted into storage forms, glycogen or fat. Fat and carbohydrate are somewhat interchangeable as "fuelstuffs." Some people, for example, consume 40 percent of their calories as fat (the approximate average figure for the United States of America), while others eat less than 25 percent of their calories as fat, more of the energy coming from carbohydrate foods. The worldwide range of the amount of fat eaten per person per year is from 1 to 20 kilograms (approximately 2 to 40

1. Particularly in discourses on the subject of food or nutrition, the singular and plural of the word "protein" are interchanged. In such context, the word "protein" does not refer to a single chemical entity, but to the class of proteins comprising many individual members.

pounds). Proteins may also be metabolized for energy, and this happens when an excess of protein is eaten or when there are insufficient calories from other sources. As a source of energy they have the same value as carbohydrate, but utilization as energy is not the primary function of protein in foods.

Some foods furnish materials which are needed constituents of the body, such as calcium and phosphate in the bones and teeth, or which are part of the living and regulatory processes such as the vitamins and trace minerals. Even fats are needed to a minor extent for purposes other than energy; the so-called essential fatty acids are needed for proper body function, and fats generally promote the absorption of fat-soluble vitamins. Proteins are also in this class of foods, as they are primarily sources of "building blocks" for the protein of new tissue. Protein that is eaten is converted into the individual proteins of the organism— into the proteins of blood and muscle, the enzymes and hormones, the proteins of skin and hair. Some of the "building blocks," the *essential* amino acids, can come only from protein in food. If the supply of protein from food is cut off, synthesis of body protein is impaired and finally ceases.

Proteins as a food, then, are in a class by themselves. They are a major food but not a major "fuelstuff"; they supply essential ingredients but are required in much larger quantities than the vitamins, minerals, and essential fatty acids. We might say that we eat protein because we need protein, and we need substantial amounts because a substantial part of us is protein.

## Protein in Life

The word "protein" also calls to mind life processes and living things in general, for proteins are essential to all living processes; wherever there is life, there is protein. Hemoglobin of red cells, antibodies in the blood plasma, insulin and other hormones, hair, skin, muscle—all are proteins or are composed primarily of proteins. All enzymes, the biological catalysts which make possible the myriad of living processes, are proteins. Such, for example, are the digestive enzymes, or the enzymes of respiration which permit transfer of the energy of metabolism into muscle action, into the energy of synthesis of new matter, into heat energy, and for many other living functions—or the enzymes of the chloroplasts which harness the sun's energy in the complex of processes called photosynthesis.

The confluence of proteins and living things is the outcome of millions of years of evolutionary development. Consider the properties of living things, the enormous complexity of their chemical and physical operations, the versatility of man which enables him to withstand wide variations in environment and still maintain a stability of the *milieu intérieur.* This calls for a system of controls, of checks and balances, which can provide for orderly response to the multitude of stresses. Certainly it cannot be expected to be a simple system. But more is involved: some of the components of the complex system must themselves be complex to account for the selectivity, for the control, the direction, and the stability of the processes. Proteins were tailor-made to be complex components of complex systems. They are the solution by evolution to the problem of creating and maintaining mechanisms which we call living.

## Proteins as Chemicals

We must not suppose because proteins are so intimately connected with the living process that they themselves are mysterious, indefinite, vague sorts of things. Ever since 1828 when Friedrich Wöhler synthesized urea, the notion has been dispelled that chemicals contained in or produced by living matter were in any way different from chemicals not connected with living processes—they obeyed the same

chemical laws and responded similarly to chemical manipulations. Since then many natural substances have been synthesized from nonliving starting material; indeed, the building blocks of proteins, amino acids, have been synthesized
from petroleum derivatives. Proteins are chemical compounds, and are large in terms of molecular size; they are
polymers, which is the generic term for large molecular
compounds made up of chains of repeating units. The repeating units in proteins are the amino acids. Twenty of
these are found in various combinations to make up the
common proteins. A few others occur in some particular
proteins. All amino acids have some properties in common,
but each one has, in addition, its own individual characteristics which set it apart from the others. Since their relative amount in proteins can vary widely, their order as they
are linked together also varies widely, and since each protein
contains large numbers of amino acids, the number of possible combinations is enormous. The surprise is that the
number of known proteins is not astronomical and shows no
tendency to approach anywhere near the number of arith-
metically possible combinations.

No protein has as yet been synthesized chemically, but
the time is not long away when this will be done. Several
peptide hormones have been synthesized. One of these, the
β-corticotropic hormone (ACTH), contains 39 amino acids.
The complete amino acid sequence of the hormone insulin
has been elucidated by Sanger and his colleagues. This protein contains 17 different amino acids. The total number is
51. It has a molecular weight of 6000 and is considered a
small protein. Since Sanger's work the amino acid sequence
of several other proteins has been determined and the procedures for doing this have almost become standardized.

This, then, is a third aspect of proteins: they are well-
defined chemical compounds and their composition in
many instances is known, but their size is such that they
have an order of complexity approached by only a few other
chemical materials.

## Proteins in Nutrition

For the most part, the selection of ingredients of a meal is not based particularly or often on their composition or value as a food. Hidden in the recesses of folklore there may have been a selection, conscious or unconscious, of foods that were best adapted to the regions, to the peoples and their welfare. If so, the reasons have long since been forgotten and only the epicurean delight remains.

It is only in times of food stress that the ingredients of foods come in for attention. But more often than we are apt to recognize, there do exist in everyone's lifetime these special situations when the amount and kind of food become particularly important. Pregnancy and childhood put a stress on nutrition; so do illness and old age. Where there is insufficient food, there is an obvious nutritional strain, and choice of food from the limited resources becomes the more important. Livestock raising, for economic reasons, puts a strain on nutrition; the objective is to bring the animals to market at the lowest possible cost in labor and foodstuff. Protein is an important consideration in all of these problem areas.

The growth of the embryo puts a strain on the mother that must be met by increased consumption of food. And when the baby is born there is the extra requirement of food to support lactation. Growth is most rapid (proportionately) at the beginning of life; the newborn infant grows at a faster rate than at any later stages. Its needs for food are higher than for the adult and taper off gradually until adulthood is reached. While these increased needs are met by a generally increased consumption of food, there are specialized needs which are met only by supplying extra amounts of particular items—among them protein. Ample protein is needed, for example, to support growth of muscle which is most rapid in the preschool years, more rapid than the growth of the body as a whole. Moreover, the years from 4 to 10 are those wherein incidence of fibrile illness is highest; protein allowance must be large enough not only for normal growth but also to permit rapid recovery of muscle and other tissue inevitably lost during illness.

Illness puts a stress on nutrition in many ways. There is impaired function which requires adjustments in the kind of food that may be eaten. The risk in surgery is reduced by good nutritional status and its aftermath requires special nutrition, particularly good protein nutrition, to promote healing and tissue repair. Convalescence, in general, is promoted and shortened by good nutrition.

There are the many diets prescribed for specific illnesses which require a drastic change in food habits. In many instances, amount and type of protein are important considerations. Even when the dietary change does not deal directly with protein, the effect on that constituent may be as profound as on any other. A diet high in rice content increases the relative contribution of rice protein to the total amount of protein eaten. A diet low in animal fat will also be reduced in animal protein. This illustrates a point which will arise time and again: foods, by and large, contain appreciable amounts of many dietary constituents. Only purified and concentrated foods such as sugar or shortening contain a single dietary component, the one carbohydrate and the other fat. The natural complexity of foods is at once an advantage (making possible many and varied approaches to good, balanced nutrition) and a disadvantage (when compounding diets to meet specialized needs). We should emphasize the dangers that arise from arbitrary, self-imposed changes in diet based on hearsay or whim, without the benefit of sound nutritional advice.

Actually the entire lifetime can be considered sensitive to nutritional status; we single out particular periods or circumstances only because we cannot always measure the consequences of good nutrition. It is relatively easy to see and measure the obvious effects of good maternal or infant nutrition. It is less simple to measure general good health and happiness and relate them to good nutrition. It is even more difficult to assess long-range effects of nutrition, of eating too little or too much, of the subtle effects of childhood habits which show up in middle and old age. Yet there is a general feeling among scientists that more can be done to improve health and prevent diseases through improved nutrition; that for each individual there is a pattern of nutrition which suits him best. What is needed is augmented knowledge of the relationship between health and nutrition; included is more knowledge of the role of proteins.

## Proteins in Livestock Feeds

Animal husbandry is one of the oldest of human enterprises; it came with the great agricultural revolution which was the beginning of modern man. Nomadism was prompted by the need to provide pasturage for animals. With the advent of agriculture, of planned production of crops, pasture did not have to be depleted, and a stable life for man and his animals could be assured in one location. The history of animal husbandry is one of continuous improvement in the production of animals and in decreasing the cost of feeding them. This has been brought about in part by selective breeding, by producing stock which grow better, produce better quality and larger quantities of milk, and are more efficient egg producers. For such efficient animals it has become profitable to embark on more intensive programs of feeding, to spend more time and effort on their feeds, and to improve the amount and nature of the ingredients so as to gain the most out of each animal unit.

Great strides have been made in poultry raising by selective breeding to produce birds which grow better and faster and by better use of nutrition information. In 1960 in the United States, a three-pound bird could be produced in eight to nine weeks on a total consumption of 6–7 pounds

of feed as compared with 12–14 weeks of growing time
and 12 or more pounds of total feed used previously. This
kind of improvement is happening every year. Instead of
haphazard feeding from scraps and leftovers, poultry feeds
are compounded scientifically and with the use of com-
puters with strict attention to sound nutritional principles.
The amount and quality of proteins are major considerations.

Actually more is known about animal nutrition than
human nutrition. There is a great incentive to know and
apply nutrition in animal husbandry because this constitutes
a stress condition on nutrition—but only for economic reasons. Here, as against human nutrition, there are clear
measures of success and failure, and relatively few subtle-
ties; only cost per unit weight gain or per unit amount of
milk or eggs is important.

Human nutrition has much to gain from the knowledge
and techniques developed by the animal feeders, and
human society benefits from the lowered cost of animal
products arising from practical application of sound nutritional practice.


## Malnutrition


Of course, when there is not enough to eat, then there is
compounded to the individual nutritional problems the general one of insufficiency. Hunger is the beginning of a
downward spiral; begotten by it are impaired growth, reduced resistance to infection, and loss of ambition and
ability to work. There is a lowering of the standard of living
and a further reduction in the ability to produce food,
thereby starting another downward turn of the spiral. Eventually equilibrium is reached, but at a low level. In the acute
stages the well-known deficiency diseases such as pellagra
or beri-beri are encountered, and in many instances the
protein-deficiency disease kwashiorkor, which is most preva-

lent among children. But even when there is no acute syndrome, the ravages of insufficiency are still there on the body and the mind. So enormous is this problem that it staggers the imagination to comprehend it in its entirety.

In a description of a trip down the Nile in a river boat we find a poignant picture of some ravages of hunger:

"We were now entering the territory of the Nuers, a kindred tribe to the Dinkas, though shorter and less handsome. They also seemed to me to be poorer, and their poverty increased steadily. The people were pitifully thin and listless, and clearly they were hungry; I saw one group of men flaying a dead crocodile, which can hardly be a palatable diet. It was interesting to watch the tribesmen's reactions to our boat. It made quite a commotion on the river and was certainly the most imposing object for many miles around, and in the more highly developed settlements upstream it had been a great center of interest. But here we did not attract much attention. The men and women sitting outside their huts hardly bothered to look up, and some of them elaborately turned their backs.... Our arrival, having no purpose or meaning in their existence, was nothing more than an intrusion and an interruption; they were absorbed in their dullness. And their dullness could merge into moments of really desperate sadness...." (Moorhead)

These are ravages short of death—ravages that can be described but cannot so easily be measured. Is it possible to assign a figure to ambition and a percentage to dullness? But death is absolute and a comparison of death rates shows clearly the difference between well-fed and undernourished countries. In the 1950s in Australia, United Kingdom and Sweden, for example, the death rate of children of ages 1 to 4 was 2 per thousand; in a group of countries including Brazil, Costa Rica, Egypt, El Salvador, Mexico, and Thailand the death rate in the same age group ranged from 15 to 50 per thousand. This is the age group for which protein malnutrition is the greatest hazard. Granted that many factors in addition to malnutrition combine to produce these differences, most medical observers nevertheless believe that nutritional deficiencies are a potent factor not only in themselves but as contributing to other causes of death such as from infectious diseases.

We would not claim that all or even most hunger is protein hunger. For adults, hunger is probably of a more general type, but for children and women with children, protein hunger is common.

## Is There Enough Protein?

There is a great disparity in protein usage by the various nations and geographical areas. Consider that the average person in the Far East eats about 50 grams of protein per day of which 39 grams are of vegetable origin, whereas in Northern Europe the total eaten per day is about 95 grams of which 53 or so are of animal origin. The difference is both in amount and kind. This is not to say that the one pattern is altogether bad and the other good, but by all standards the lower is not enough in quantity and not good enough in quality. In succeeding generations, as the world population increases the problem will become more acute and will spread to larger areas.

This is a general food problem but the protein aspect will become acute faster—indeed, it is so already. Protein is costlier to produce than calories and the need for protein is constant throughout adult life, whereas the caloric requirements decrease with age. This same situation holds for most vitamins and minerals, the allowance remaining the same over the entire adult period. We can expect that protein and vitamins, as they are costlier to produce, will become scarcer faster as the world population increases than will general calories (carbohydrate and fat).

It is not our purpose to enter into a general demographic discussion of world population pressure, to speculate how big the population will become, to analyze means for controlling its size, or even to debate the desirability of doing so. This is a vast problem, of which food, and particularly protein, is but one aspect. But of this we can be sure: there will be no cheap way of increasing the world food supply, there will be no panaceas to improve the food picture, there will be no easy road to adequacy. Success in solving our food problems will come slowly and painfully and only if we understand the issues clearly.

## SELECTED BIBLIOGRAPHY

Boyd Orr, Lord John. *Feast and Famine.* London: Rathbone, 1957. (Although intended for younger people, this should be of interest to adults as well.)

Butler, J. A. V. *Inside the Living Cell.* New York: Basic, 1959.

Curwen, E. C., and G. Hatt. *Plough and Pasture.* New York: Collier, 1961.

Gortner, H. A. "The Plant Proteins," *Cereal Chemistry* (supplement), vol. 19, no. 6 (November 1942).

Haurowitz, F. *The Chemistry and Function of Proteins.* 2nd ed. New York: Academic, 1963.

Hundley, J. M. "Enrichment of Foods with Protein," *Ann. N. Y. Acad. Sci.,* vol. 69 (1958), p. 1042.

McCollum, E. V. *A History of Nutrition.* Boston: Houghton, 1957.

*Man and Hunger: World Food Problems, No. 2.* Rome, Italy: Food and Agriculture Organization of the United Nations, 1957.

Moorhead, A. "To the Beginnings of Memory," *The New Yorker,* Sept. 27, 1958, p. 135.

Todhunter, E. N. "The Story of Nutrition," in *Yearbook of Agriculture: Food.* Washington, D. C.: U. S. Dept. of Agriculture, 1959.

CHAPTER 2

# The Protein Content
# of Tissues

## Determination of Protein Content

Can proteins be distinguished from other substances by
inspection, by taste or smell or feel? Many proteins are
sticky when moist, but so are starches and dextrins. Some
proteins set up in gels as do gelatin and fibrin, but so do
solutions of complex carbohydrates, such as alginic acid.
Many proteins are coagulated by heat, but some are not.
Pure proteins are bland in taste; it is the accompanying
materials which give the characteristic taste to the proteins
in eggs and milk. Some proteins, like those in fingernails
and horns, are hard, while others, like those in silk, are soft.
Some, such as the blood proteins, are soluble in water and
dilute salt solutions; others, like the proteins of hair, are
insoluble in almost every solvent. The first glance at a
sample of pure protein might be disappointing: it appears
no different from other crystals or powders which might
be found on the chemist's shelf. Most pure proteins are
colorless, but some are colored, as is hemoglobin from red
blood cells. Proteins have such a diversity of physical properties that these alone are insufficient to distinguish them
from other materials. Only chemical analysis can determine
which are proteins. The odor of burning protein and the

15

characteristic odor of putrefaction are reflections of breakdown of proteins into products with typical odors, the one by heat and the other by the action of microorganisms—a sort of chemical analysis.

One of the characteristics of proteins noted by the early investigators was that they always contain nitrogen. This, then, is the first clue to the presence of proteins: if a tissue contains nitrogen, it could contain protein. Certainly the converse is true: if a tissue does not contain nitrogen, it does not contain protein.

The amount of nitrogen which each protein contains will depend upon its composition, and will vary from protein to protein; on the average, proteins contain 16 percent nitrogen. It is possible, then, in a crude way, to estimate the protein content of a tissue by analyzing for its nitrogen content and multiplying this percentage by the factor, 6.25 (100/16). But this procedure of estimating protein content has many pitfalls because there are numerous constituents which are not proteins and yet contain nitrogen, and they are present in tissues in not negligible amounts. Nucleic acids which are vital components of each cell contain nitrogen and are present in various amounts in different tissues. There are certain complex lipids (fatty substances), such as some phosphatides, which contain nitrogen; so do some complex carbohydrates which contain hexosamine and sialic acid. In theory, only complete separation of proteins from a tissue yields an unequivocal measure of protein content. Although pure proteins have been isolated from tissues, recovery is usually low. Hence the quantitative separation and recovery of all the protein from a given tissue is impractical as a method of analysis. Protein content when given as nitrogen times 6.25 is at best an estimate, often a crude one.

Because of the difficulty of doing otherwise, the science of protein nutrition depends on such a crude estimate of protein content. On this basis foodstuffs are classified as high or low in protein content, mixed diets are compounded, and the adequacy of foods as protein substances is judged. Were this the only measure of protein, it would indeed be an insecure one, but parallel to the chemical measurements is a history of extensive feeding tests on animals and humans. Most of the common foodstuffs have been tested as sources of protein in nutrition; a relationship has been developed between their protein content as estimated chemically and their protein value as exhibited nutritionally. This has provided a correlation by which to evaluate and use foodstuffs as sources of protein for men and animal. Obviously, this is not the last word.

More information is gained by hydrolyzing the tissues and analyzing for amino acid content. Hydrolysis means, simply, the splitting of the material in the presence of water. With water alone, even at high temperatures, the splitting goes slowly; hence, acid or other catalysts, as well as elevated temperatures, are employed. When starch is so treated, simple sugars are the result; fats on hydrolysis yield glycerine and fatty acids; proteins yield amino acids. Any tissue containing protein can be treated with acid at temperatures slightly above the boiling point of water: the proteins will be hydrolyzed and the resulting amino acids can be separated, collected, identified, and measured quantitatively.

Amino acid composition of a tissue, in itself, provides useful information: it describes the composition of a hypothetical average protein comprising all the diverse proteins of the tissue. For evaluation of a foodstuff as a source of protein, this type of information is more meaningful than protein content. The amino acid composition of numerous pure proteins is known, and many tissues containing protein have been analyzed for their amino acid content. More reliance is given to analytical values for pure proteins; the associated materials in crude protein mixtures oftentimes interfere with the analyses and produce spurious results. Even so, these values are ever becoming a closer approximation to a correct one as techniques are refined to improve accuracy of analyses and minimize the interference of other materials in the crude mixtures. The sum of the weights of the different amino acids is a good approximation of the weight of protein in a tissue; and this could be a more reliable figure than nitrogen content multiplied by 6.25.

The existing methods, despite their limitations, have provided for mapping of tissues, plant and animal, high order or low, for their crude protein content. We must emphasize, however, that no matter how we arrive at the total weight of all proteins in a tissue, we cannot tell anything about the number, size, shape, or properties of the individual proteins; no more than we can tell the shape of a house-to-be from a pile of bricks on a construction site. The bulk protein of any tissue is composed of many different types of individual proteins of various sizes, shapes, and compositions. The average of all this is the total protein.

## Proteins of Animal Tissues

The human body is composed of about ⅔ water and ⅓ solids. Protein constitutes 12 percent of the body weight of the human infant. In a few years this increases to 18–20 percent; this remains the average adult protein content, although instances of individual variation from this average figure have been reported. Lipids (fats) vary in abundance; by far the greatest variability in body composition is in fat. Fat contents of 14 percent for a normal young man and 32 percent for an obese adult have been reported (Keys and Brozek). The average for American males is about 10 percent at age 20 and 23 percent at age 55. For females the average fat content is about 20 percent for groups 20 years old and 30 percent for those of age 55 (Shank). Carbohydrates (sugars, glycogen, etc.) constitute 0.5 percent and mineral matter about 5 percent of body weight. While there are individual variations among species and induced differences imposed by feeding practices, these general ranges in composition hold for many other types of mammals as well.

The proteins in tissues might be divided roughly into three classes: (1) the structural proteins that help to support the organs, which are part of the protective tissue, supply the means for mechanical action, and organize and support subcellular structures and membranes; (2) proteins such as enzymes, hormones, antibodies, and the like, which support living processes; and (3) food proteins such as those in milk and eggs. These classifications are not clear-cut; there is such a great interdependence of body constituents that classification is only a convenience and a rough approximation.

Hair and nails and the outer layer of the skin are primarily structural protein of the type called keratin (not to be confused with carotene, a plant pigment, some forms of which serve as pro-vitamin A). Another structural protein is collagen of the connective tissue. It is the most abundant of the body—30 percent of all protein. The same sort of proteins are widespread in the animal kingdom. Wool and feathers, for example, are of the keratin class; silk is of a class called fibroins; leather is modified keratin protein, stabilized and preserved by a tanning agent; gelatin is produced from collagen by heat and chemical treatment.

Beauticians take advantage of a chemical reaction involving proteins when they set permanent waves in hair. First the hair proteins are untied slightly (some of the chemical bonds which hold the proteins in their original form are broken temporarily by chemical means), the hair is set into the desired form, and the bonds are then remade under these new conditions. These are reactions involving cystine, a sulfur-containing amino acid.

Another group of the so-called structural proteins are those of muscle. There are two important components of muscle protein—myosin and actin, which bind together to form a complex, actomyosin. In solution it can exist as long threads. In the presence of the biological reagent, adenosine triphosphate, this complex will contract and lose its fibril properties, not unlike muscle contraction. Since adenosine triphosphate is a high-energy compound capable of capturing the energy of respiration and glycolysis and transmitting it to other groups, this is an illustration of the conversion of the energy of metabolism into muscular work.

Virus protein might be considered a structural protein since it makes possible the organization and protection of the components of the virus. So might the major structural protein of subcellular units, such as mitochondria. Such proteins make possible the organization of certain enzyme systems into units to provide for an integrated relationship between respiration and energy transfer.

The second group of proteins, those that support living processes, is typified by enzymes. Enzymes are biological catalysts. This puts them in the general category of agents which promote chemical reactions, and makes it possible for them to proceed faster and at lower temperatures. Catalysis is not confined to living substances. Many industrial chemical processes require the presence of small amounts of promoters (catalysts). The "hardening" of vegetable oils to produce shortening requires the presence of metal catalysts (catalytic hydrogenation); other catalysts are needed for the formation of polymers such as nylon or Dacron. But the enzymes do more than mere catalysis—they are selective, they do very specific chemical jobs. There are many enzymes, chains of chemical events, each presided over by a particular enzyme; together they form an integrated biological operation.

It is characteristic of enzymes and of catalysts in general that only small quantities of these reagents are required to promote chemical reaction. For this reason we would expect that, particularly in adult tissue but even generally in all animal tissue, enzymes and other aspects of the "biological machinery" would comprise a relatively small proportion of the proteins in the tissue.

Then there is the group of proteins which serves as food for the young of the species. Cow's milk contains about 3.3 percent protein, and this represents roughly 25 percent of the solids of the milk. Mature human milk contains 1.2 percent protein, and this is about 10 percent of the solids. The predominant protein in cows' milk is casein, a phosphoprotein which is precipitated as a curd by acidification or by clotting by the enzyme rennin. Casein, one of the first proteins to have been characterized, was separated out of milk in 1838 by G. J. Mulder. Although it is a relatively pure protein, free of nonproteinaceous material, it is not pure in the sense of being one single protein species. The other proteins of milk, which are not precipitated with the casein, are called whey proteins. In human milk they are the majority of the protein; in cow's milk they represent a little less than 20 percent of the total protein.

Egg contains protein which serves as food for the embryo. Egg white contains about 88 percent water, 11 percent protein, and 1 percent carbohydrate. Ovalbumin, the major protein constituent in egg white, was isolated in a crystalline form by Hofmeister in 1890. There are a number of other proteins in egg white; among them is lysozyme, which destroys bacteria, ovomucoid, a heat stable protein, and avidin, a protein which combines with biotin, a vitamin, rendering it unavailable for biological activity. Egg yolk is not quite so high in protein on a water-free basis: it contains 49 percent water, 17 percent protein, 33 percent fat, and 1 percent carbohydrate.

## Proteins of Plant Tissues

In plants, structural support is assumed by carbohydrates instead of proteins; hence, there are not generally the analogs of the keratins and collagens of animals in plants. Most of the proteins of the growing portions of plants carry out biological functions. They might be considered as the biological machinery; they would form a major proportion of the total protein in these tissues. For example, in growing leaves 75 percent of the protein is in the chloroplasts.

A second type of protein in plants is storage protein, either of a temporary sort as may be found in some parenchymatous cells of growing portions, or longer-lived as those found in the tissues of seeds. Proteins of seeds are of particular interest because they are the great economic source of protein foods; by far the largest amount of protein is the protein of seeds. There is an accumulation of evidence that the majority of the protein in these tissues, particularly in protein-rich seeds, is in subcellular particles or packets which might be called protein bodies.

## Protein in Foodstuffs

Information on a selected number of tissues which double as food material is given in Table 2-1.

### TABLE 2-1

#### Protein Content of Some Foodstuffs[1]

| Food Source | Crude Protein Content, Percent |
|---|---|
| Cereals and Cereal Products | |
| Barley, pearled, *Hordeum vulgare* | 8.2–11.6 |
| Buckwheat, whole, *Fagopyrum esculentum* | 9.2–11.7 |
| Corn or maize, meal, *Zea mays* | 7.2–9.4 |
| Corn flakes | 8.1 |
| Oatmeal, dry, *Avena sterilis* | 12.1–14.2 |
| Rice, whole, *Oryza sativa* | 7.5–9.0 |
| Rice, polished | 5.2–7-6 |
| Wheat flour, whole, *Triticum aestivum* | 12–14 |
| Wheat flour, patent | 10–12 |
| Wheat bread, white | 7–8 |
| Macaroni, spaghetti, vermicelli | 10–13 |

*Legumes*

| | |
|---|---|
| Bengal gram or chick pea, *Cicer arietinum* | 20–28 |
| Lentil, *Lens culinaris* | 23–29 |
| Lentil, *Lens esculenta* | 23–27 |
| Lima bean, *Phaseolus lunatus* | 19–21 |
| Pea, green, *Pisum sativum* | 6.7 |
| Pea, mature, dry | 21–28 |
| Soybean, *Glycine max* | 32–42 |
| Soybean curd (moist cake) | 7 |
| Soybean protein concentrates, defatted | 45–54 |

*Oilseeds and Nuts*

| | |
|---|---|
| Coconut meal, defatted, *Cocos nucifera* | 21 |
| Cottonseed, *Gossypium hirsutum*, | |
| also *Gossypium herbaceum* | 17–21 |
| Cottonseed protein concentrate, defatted | 45–55 |
| Groundnut (peanut), *Arachis hypogaea* | 25–28 |
| Groundnut protein concentrate, defatted | 46–63 |
| Pecan, *Carya pecan* | 9–11 |
| Sesame seed, *Sesamum indicum* | 25 |
| Sunflower seed, *Helianthus annuus* | 27 |
| Sunflower seed protein concentrate, defatted | 47–55 |
| Walnut, *Juglans regia* | 15–21 |

*Fruits and Vegetables*

| | |
|---|---|
| Potato, *Solanum tuberosum* | 2.8 |
| Sweet potato, *Ipomoea batatas* | 1.8 |
| Tapioca, *Manihot esculenta* | 1.3 |
| Spinach, *Spinacia oleracea* | 2.3–3.6 |
| Carrot, *Daucus carota* | 1.2 |
| Plantain, *Musa paradisiaca* | 1–2.7 |

*Milk and Milk Products*

| | |
|---|---|
| Cow's milk | |
| Whole | 3.3 |
| Whole, dried | 22–25 |
| Skimmed, dried | 34–38 |
| Cheese | 7–22 |
| Buffalo milk, whole | 3.6 |
| Human milk | 1.3 |

*Meat*

| | |
|---|---|
| Chicken | 18–31 |
| Chicken, dried | 75 |
| Beef, round, raw | 23 |
| Beef, dried | 72 |
| Beef, roasted | 81–90 |
| Ham, whole, cured | 16 |
| Gelatin | 100 |

*Eggs*

| | |
|---|---|
| Whole, fresh weight | 12 |
| Whole, dried | 35 |
| Whole, dried and defatted | 77 |

*Fish*

| | |
|---|---|
| Mackerel | 18 |
| Sardine | 18 |
| Sardine, canned, solid portion | 21 |
| Herring | 18 |
| Oyster | 14 |
| Shrimp | 14 |
| Fish meal | 76 |
| Whale meal | 86 |
| Mackerel meal | 75 |

*Miscellaneous*

| | |
|---|---|
| Alfalfa (lucerne), dried, *Medicago sativa* | 18–23 |
| Broccoli leaf meal, dried, *Brassica oleracea* | 41 |
| Seaweed, *Laminaria sp.* | 4–11 |
| Fresh water algae, dried, *Chlorella sp.* | 60–66 |
| Brewers' yeast, dried, *Saccharomyces cerevisiae* | 44–51 |
| Food yeast, dried, *Torula utilis* | 38–55 |
| Mushroom, fresh, *Agaricus campestris* | 2–4 |
| Mushroom, dried | 37 |
| Mold mycelium, dried, *Aspergillus niger* | 31–47 |

---

[1] The protein content is calculated as "crude protein" (nitrogen multiplied by 6.25) per 100 grams of edible portion. Each foodstuff is reported either on the basis of its natural moisture content or as dried; the cereals, mature legumes, oilseeds, and nuts have a low moisture content, of the order of 10 per cent or less.

Cereals do not exceed 15 percent in protein content, rice and corn have less than wheat. Nevertheless, the major source of protein for man over most of the world is the cereal grains. Legumes contain more protein, rarely less than 20 percent, and in some species, notably the soybeans, above 35 percent. The animal sources have a uniformly high percentage of protein in the solids (total weight minus water content). Dried whole milk contains 22–25 percent and dried whole egg 35 percent protein. Muscle tissue contains 21 percent protein on a fresh weight basis and 74–88 percent protein in the dry solids. The protein content of chicken meat varies from 20 to 30 percent fresh weight and 75–92 percent dry weight. The protein content of fish, shellfish, and crustacea varies from 9 to 26 percent for the different species, that of dried fish or of salted and dried fish ranges from 28 to 80 percent.

Fruits and vegetables, with a few exceptions, are generally low in protein content. The protein content of potatoes is about 3 percent, but significant quantities of the nitrogen in the potato is nonprotein nitrogen; hence, these values are actually too high. Bananas, tapioca, and plantains have a very low protein content. In some areas of the world these three are major foods despite their inadequacy as sources of protein.

All protein which we eat comes originally from green plants, on land or sea. These plant proteins are concentrated into seeds (cereals and legumes) or are transformed by animals into milk, meat, and eggs. Plankton (seaweed) likewise is transformed into fish protein. Grasses and leaves contain protein. Actually alfalfa (lucerne) is a rich source of protein: the dry material contains from 18 to 23 percent protein. The protein content of leaves ranges from 10 to 41 percent on a dry weight basis. Dried broccoli leaf contains 41 percent protein. Seaweed contains from 4 to 11 percent protein; yeast is a rich source; brewers' and torula yeast contain from 35 to 55 percent protein. And some molds contain significant qualities of protein; fresh mushrooms contain from 2.2 to 3.5 percent protein.

## Concentration of Protein

Among the foodstuffs listed in Table 2-1 are materials which have been modified from their natural state to suit the needs of the human palate. One such modification is to concentrate the proteins.

Many of the tissues which contain protein also contain considerable water. One of the first problems in "food technology" to face ancient man was to reduce the amount of water both for purposes of preservation and for concentration of protein and other food ingredients. An obvious approach is drying, by sun or by heat. This produces the sundried fish and meat products, the dehydrated eggs and dried milk, and the dried leaves, fruits, and grasses. But drying by heat is expensive, and there are other ways of removing at least part of the water. Cheese manufacture is one such way: the milk proteins are precipitated as a curd which then is fermented to a product of characteristic odor and taste, and of higher protein content.

There are other ways of concentrating protein besides removing water. Certain tissues, particularly oilseeds, contain large quantities of fat which can be removed by heat rendering, by mechanical pressure, or by extraction with solvents. The oil is valued as food—in salad oils, shortening, cooking oils, and margarine. The residue, after the oil has been removed, often has a high protein content. The art of oil extraction is probably almost as ancient as water removal; there is evidence that sesame oil was part of the diet of prehistoric Jarmo. But the efficient utilization of oilseed as a source of protein concentrate is of relatively recent vintage. It is only in the last century or two that such "residues" were fed to cattle, and only within the present century that they have been fed to monogastric animals with more demanding requirements, such as poultry, swine, and dogs. The supplementation of human diets with oilseed protein concentrates represents one of the great untapped sources of protein—a source which could supply millions of tons of additional protein yearly.

Protein may also be concentrated by separating it from the surrounding tissue. Gelatin is one such product; it is manufactured from collagen, the protein of tendons and joints, and it is practically 100 percent protein. Another protein product is casein, the major protein of milk. There was a time when considerable quantities of casein were consumed in the manufacture of plastics, adhesives, and sizes. This market has dwindled in the face of competition from synthetic polymers. Soybean protein has been manufactured in small quantities by isolation, and so has peanut protein.

Here again, the potential for isolated protein, from 95 to 100 percent, in human food products is practically untapped, particularly for the protein from plant materials.

## Conclusion

These are but a few examples of proteins in the living world. Protein is as widespread as life itself and appears in countless forms. The extensive variation in size, shape, and appearance of living organisms is reflected in an equally immense variation in the appearance, shape, structure, and the properties of proteins. It would seem impossible to develop out of this diversity any organized idea of proteins as a class. Yet beneath these differences the chemistry of the proteins is essentially the same: proteins have common ingredients and are put together similarly. But they are so large in size and so complex compared to most other chemical compounds that it is possible for the same ingredients to appear in a vast variety of physical and biological forms.

### SELECTED BIBLIOGRAPHY

COMPOSITION OF FOODSTUFFS

Altschul, A. M. (ed.) *Processed Plant Protein Foodstuffs.* New York: Academic, 1958.

American Academy of Pediatrics. "Composition of Milks: Report of the Committee on Nutrition," *Pediatrics,* vol. 26 (1960), p. 1039.

Chatfield, C. *Food Composition Tables for International Use.* Washington, D. C.: Food and Agriculture Organization of the United Nations, 1949.

*Report of the FAO/CCTA Technical Meeting on Legumes in Agriculture and Human Nutrition in Africa, No. 1958/22.* Rome, Italy: Food and Agriculture Organization of the United Nations, 1959.

Guggenheim, K. *Tables of Food Composition.* Jerusalem, Israel: Government of Israel, Ministry of Education and Culture, Nutrition Division, 1959.

Harvey, D. *Tables of the Amino Acids in Food and Feedingstuffs.* Technical Communication No. 19. Farnham Royal, Slough, Buckinghamshire, England: Commonwealth Agricultural Bureaux, 1956.

Hutchinson, R. C. *Food for the People of Australia.* Sydney: Angus & Robertson, 1958.

Kuppuswamy, S., M. Srinivasan, and V. Subramanyan. *Proteins in Foods.* New Delhi: Indian Council of Medical Research, 1958.

Watt, B. K., and A. L. Merrill. *Composition of Foods.* Agricultural Handbook No. 8. Washington, D. C.: U. S. Dept. of Agriculture, 1950.

*Yearbook of Agriculture: Food.* Washington, D. C.: U. S. Dept. of Agriculture, 1959.

GENERAL

Fox, S. W., and J. F. Foster. *Introduction to Protein Chemistry.* New York: Wiley, 1957.

Keys, A., and J. Brozek. "Body Fat in Adult Man," *Physiol. Rev.,* vol. 33 (1953), p. 245.

Shank, R. E. "Weight Reduction and Its Significance," *Nutr. Rev.,* vol. 19 (1961), p. 289.

West, E. S., and W. R. Todd. *Textbook of Biochemistry.* New York: Macmillan, 1956.

# II

# AMINO ACIDS, PROTEINS, AND PROTEOLYSIS

# CHAPTER 3

# Amino Acids

### History of Discovery

Amino acids were discovered as constituents of natural products even before they were recognized as components of proteins; asparagine was discovered in 1806 in juice of the asparagus plant, and cystine in 1810 in urinary stones. Indeed, their names are based on the sources from which they were isolated. The first discovery of an amino acid derived by hydrolysis of a protein was that of glycine in 1820. This prefaced the beginning of a hundred-year period in which were discovered all but a few of the 20 amino acids which are regular constituents of proteins and which can be recovered by hydrolysis. Even though a large number of these had already been discovered by the end of the nineteenth century, it was not until 1902, with the publication of the works of Hofmeister and of Fischer, that an explanation was offered for the mode of combination of the amino acids in proteins. Their development of the peptide hypothesis of protein structure is regarded as one of the most important events in the history of protein chemistry.

The story of the discovery and identification of the amino acids is a brilliant chapter in the history of chemistry; many of chemistry's "greats" participated in this venture. The names which they gave to these amino acids are for the most

31

part trivial, reflecting the momentary impressions and interests of the discoverer. Like too many other names, these make little sense; their connection to chemistry and biochemistry must be drawn from memory.

The amino acids listed in Table 3-1 are those found in proteins; close to 100 others have been isolated from natural products, but not as components of proteins. Many of the

TABLE 3-1

*History of Discovery of Amino Acids Found in Proteins*

| Amino Acid | Basis of Name[1] | Date Isolated from Protein | Credited with Discovery | Protein Source from Which Isolated |
|---|---|---|---|---|
| Glycine | Γλυχνs, sweet (Berzelius) | 1820 | Braconnot | Gelatin |
| Leucine | Λενκοs, white (Braconnot) | 1820 | Braconnot | Muscle fiber, wool |
| Tyrosine | Τυρόs, from cheese (Liebig) | 1849 | Bopp | Casein |
| Serine | From serecine (Cramer) | 1865 | Cramer | Silk serecine |
| Glutamic acid | From gluten (Ritthausen) | 1866 | Ritthausen | Wheat gliadin (gluten-fibrin) |
| Aspartic acid | Related to asparagine | 1868 | Ritthausen | Pea legumin, conglutin from lupine |
| Phenylalanine | Related to alanine (Erlenmeyer and Lipp) | 1881 | Schulze and Barbieri | Lupine seedlings |
| Alanine | First syllable is from "aldehyde" (Strecker) | 1879 1888 | Schutzenberger Weyl | Silk fibroin |
| Lysine | Λνσιs, "loosing" urea (Drechsel) | 1889 | Drechsel | Casein |
| Arginine | (Schulze and Steiger)[2] | 1895 | Hedin | Horn |

| | | | | |
|---|---|---|---|---|
| Diiodotyrosine | First called iodogorgoic acid from its source (Drechsel) | 1896 | Drechsel | Skeleton of *Gorgonia cavolinii* (coral) |
| Histidine | Ιστος, tissue (Kossel) | 1896 | Kossel<br>Hedin | Sturine from salmon sperm<br>Various protein hydrolyzates |
| Cystine | Κυστις, bladder (Berzelius) | 1899 | Mörner | Horn |
| Valine | From its formula, α-aminovaleric acid (Fischer) | 1901 | Fischer | Casein |
| Proline | Short for α-pyrrolidinecarboxylic acid (Fischer) | 1901 | Fischer | Casein |
| Tryptophan | From θρυπτομαι, to be broken, and φαιγω, to bring to light (Neumeister) | 1901 | Hopkins and Cole | Casein |
| Hydroxyproline | Related to proline (Fischer) | 1902 | Fischer | Gelatin |
| Isoleucine | Isomer of leucine (Ehrlich) | 1904 | Ehrlich | Fibrin (blood clot), beet-sugar molasses residue |
| Thyroxine | From thyroid (Kendall) | 1915 | Kendall | Thyroid tissue |
| Methionine | After characteristic grouping of the compound, γ-methyl thio-α-amino butyric acid (Barger and Coyne with Mueller) | 1922 | Mueller | Casein |
| Hydroxylysine | Related to lysine | 1925 | Schryver, Buston and Mukherjee | Fish gelatin |

| Threonine | Similar in structure to sugar, D (−) threose (Meyer and Rose) | 1925 | Schryver and Buston Gortner and Hoffmann | Oat protein, Teozein from seeds of Euchlaena Mexicana |
|---|---|---|---|---|
| Asparagine | From ασπαραγος, asparagus (Dulong, 1826) | 1932 | Damodaran | Hempseed edestin |
| Glutamine | Related to glutamic acid | 1932 | Damodaran, Jaabach, and Chibnall | Wheat gliadin |

Source: Based on H. B. Vickery and C. L. A. Schmidt, "The History of the Discovery of the Amino Acids," Chem. Rev., vol. 9 (1931), p. 169.

[1] Person(s) in parentheses named the amino acid.
[2] Probably from the name of the silvery lupine, Lupinus argenteus, from which it was isolated by Schulze and Steiger.

latter are found in plants and bacteria, some are components of antibiotics, and a lesser number are in animal tissues. It is interesting to speculate on the relatively small number of amino acids found in proteins. Oparin felt that this was the outcome of the evolutionary process:

If we assume, on the basis of evolutionary theory, that the proteins of highly organized beings become progressively more and more efficient in carrying out their particular function, then it is reasonable to suppose that their component parts (as it were, the nuts and bolts of the mechanism) have been to a great extent standardized, just as in modern engineering the component parts are standardized, so that they can be used to make all kinds of things from sewing machines to motor car engines. This idea is supported by the fact that many lower organisms have peculiar or uncommon amino acids.

## Peptide Bond

The chemical structures of the more common amino acids in proteins are listed in Table 3-2, together with their accepted abbreviations. Obviously the single most impor-

tant property of amino acids is that they can be linked
in chains called peptide chains. A glance at the generalized
formula for an amino acid shows that each has an amino
and a carboxyl group—that is, at least one acid and one

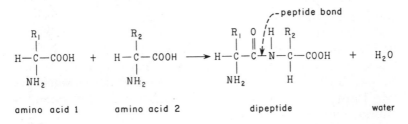

amino acid 1        amino acid 2            dipeptide            water

basic group. (Proline and hydroxyproline are exceptions
to this general rule, but for  purposes of the generalized
discussion we need not be concerned with individual cases.)
The amino group of one amino acid is capable of combining with the carboxyl group of another to yield a dipeptide (two amino acids joined together by a peptide bond).
The peptide bond is the fundamental linkage in protein
chains; this is the linkage proposed by Hofmeister and by
Fischer. Such chemical combinations can be brought about
in the laboratory between individual amino acids; it is one
of the fundamental synthetic operations of living matter.

## Asymmetry

Amino acids contain at least one asymmetric carbon atom,
i.e., they are able to appear in two forms or isomers which
are mirror images of each other (optical isomers). This is
best demonstrated by the two tetrahedra shown below:

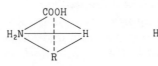

Optical isomerism is not a property solely of amino acids, it is a property of many compounds and was first discovered by Pasteur. The two forms can be distinguished from each other by their physical properties, particularly optical rotation: one rotates polarized light clockwise and the other counterclockwise. When amino acids are synthesized chemically, 50 percent of the resulting product is of one form, and 50 percent is of the other; the production of each form has the same chance of occurring, hence the equal distribution. Such products exhibit no optical rotation since the two forms cancel out each other's properties. But when an amino acid is synthesized by living organisms, only one form results; this is one of the unique properties of living organisms. In general, whenever a molecule which can exist in the two optical forms is synthesized biologically, only one of the forms is synthesized. The forms which are synthesized and exist in proteins are called L-amino acids, so named by comparison with optically active sugars which are the standards for this nomenclature. But there are examples of the occurrence of D-isomers in certain tissues and in specialized compounds. It is noteworthy that the L-amino acids are generally tasteless or bitter and the D-amino acids are generally sweet.

The taste of L-glutamic acid makes it particularly suitable as a condiment. It accentuates other flavors, particularly meatlike flavors, and hence is a favored additive to soups and other food servings. It is a major ingredient of vegetable protein hydrolyzates such as soy sauce and is available commercially as monosodium glutamate.

In nutrition, it is the L-isomer which is significant. With but a few exceptions, in mixtures of the D- and L- forms of essential amino acids, it is only the L-form which is effective as a source of amino acid. D, L-Methionine and D, L-phenylalanine are exceptions; they are utilized by man equally as well as the L-isomers; apparently biological systems exist to convert the D-form of these amino acids into the L-form.

It is not surprising that the unnatural and unusual forms

of amino acids occur in some antibiotics, the natural antagonists of living organisms. D-Leucine, D-phenylalanine, and D-valine are found in gramicidin. D-Serine is in polymycin and D-penicillamine, a derivative of D-cystine ($\beta$, $\beta$-dimethyl-D-cystine), occurs in the penicillins.

## Individual Properties

We have discussed some of the properties which amino acids have in common. But each amino acid has also its individuality and this is determined by the nature of the side groups. We might say that amino acids which are linked together in peptide bonds have a backbone, which is made up of the peptide linkage, and side chains, the groups which characterize the individual amino acids. The nature of the characteristic groups which become the side chains in proteins has been indicated for the common amino acids in Table 3-2. We do not intend to discuss any further the chemical individuality conferred by these groups on amino acids and on proteins; the references at the end of this chapter will prove interesting to those who wish to know more about the chemistry of the amino acids. Suffice it to point out that the nature of the characteristic groups affects chemical reactivity and physical properties such as solubility and absorption of light; these differences are compounded when amino acids are put together in diverse order in proteins.

Brief mention might be made of a property of the sulfur-containing amino acid, cystine. This amino acid exists in two forms: the oxidized form in which it is a double molecule bridged together by sulfur bridges, and the reduced form which is the single molecule. The same relationship occurs when cystine is incorporated into a peptide chain. Under these conditions, its side-chain bridges together two peptide chains; this is a means for forming cross-linkages. We mentioned this property briefly in Chap. 2 when we

## TABLE 3-2

### The Common Amino Acids of Proteins

General Formula $R-CH \underset{\displaystyle \diagdown COO^-}{\overset{\displaystyle \diagup NH_3^+}{}}$

| Name | R | Name | R |
|---|---|---|---|
| Glycine(Gly)[1] | H− | Aspartic acid (Asp) | $^-OOC\text{-}CH_2\text{-}$ |
| Alanine(Ala) | $CH_3-$ | Asparagine(Asp-$NH_2$) | $H_2NOC\text{-}CH_2\text{-}$ |
| Valine (Val) | $(CH_3)_2CH-$ | Glutamic acid(Glu) | $^-OOC\text{-}CH_2CH_2\text{-}$ |
| Leucine(Leu) | $(CH_3)_2CHCH_2-$ | Glutamine (Glu-$NH_2$) | $H_2NOC\text{-}CH_2CH_2\text{-}$ |
| Isoleucine(Ileu) | $C_2H_5 \diagdown$ $CH_3 \diagup$ $CH-$ | Lysine(Lys) | $^+H_3N\text{-}CH_2CH_2CH_2CH_2\text{-}$ |
| Serine(Ser) | $HO\cdot CH_2-$ | Histidine(His) | $^+HN - CH$ $HC \quad C\text{-}CH_2\text{-}$ $N$ $H$ |
| Threonine(Thr) | $CH_3\text{-}CHOH-$ | | |
| Tyrosine(Tyr) | $HOC_6H_5CH_2-$ | Arginine(Arg) | $^+NH_2\text{=}C(NH_2)NHCH_2\,CH_2\,CH_2\text{-}$ |
| Phenylalanine(Phe) | $C_6H_5CH_2-$ | Cysteine(CySH) | $HS\text{-}CH_2\text{-}$ |
| Tryptophan(Try) | (indole ring)$-CH_2-$ NH | [2]Cystine(CySSCy) | $^-OOC \diagdown$ $^+H_3N \diagup CH\text{-}CH_2SSCH_2\text{-}$ |
| Methionine(Met) | $CH_3\text{-}S\text{-}CH_2CH_2\text{-}$ | [3]Proline(Pro) | $H_2C - CH_2$ $H_2C \quad CHCOO^-$ $N+$ $H_2$ |

Sources: S. W. Fox and J. F. Foster, *Introduction to Protein Chemistry*, (New York: Wiley, 1956); J. P. Greenstein and M. Winitz, *Chemistry of the Amino Acids*, vol. 1 (New York: Wiley, 1961); nomenclature explained in vol. 2, p. 767.

[1] The letters in parentheses are the commonly accepted abbreviations for the amino acids.

[2] Cysteine and cystine are two forms of the same amino acid: the first is the reduced and the second is the oxidized form which exists as a double molecule bound together by a disulfide linkage.

[3] Proline is not an amino acid; it is an *imino* acid. The amino group of the other acids is part of a ring in this one. The formula given is for the complete imino acid.

discussed hair waving, in which these cystine cross-linkages are broken temporarily and then reformed. We will have further occasion to notice these cross-linkages as we examine the structure of proteins. There are other ways in nature of producing chemical cross-linking in proteins, such as by phosphate diesters and other esters, but that which involves cystine is the more common one.

## Analysis

The remarkable strides in improvement of methods of chemical analysis which accompanied the phenomenal advances in chemistry and biochemistry of this century are well illustrated in analyses for amino acids. The pioneer discoveries and analyses for amino acids of the nineteenth century were painstaking and slow. Analysis for an amino acid was by actual isolation and conversion to a derivative which could be identified. Aside from taking quite a bit of time and requiring considerable skill, such a procedure also needed fairly large quantities of the material for analysis, and this often was the factor limiting progress.

Modern methods on a scale which permitted wholesale analysis for the amino acid composition of proteins began with the application of microbiological techniques (Lyman). The lactobacillus *Leuconostoc mesenteroides* P-60 requires 17 amino acids for growth. Nutrient media for this species can be designed to be lacking in one amino acid—the one to be analyzed for—and then the amount of that amino acid supplied by a suspected source can be measured. The growth of bacteria is rapid, and their quantity is estimated simply by densitometry. Appearance of this method was a great boost to analysis of amino acids in proteins; indeed, many of the published analyses of foodstuffs and other protein tissues were made by the microbiological assay. There are some difficulties with this method. The protein hydrolyzate, which is the source of amino acids, may also contain unknown nutrients for the microorganism; these materials would support growth in a manner unrelated to the amino acid supply. This procedure has now been largely supplanted by physical methods involving chromatography.

Chromatography is a procedure for separating materials on the basis of their relative strength of adsorption onto certain media; the least tightly held member of a mixture will move faster, followed by the next one, and so on. This can be done on paper or on certain specially prepared resins. It can be done by washing the medium with liquids or by flushing it with gases.

It is possible to put a drop of protein hydrolyzate on the corner of a sheet of paper and produce a two-dimensional "map" of the amino acids in the mixture. Or a mixture of amino acids is put on a suitable column and eluted by a programmed succession of solvents. Each amino acid comes off separately, can be identified, and its quantity measured. Volatile derivatives of amino acids are now also being separated and identified by gas chromatography and mass spectroscopy.

## Synthesis

Some of the amino acids (proline, for example) were synthesized chemically even before they were isolated from proteins. All of the common ones can now be synthesized chemically. In some instances, the synthesis is difficult and expensive and in others, particularly where there is a commercial basis for producing them in large quantities, their cost approaches that of industrial chemicals. This applies particularly to methionine and, to some extent, to lysine. The amino acids produced synthetically are, of course, a mixture of optical isomers, the DL forms. The two forms may be separated chemically, or the unnatural form removed by selective destruction of the D form with certain enzymes.

An alternative practical method for producing lysine is by large-scale fermentation in a two-stage process: first a precursor of lysine is formed and then it is converted enzymatically into lysine. This is a practical process competitive with chemical synthesis. We shall have occasion in later chapters to come back to the practicality of synthesis of amino acids as we consider the economics of increasing the protein supply.

## *Protein Synthesis*

The major metabolic fate of amino acids is to be incorporated into proteins; living cells require a supply of amino acids to support protein synthesis. There are biological systems for synthesis of amino acids from other constituents. But some organisms are unable to synthesize all of the amino acids or to synthesize them rapidly enough to meet their requirements: this is the basis for the concept of "essential" amino acids which are required for growth and maintenance. There is a wide and unpredictable range in the requirements for amino acids among the bacteria. Among higher organisms, the similarities between species become clearer. Isoleucine, leucine, lysine, methionine, phenylalanine, threonine, tryptophan, and valine are generally required. Histidine is required for most species with the exception of adult man, and arginine is required for some vertebrates such as the chick and salmon, and for insects.

The other amino acids needed for protein synthesis come from endogenous sources. Alanine, for example, may be formed by amination of pyruvic acid which itself is a product of the metabolism of carbohydrates. This amino acid may also arise from aspartic acid or from kynurenine, a metabolic product of tryptophan. In turn, in a reversal of the pathway of its formation, alanine may be converted into pyruvic acid which then may be the source for formation of serine, glycine, cysteine, valine, leucine, and isoleucine.

Phenylalanine is converted to tyrosine in the animal. Since phenylalanine is an essential amino acid for animals, the inclusion of its metabolic product tyrosine should "spare" the phenylalanine. Methionine is converted to cysteine in animals; here again advantage is taken of this metabolic relationship to reduce the requirement for methionine, an essential amino acid, by including cystine in the diet.

Isolated animal cells will proliferate in a medium containing amino acids, vitamins, salts, glucose, antibiotics, and some as yet unidentified components in blood serum. Thirteen amino acids are required for growth of human carcinoma cell (H La) and mouse fibroblast: arginine, cystine-cysteine, glutamine, histidine, isoleucine, leucine, lysine, methionine, phenylalanine, threonine, tryptophan, tyrosine, and valine. The need for both methionine and cystine and for each of the pair, tyrosine-phenylalanine, whereas one of each pair can spare the requirement of the other in the entire animal, indicates that the biological systems for conversion of one member of the pair into the other are absent in the isolated cells. The amino acids must be of the L configuration.

## Other Metabolic Roles

Aside from their role as constituents of proteins, amino acids are found in a number of important nonprotein compounds. Folic acid (N-pteroyl-L-glutamic acid) contains glutamic acid incorporated in its structure. $\beta$-Alanine is a component of coenzyme A. Many antibiotics contain amino acids; we mentioned earlier that some of these are D-amino acids. Glutathione, a ubiquitous cell constituent, is a combination of three amino acids; cell walls contain amino acids combined with nonprotein constituents. The posterior pituitary hormones, vasopressin and oxytocin, are polypeptides.

There are also many instances where parts of the amino acids are incorporated into the structure of important biological chemicals. Purine, one of the important structures in nucleic acids, contains four nitrogen atoms. In the course of its biological synthesis, two of the nitrogen atoms come from glutamine, one from aspartic acid, and two carbons and one nitrogen are incorporated directly from glycine. Hence, three amino acids supply ingredients for the biological synthesis of this purine base. Glycine is incorporated into the porphyrin portion of hemoglobin, the red pigmented protein in blood cells. Tryptophan is the source from which indolacetic acid, a plant growth hormone, and the vitamin niacin are derived by biological modification. The hormones adrenaline and thyroxine are formed from tyrosine. Phenylalanine, tyrosine, and tryptophan are precursors of alkaloids. Methionine is a methyl group donor; it is involved, for example, in the synthesis of creatine. Histidine is the precursor of histamine.

Ammonia, one of the by-products of amino acid metabolism, is toxic; it must be removed from the cell as it originates. The removal of ammonia is handled differently by various organisms—a study of how this is done reveals interesting evolutionary implications. In plants, ammonia is removed by being incorporated into aspartic or glutamic acids to yield the amides, asparagine or glutamine. In aquatic animals, ammonia may be released unchanged into the water milieu where its dilution is the detoxification. Amphibians and land animals convert ammonia into urea which is excreted in the urine. Dry-living reptiles and birds transform ammonia into uric acid. This has been attributed by Needham to the conditions under which the eggs hatch. For snakes, lizards, and birds, the eggs are laid with a supply of water just sufficient for their needs in development. Formation of ammonia would be disastrous, that of urea less serious but not satisfactory. Hence, embryos which develop in cleidoic eggs convert ammonia into uric acid which is insoluble and can be disposed in a solid form. The detoxification of ammonia is intimately related to the water supply (Brown and Cohen).

## Metabolism

There is a dynamic interchange between the major body constituents. There is a general interchange between carbohydrates, fats, and amino acids. For example, it is possible to convert parts of carbohydrates into fats as is done regularly in animal tissue and in growing plants. It is also possible to convert fats into carbohydrates as is done in germinating seedlings. This interconversion comes about because all three of these categories have in common a number of relatively simple metabolites. These are the "intersections" of the diverse metabolic pathways; it is possible, for example, to form these metabolites by starting with carbohydrates and to go from them to lipids or amino acids.

The metabolism of amino acids is related in a general way to the presence of adequate vitamin supply. Amino acid metabolism is influenced by the general state of health of the organism just as are other vital functions. But vitamin $B_6$, pyridoxal phosphate, is of particular interest since it participates in a large number of metabolic reactions involving amino acids.

## Error of Metabolism

When amino acid transformations are interfered with because of absence of a particular enzyme, the result is a metabolic block or an inborn error of metabolism. Consider the transformation of phenylalanine into tyrosine. The excess of tyrosine which is not incorporated into proteins undergoes further metabolic changes. There are known instances in which the biological apparatus for transforming phenylalanine into tyrosine is missing. Under these conditions there is an accumulation of phenylalanine in the blood and the presence of phenyl pyruvic acid in the urine; this is the metabolic disorder called phenylketonuria which is characterized by mental retardation and can lead to imbecility. The treatment, which is to place the affected child on a diet extremely low in phenylalanine, if begun soon after birth, may be of value.

## Conclusion

Amino acids have a variety of functions and are related to each other and to cell constituents by a variety of metabolic pathways. By far the main outcome of amino acid metabolism is incorporation into proteins. But many other vital functions require amino acids. The excess amino acids over and above those needed for protein synthesis and for transformation into vital materials can be converted into the pool of materials such as dicarboxylic acids which are transformed into carbohydrates or fats or back into amino acids. And when there is a deficiency of one amino acid, this can, in part, be overcome by drawing from other sources of either this amino acid or its precursors. Since there is a remarkable degree of interchangeability, this can be done to a great extent without interfering with normal functions. There is, no doubt, an order of priority in which the available supplies of an amino acid are directed into those functions which are most critical. But finally, if there is a serious enough deficiency, it will be recognized by failure of certain vital functions. It may be reflected as reduced synthesis of proteins or it may be observed as a deficiency in the synthesis of other vital biochemicals which draw upon any given amino acid as part of their construction material.

In general, there is a great flexibility and interchange of biological materials, and of carbon and nitrogen compounds among living matter. The position of amino acids in this interchange is one more example of the flexibility of living organisms which provides a built-in factor of safety to help overcome uncontrolled changes in the environment.

## SELECTED BIBLIOGRAPHY

Baldwin, E. *Dynamic Aspects of Biochemistry.* 3d ed. London: Cambridge U. P., 1957.

Brown, G. W., Jr., and P. P. Cohen. *"Biosynthesis of Urea in Metamorphosing Tadpoles,"* in W. D. McElroy and B. Glass (eds.), *The Chemical Basis of Development.* Baltimore, Md.: Johns Hopkins, 1958.

Greenstein, J. P., and M. Winitz. *Chemistry of the Amino Acids.* 3 vols. New York: Wiley, 1961.

Lyman, C. M. "Proteins," in A. M. Altschul (ed.), *Processed Plant Protein Foodstuffs.* New York: Academic, 1958.

Meister, A. *Biochemistry of the Amino Acids.* New York: Academic, 1957.

Oparin, A. I. *The Origin of Life on the Earth.* Translated by Ann Synge. 3d ed. New York: Academic, 1957, p. 229.

Stein, W. H., and S. Moore. "Chromatography," *Sci. Am.,* vol. 189 (March 1951), p. 35.

Vickery, H. B., and C. L. A. Schmidt. "The History of the Discovery of the Amino Acids," *Chem. Rev.,* vol. 9 (1931), p. 169.

# CHAPTER 4

# *The Primary Structure of Proteins*

PROTEINS ARE LONG CHAINS of amino acids joined together in peptide bonds. Most often, all of a protein is amino acids. But there are numerous proteins with significant quantities of nonprotein materials chemically bound to the peptide chains; as a class these are called conjugated proteins. When the nonprotein material is lipid, the protein is called a lipoprotein; and when it is carbohydrate, it is a glycoprotein. Sometimes a metal ion is firmly bound with the protein—this is a metalloprotein; and often small molecules are bound with the proteins, such as in hemoglobin or in flavoproteins.

In this chapter and the next we will deal with some aspects of protein structure. First we will consider the arrangement of amino acids along the protein chains; this is the primary structure. The special arrangement of that protein chain or chains will be discussed in the following chapter.

## The Question of Purity

Proteins in tissues are in admixture with other proteins and with nonprotein materials. By careful removal from the tissue and by means of operations, such as fractional precipitation and selective adsorption, it is possible to remove most contaminants. Numerous specialized techniques exist for eliminating the last traces of chemicals not affixed to the protein. Finally, the problem resolves itself into separating the particular protein from closely related ones.

It is obvious that any reliable work on protein structure or on the chemistry or biochemistry of proteins must be on a pure specimen and a single species. For small chemical molecules, purity is defined by chemical composition, by physical properties such as melting point and absorption spectra, and by the characteristics of their crystals. But ordinary chemical composition of large molecules such as proteins has little meaning in defining purity. Nor can one rely on formation of crystals, a favorite criterion of purity in the early days of investigations on proteins.

The concept of purity in proteins is an evolving one. As the knowledge of proteins increases and methodology is refined, the notions of purity change. What was once considered pure can now be shown by more refined techniques to be a gross mixture. Proteins pure by one criterion may be separated into several components by a more sensitive procedure.

Physical-chemical observations were until recently the sole criteria of purity of proteins. If a protein in solution sediments as a single species in a high centrifugal field (ultracentrifugation), this is one item of evidence in favor of it being pure. Other observations include migration in an electric field (electrophoresis) and solubility. More sensitive physical methods of fractionation have been developed in recent years. These include column chromatography, zone electrophoresis, countercurrent extraction, and reactions based on immuno chemistry. The techniques which are used to determine the number of components in a protein solution may be scaled up to become preparative procedures. Indeed, after preliminary fractionation by simpler techniques, the final purification is often by column chromatography or by one of the various modifications of electrophoresis.

No single method is sufficient to provide unequivocal evidence of purity; hence it is necessary to draw upon several independent criteria. There is the additional complication that a preparation may sometimes appear impure when, in fact, the several species may be isomers or association-dissociation complexes of the same species.

Finally, we may now draw upon chemical criteria to supplement the physical-chemical observations. But this comes about only because it has been established that each protein has a unique primary structure.

## Fundamental Questions about Primary Structure

With improved chances that some proteins are pure, it became possible to raise certain fundamental questions. Are proteins chemicals in the same sense as other chemicals? Are all of the molecules of a single species of proteins exactly the same? Are all of the amino acids in a single pure protein arranged in the same order, or is there a population of proteins which have the same over-all amino acid composition and the same size but which differ slightly or considerably in the order of amino acids? Physical-chemical methods might not detect such differences. Answers to these questions could come only from an unequivocal determination of the order of amino acids in a protein chain.

Actually, a first step in the consideration of this question was made by study of small peptides such as some of the posterior pituitary hormones. The sequence of amino acids in oxytocin and vasopressin was determined first by degrading the chains and then confirmed by synthesizing the hormones from their constituent amino acids (du Vigneaud). Each are peptides containing nine amino acids. Though there is a general similarity between these two molecules, each has a unique composition and arrangement of amino acids. It is clear, then, that for small chains of amino acids there is, indeed, a unique arrangement of amino acids: all of the same molecules have the same amino acid arrangement.

## Insulin

The historic and pioneering effort on the primary structure of a protein was on the insulin molecule. Insulin was discovered as a secretion of the pancreas. Great practical medical interest in this material for control of diabetes led to vigorous chemical studies on its purification. When insulin was first crystallized by Abel in 1926, there was a general reluctance to believe that this was a protein, because it was difficult to conceive that a protein could possess hormone activity. It was thought that this crystalline protein material contained small quantities of a very active impurity which was the hormone: the protein itself was not involved. As the purification continued, it became increasingly clear that indeed the protein was the hormone: no other nonprotein material could be found. Then there began a search for unique bonds or for unique amino acids to account for the hormone properties. But even these were not found; insulin is a typical protein with normal peptide linkages.

The choice of insulin as the model for studying the primary structure of proteins was a logical one. Insulin was available as a pure chemical by all existing criteria, and it was a small molecule. When studies on structure were first begun, it was thought that its molecular weight was 12,000; only later did it turn out that its minimum molecular weight was actually 6,000. Sanger and his associates undertook and solved the problem of elucidating the complete amino acid sequence of this molecule. The story of this endeavor makes exciting reading; we will leave the details to the reader who wishes to pursue this matter further (Sanger). We shall point out some of the significant aspects of this approach and of the conclusion which came with the culmination of the work.

First it was found that insulin consisted of two peptide chains held together by two disulfide bonds. These bonds were broken by a mild oxidation procedure and each chain was studied separately. The strategy was to split each chain into a number of well-defined fragments, separate out each fragment and purify it, and determine its amino acid sequence. It was necessary to rupture each chain in a number of ways to produce overlapping fragments in order to decide how to piece together the information from the analysis of the individual fragments. Most of the fragments were produced by partial acid hydrolysis; some of the larger fragments were made by enzymic hydrolysis. (Hydrolysis by enzymes has the advantage that the points of rupture of the chains are better controlled by the choice of

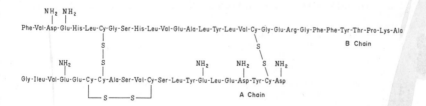

FIG. 4-1. The Primary Structure of Insulin.*

*Source: F. Sanger, "Chemistry of Insulin," *Science*, vol. 129 (1959), p. 1340.
The amino ends of the chains are the phenylalanine and glycine residues; the carboxyl ends of the chains are the alanine and asparagine residues.

EDINBURGH COLLEGE DOMESTIC SCIENCE LIBRARY

enzymes.) And finally, it is like piecing together the parts of a jigsaw puzzle—the structure of the so-called A and B chains was determined, and the positions of the disulfide cross-linkages were located; the structure which evolved is given in Fig. 4-1. You will notice that in addition to the two sulfide bridges connecting the two chains, there is a third disulfide loop within one of the chains.

Sanger confirmed, if it was then yet necessary to confirm, the peptide hypothesis of Fischer and Hofmeister. And the question was answered, at least for insulin, that proteins are indeed composed of well-defined chains of amino acids.[1]

The chains of insulin contain 21 and 30 amino acid residues, respectively.[2] These are uniquely short. But Sanger felt that other proteins could be studied as well and predicted that many would be analyzed for their sequences in a short time to come.

## The Primary Structure of Other Proteins

Beginnings made with insulin have been extended to include several more proteins, each in turn larger than the preceding one. Ribonuclease, an enzyme which catalyzes the splitting of ribonucleic acid, has a molecular weight of 13,683 and contains 124 amino acid residues. An outline of the primary structure of this molecule is given in Fig. 4-2.

1. "Thus, until more definite evidence to the contrary is produced, we are probably justified in concluding from the results with insulin that proteins in general will be found to obey the simple laws of protein chemistry and that they are composed of polypeptide chains having a unique arrangement of amino acids. This arrangement differs from protein to protein, but does not differ from one molecule to another molecule of the same protein. Each position in the insulin chains is occupied by one, and by only one residue, at least to within the limits of the methods used." (Sanger, 1956; see also Vaughan and Steinberg.)

2. When amino acids are combined together in peptide chains, a molecule of water is removed in formation of each linkage. The amino acid minus this molecule of water is called an amino acid residue.

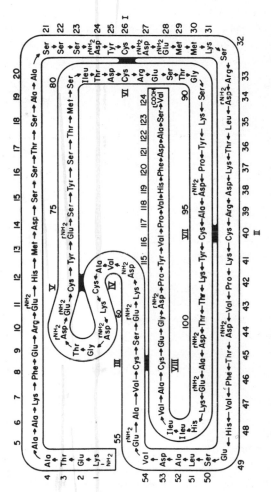

FIG. 4-2. The primary structure of bovine pancreatic ribonuclease. The free amino end of the chain is lysine (Number 1); the free carboxyl end is valine (Number 124). The Roman numerals denote the order of the ½ cystine residues counting from the no free amino end.*

*Sources: Reproduced by permission from H. A. Scheraga and J. A. Rupley, "Structure and Function of Ribonuclease," *Advan. Enzymol.,* vol. 24 (1962), p. 174. See also C. H. W. Hirs, "The Structure of Ribonuclease," *Ann. N.Y. Acad. Sci.,* vol. 88, art. 3 (1960) p. 611; W. H. Stein and S. Moore, "The Chemical Structure of Proteins," *Sci. Am.,* vol. 204 (1961), p. 81; and C. B. Anfinsen, *The Molecular Basis of Evolution* (New York: Wiley, 1959), Chap. 5, p. 99.

One tobacco mosaic virus rod contains 2200 protein sub-units, each of which has a molecular weight of about 18,000. This subunit contains 158 amino acid residues; its primary structure has been determined (Anderer et al., Tsugita et al.).

Many more proteins are being extensively studied by these and improved techniques, and more precise definitions of the primary structure of additional proteins can be expected in the near future.

## A Chemical Measure of Purity

Now that it is established that the position of amino acids in a protein chain is uniquely determined, it becomes possible to add chemical measures to the existing physico-chemical criteria of purity. If a given protein consists of a single chain, at one end there should be a free amino group and at the other a free carboxyl group. In the previous chapter we sketched the formation of a dipeptide by combination of two amino acids. We can extend the same description to a chain of any length:

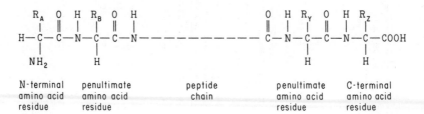

A pure chain, therefore, will contain only one set of terminal amino acids; a mixture of chains will show several kinds of terminal amino acids. Of course, if the molecule consists of more than one chain, there will be additional sets of terminal amino acids. And if the chain is closed to form a complete circle, there will be no terminal amino acids. Analysis for terminal amino acids adds a dimension to protein analysis and to the determination of purity.

It is possible to fragment a protein in a reproducible way and separate the fragments by a combination of paper chromatography and electrophoresis. The resulting pattern (often called fingerprint) is reproducible for pure proteins and characteristic of the protein.

### *Variations in Amino Acid Sequence*

For any given protein molecule, the amino acid sequence in the peptide chains is uniquely determined. But the same protein may vary in sequence from species to species.

Insulin molecules of a number of species are identical except for variations in the amino acids within the disulfide loop of the A chain. It might be that the three amino acids within this disulfide loop are not critical to biological activity. But the rest of the molecule is critical to activity; it has evolved similarly in all the species tested. Examples are multiplying of differences in amino acid sequences of like proteins from several species as more information becomes available on primary structure. Cytochrome c, an important protein of biological oxidation, shows species variation in the amino acid sequence of sections of the chain; so do the peptide hormones adrenocorticotropin, hypertensin, mela- nocyte-stimulating hormone, and vasopressin.

Even within the same species there may be several vari- ants of the same molecule. One such variation studied ex- tensively is in hemoglobin from erythrocytes. Hemoglobin of most vertebrates is composed of four polypeptide chains, each one of 17,000 molecular weight. These are folded to- gether to yield a single molecule of 68,000 molecular weight. The majority of hemoglobin molecules of normal adults (Hemoglobin A) consist of two pairs of chains; these have been named the $\alpha^A$ and $\beta^A$ chains; they are roughly of equal size (141 and 146 residues) and differ from each other in composition of 21 amino acids (Ingram, 1961). There are other hemoglobins in the normal adult. One such is found principally in the foetus but is carried over to some extent in the adult. Instead of the two $\beta^A$ chains this hemoglobin molecule contains two other chains, $\gamma^F$ chains, which differ from the normal $\beta^A$ chains in perhaps 17 amino acids (Ingram, 1961). Foetal hemoglobin, therefore, consists of two normal $\alpha^A$ and two $\gamma^F$ chains. ($\alpha_2^A \gamma_2^F$ compared to $\alpha_2^A \beta_2^A$.)

Over a dozen different normal and abnormal hemoglobins have been identified. In some instances the difference in the composition of the molecules is readily manifested in the properties of the molecule or even in the behavior of the erythrocyte. An example is sickle cell anemia; here the erythrocytes in the absence of oxygen are not spherical, they are crescent shaped. In those adults who have this trait, some hemoglobin molecules differ from the normal in having $\beta^S$ chains instead of $\beta^A$ chains ($\alpha_2^A \beta_2^S$). And these differ by one amino acid in the N-terminal sequence of the $\beta$ chain.

| | |
|---|---|
| $\beta^A$ (Normal adult) | Val. His. Leu. Thr. Pro. *Glu.* Glu. Lys. ---- |
| $\beta^S$ (Sickle cell trait) | Val. His. Leu. Thr. Pro. *Val.* Glu. Lys. ---- |

This is an inheritable trait; those adults who suffer from severe anemia with this disease have been shown to be homozygous for this form of gene: all of their hemoglobin molecules are abnormal, i.e., all of the beta chains are $\beta^S$.

Here is an instance of chemical changes obeying the laws of heredity. Since these are relationships on the molecular level, they are making possible a precise chemical correlation of phenotype with genotype (Ingram, Hunt and Ingram, Itano et al., Anfinsen).

We have provided examples of extreme sensitivity of biological function to primary structure, e.g., the effect of substitution of one amino acid for another in the $\beta$ chain of hemoglobin. And we have shown that substitution of amino acids in certain locations, as within the disulfide loop of insulin, does not interfere with function. There are numerous examples of both points. One must not forget that the structures shown in the figures are linear projections of three-dimensional objects. Since the protein is a large molecule and can fold and refold, it is entirely possible that an amino acid might influence another amino acid many residues away on the chain more than its nearest neighbor.

### Proof of Structure, Chemical Synthesis

When an organic chemist discovers a new molecule, he determines its structure by physical means and by degradative procedures. This is what was done for the primary structure of the proteins. But the final proof requires that the chemical be synthesized from known materials. Then, and only then, is there unequivocal proof of structure.[3]

Chains containing up to 39 amino acids arranged in a specific order have been synthesized; the resulting compounds (hormones) have had the same structure as determined by chemical degradations and the same kind and order of biological activity (Anderson, Hofmann). The principle of these syntheses is to block all but one of the reactive groups (e.g., the alpha amino group) in one amino acid so that only it will react with another amino acid blocked so as to leave free only the carboxyl group. This process is continued; the peptide chain is lengthened each

3. "Degradative experiments, in which molecules are broken down, do not offer final proof for an organic chemical structure; the last word comes when a postulated structure is synthesized and then shown to have all the same properties as the natural product. In spite of the substantial advances in the past few years in the synthesis of complex peptides, it will probably be sometime before a molecule of the size of ribonuclease is put together. Until then we must be on the lookout for surprises, because it is entirely possible that ribonuclease contains chemical linkages that are not revealed by the degradative techniques that were employed." (Stein and Moore, 1961.)

time. When the blocking agents are removed, then the result is a peptide chain with a specific order of amino acids.

The greatest accomplishment, of course, will be the synthesis of a protein such as insulin or ribonuclease. The strategy here is first to synthesize large fragments and then put them together in the special way in which they are put together in the natural protein. One major problem is to place the cross-links—the SS bridges—at the proper position.[4] A fundamental biological question is involved. If large enough fragments are synthesized and put together, will there be a preferred way of folding so that the cross-links come out at the right places?

4. There are reports of the synthesis of both the A and B chains of insulin. Upon combination, slight but definite insulin activity was produced. (*Chem. & Eng. News,* October 21, 1963, p. 45.)

SELECTED BIBLIOGRAPHY

"Amino Acids, Peptides, and Proteins," *Ann. N. Y. Acad. Sci.,* vol. 88, no. 3 (1960). This issue includes the following papers: V. du Vigneaud, "Experiences in the Polypeptide Field: Insulin to Oxytocin," p. 537 [*see also Science,* vol. 123 (1956), p 967]; C. H. W. Hirs, "The Structure of Ribonuclease," p. 611; G. W. Anderson, "New Approaches to Peptide Synthesis," p. 676; K. Hofmann, "Synthesis of Melanocyte-stimulating Hormone Derivatives," p. 689.

Anderer, F. A., H. Uhlig, E. Weber, and G. Schramm. Primary Structure of the Protein of Tobacco Mosaic Virus," *Nature,* vol. 186 (1960), p. 922.

Anfinsen, C. B. *The Molecular Basis of Evolution.* New York: Wiley, 1959.

Hill, R. L., J. R. Kimmel, and E. M. Smith. "The Structure of Proteins," *Ann. Rev. Biochem.,* vol. 28 (1959), p. 97.

Hunt, J. A., and V. M. Ingram, "The Genetical Control of Protein Structure: The Abnormal Human Haemoglobins," in G. E. W. Wolstenholme and C. M. O'Connor (eds.), *Ciba Foundation Symposium on Biochemistry of Human Genetics.* Boston: Little, Brown, 1960.

Ingram, V. M. "Gene Evolution and the Haemoglobins," *Nature,* vol. 189 (1961), p. 704.

Itano, H. A., S. J. Singer, and E. Robinson. "Chemical and Genetical Units of the Haemoglobin Molecule," in G. E. W. Wolstenholme and C. M. O'Connor (eds.), *Ciba Foundation Symposium on Biochemistry of Human Genetics.* Boston: Little, Brown, 1960.

Sanger, F. "Chemistry of Insulin," *Science,* vol. 129 (1959), p. 1340.

Sanger, F. "The Structure of Insulin," in D. E. Green (ed.), *Currents in Biochemical Research.* New York: Interscience, 1956.

Stein, W. H., and S. Moore. "The Chemical Structure of Proteins," *Sci. Am.,* vol. 204 (February 1961), p. 81.

Tsugita, A., D. T. Gish, J. Young, H. Fraenkel-Conrat, C. A. Knight, and W. M. Stanley. "The Complete Amino Acid Sequence of the Protein of Tobacco Mosaic Virus," *Proc. Nat. Acad. Sci. U. S.,* vol. 46 (1960), p. 1463.

Vaughan, M., and D. Steinberg. "The Specificity of Protein Biosynthesis," *Advan. Protein Chem.,* vol. 14 (1959), p. 115.

# CHAPTER 5

# The Size and Shape of Protein Molecules

THE ORGANIZATION OF PROTEINS already manifest in the unequivocal sequence of amino acids in chains of like molecules extends to the three-dimensional structure as well. It would be presumptuous indeed to present in these few pages anything but a rough overview of the picture; our objective rather is to provide a qualitative notion of the complexity of the protein molecule. And complex it is. And this complexity makes possible a degree of organization which superimposes a new chemistry upon the chemistry of the constituents. In general for simple molecules, one might predict the chemistry of the molecule by the chemistry of the constituents. One might even predict interactions between the constituents and their effects on the overall chemistry. The chemistry of simple peptide chains is a reflection of the chemistry of the individual amino acids. The reactions of these chains are primarily the reactions of the side groups of the amino acids—those groups not involved in the peptide bond. For longer peptide chains there develops a three-dimensional organization; many of the otherwise active groups of the constituent amino acids are modified in their activity by virtue of this three-dimensional structure. These can, however, revert to normal if there is a lowering in the degree of organization. A highly disorganized protein molecule will approach in its chemistry the chemistry of the constituent amino acids, and this indeed is one way of noting that there has been disorganization.

## Molecular Weight

Proteins are large molecules; hence, their molecular weights are big compared to most ordinary molecules. We get an idea of their relative size by listing first the molecular weights of familiar nonprotein materials and then comparing these to the molecular weights of a number of proteins, as is done in Table 5-1. Water has a molecular weight of 18; glucagon, one of the largest natural peptides not quite

### TABLE 5-1

#### Molecular Weights of Some Natural Compounds

| Compound | Molecular Weight | Comments |
|---|---|---|
| Water | 18 | |
| Ethyl Alcohol | 46 | |
| Alanine | 89 | An amino acid |
| Vitamin A | 286 | |
| Glutathione | 307 | A tripeptide |
| Sucrose | 342 | Common table sugar |
| Cholesterol | 387 | |
| Triolein | 885 | A liquid oil |
| Glucagon | 3,485 | A peptide hormone |
| *Protein* | | *Origin* |
| Ribonuclease | 13,000 | Beef pancreas |
| Trypsin | 15,000 | Beef pancreas |
| Pepsin | 35,500 | Hog gastric mucosa |
| Albumin | 64,500 | Bovine plasma |
| γ-Globulin | 153,000 | Human serum |
| Edestin | 310,000 | Hempseed |
| Thyroglobulin | 650,000 | Hog thyroid |
| β-Lipoprotein | 1,300,000 | Human plasma |

Source: K. O. Pedersen, "The Molecular Weight of Proteins," in R. Stoops (ed.), *Les Protéines*. Brussels: Institut International de Chimie-Solvay, 1953, p. 19.

big enough to be called a protein, has a molecular weight of 3485. In between these values lie the molecular weights of most of the common nonpolymeric natural substances. The molecular weights of proteins start at 6000 for the insulin monomer and go up to values of over a million for some lipoproteins of the blood serum, and for hemocyanins.

It is difficult to generalize about ranges of sizes of proteins of different origins and of different functions. In general, the protein hormones as a group have the lowest molecular weights, none of them have molecular weights above 100,000 (Pedersen). And many of the hormones have molecular weights below 6000; these are generally not to be considered as proteins but as large peptides. Aside from the hormones, proteins range oddly in size regardless of origin or function.

Protein molecules have a tendency to "stick together." They tend to associate with each other and often with other protein molecules. It is therefore proper to inquire whether the particle whose molecular weight is being measured is uniquely the protein molecule or an association of this molecule with other like molecules to produce dimers, trimers, or bigger polymers. In some instances it has been possible to demonstrate such association-dissociation phenomena; and particularly for those proteins for which the primary structure has been determined, it is possible even to be more certain about this relationship. For a long time the molecular weight of insulin was considered to be 12,000 because this was the only size particle encountered in solution. It was only with difficulty that conditions are obtained which demonstrate that the minimum size particle has a weight of 6000.

Some years ago, Svedberg, the pioneer of ultracentrifugation, stated that he thought that all proteins were associations of particles of about 17,000 molecular weight. (See Pedersen.) Indeed, as we have shown in the previous chapter, hemoglobin, which has a molecular weight of 64,000, consists of four chains. But all four chains are not alike, there are two pairs; this is not simply a matter of association of like molecules. Svedberg's hypothesis has not been supported as a general principle. There are, for example, many proteins with molecular weights below 17,000. But it is quite possible that some larger particles will turn out to be aggregates of smaller particles.

Regardless of whether they are aggregation products or not, there is no question that proteins as a class belong to those groups of chemicals which are considered to be large molecules; this largeness, as we will show later, imposes certain pecularities to those molecules not found in small molecules.

## Size

Molecular weight is a convenient way of comparing size of chemical molecules. For larger molecules, however, it is possible to obtain other measures of size either directly by electron microscopy or indirectly from X-ray analyses. In Fig. 5-1 are brought together the two-dimensional projections of a number of protein molecules and familiar unicellular objects (Butler).

## Organization. The Secondary Structure

Beside the primary structure, other structures have been recognized. The primary structure is the bona fide chemical structure; it is the structure determined by chemical bonds between amino acids and between chains of amino acids. The other structures depend on weaker bonds which are much less stable than the chemical bond, but because of their large number are effective in stabilizing certain types of organization and in favoring these over other alternative possibilities. A peptide chain consisting of many amino acids may be folded or may be stretched out. X-ray

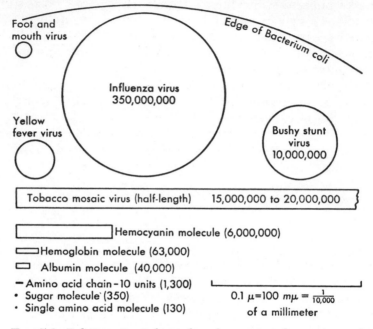

FIG. 5-1. Relative sizes of simple substances and proteins and of various particles and bacteria.*

*Source: J. A. V. Butler, *Inside the Living Cell* (New York: Basic Books, 1959), p. 19.

studies of silk fibroin indicate that it approaches a fully stretched out form. This will be referred to as the *beta* form. Keratin, the protein of hair and wool, exists naturally in a form approaching complete folding, called the *alpha* form. But upon stretching, this can be changed to show the characteristics of a *beta* form. Either form represents a high degree of organization stabilized by weaker chemical forces such as hydrogen bonds. For the *beta* form, the stabilizing forces act between protein chains; hence, the stabilized form may be represented by pleated sheets. The folded form, the *alpha* form, is stabilized by *intra*chain bonds which act between amino acid residues on the same chain holding it together in a folded form. Not all of the

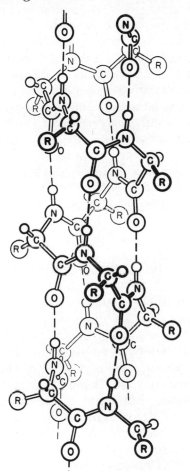

FIG. 5-2. Diagrammatic representation of the alpha helix according to Pauling and Corey. R represents the side chains of amino acids; the dotted lines represent the hydrogen bonds which are between points on the same chain.°

°Reproduced by permission from J. T. Edsall and J. Wyman, *Biophysical Chemistry* (New York: Academic, 1958), Chap. 3.

segments of chains are organized; there exist also regions which do not show either characteristic structure but which apparently are arranged in a random manner.

Thus far we have cited as examples insoluble fibrous proteins. Proteins in solution may also exhibit segments of organization where there is folding, together with portions of unorganized or random regions; and methods have been developed for estimating the percentage of organization. For example, beta lactoglobulin, a protein of milk, is considered to have a high percentage of the amino acid chain in folded configuration; the enzyme ribonuclease is considered to have less than 50 percent of its chains folded; insulin, ovalbumin, and bovine serum albumin occupy intermediate positions. A concept of the organization of a folded chain which has been widely accepted is the alpha helix shown in Fig. 5-2.

## Organization. The Tertiary Structure

We now come to the question of the general three-dimensional arrangement of the chains. And the first question, which in a sense is similar to the one Sanger faced, is whether there is indeed a single shape characteristic of a protein. Some proteins consist of stretched out peptide chains; the molecules are long and narrow. Such are the fibrous proteins. But many proteins are globular and approach spherical shape. Hence their chains would have to be folded and twisted in some sort of a manner to yield a compact arrangement.

An answer to this question has virtually been completed for crystals of hemoglobin and myoglobin as the result of an elegant X-ray analysis conducted by Kendrew, Perutz, and associates in an operation too broad and ambitious to be described in simple terms (Kendrew). We have already noted that hemoglobin consists of four chains each of 17,000 molecular weight. Normal adult hemoglobin contains two pairs of identical chains. Myoglobin is a protein of lower molecular weight (17,000) which occurs in muscle and has an oxygen transfer or holding function in the muscle tissues. By function it is related to hemoglobin; now it is also shown to be related to hemoglobin by structure, since the structure of the myoglobin molecule turns out to be similar to one of the hemoglobin chains. Hemoglobin might be considered to be an orderly arrangement of four molecules each shaped somewhat like myoglobin. Fig. 5-3 shows the outline of the chain of myoglobin and conception of the arrangement of this chain in space. This type of treatment will eventually reveal the amino acid sequences along the chains and hence will be a way of confirming primary structure now deduced only by degradative procedures.

What determines the shape of the molecule? Is this shape built into the primary structure, or is some additional genetic information required to organize the protein in any given particular shape. It is the feeling of Kendrew and Perutz, and of Anfinsen, that there is sufficient information in the amino acid sequences at critical points in the chains to determine the nature and direction of the bends. It might be held provisionally that once the amino acids are put together in the proper sequence, there will be one structure which will be the most stable for that sequence.

## Organization. The Quaternary Structure

There is another aspect of structure, what might be called the quaternary aspect, which results from association of the original chains to form larger molecules. This is differentiated from random aggregation in that this is organized and orderly. Some of this association is reversible depending upon the concentration of salts in solution or on the strength of acid or base. In some instances the association

(a)

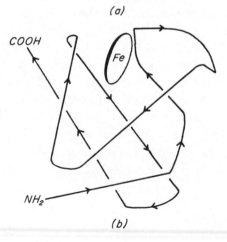

(b)

Fig. 5-3. The tertiary structure of myoglobin. (a) Conception of arrangement in space. (b) Course of the polypeptide chain. The N-terminal end is at the lower left, and the C-terminal at the upper left. The disk marked "Fe" represents the heme group.*

*Reproduced by permission from J. C. Kendrew, R. E. Dickerson, B. E. Strandberg, R. G. Hart, D. R. Davies, D. C. Phillips, and V. C. Shore, "Structure of Myoglobin. A Three-Dimensional Fourier Synthesis at 2A Resolution," *Nature*, vol. 185 (1960), p. 422. The authors note that the plane of the heme group is not correctly indicated in the drawing.

requires stronger conditions such as heating and is only reversed by more vigorous treatment such as with strong alkali.

We have already mentioned that insulin which has a molecular weight of 6000 is ordinarily found as a stable dimer in solution. This unit in turn is in reversible equilibrium with higher association products. When insulin is heated in an acid solution, it aggregates to form fibrils. These are remarkably stable and may be photographed by electron microscopy. If such fibrils are introduced into a solution of otherwise normal insulin, they will eventually incorporate all of the soluble insulin into the fibril structure. This is an organized association of insulin which depends upon the structure of the original molecule and builds upon it.

Collagen is synthesized as a molecule of tropocollagen which consists of three helices of the collagen monomer put together in a single strand. This tropocollagen molecule is the basic unit; it polymerizes to form the collagen fibrils which are the form in which collagen exists in nature.

The structure of tobacco mosaic virus is another illustration of combination of subunits in an orderly way. In this instance the organization of the subunits is aided and controlled by the strand of nucleic acid associated with the protein. Although the molecular weight of a tobacco mosaic virus particle would indicate that its protein component has a weight of 38 million, further examination shows that the protein of tobacco mosaic virus consists of subunits, each of about 18,000 molecular weight; as we have stated previously, the amino acid sequence of this subunit has been elucidated. It now seems reasonably certain that the rodlike subunits are arranged in a helix around the nucleic acid which is the core (Knight).

We have presented four categories of protein structure. It is not to be assumed that these are differentiated one from the other by well-defined means, nor that their order of importance is from primary to quaternary. It is difficult to know where one structure begins and the other ends. For example, even though disulfide bonds are part of the primary structure, they are certainly an important part of the other structures as well. Let it be said that the protein molecule has many degrees and types of organization, which are manifest in many ways: by the sequence of amino acids in the chain, by the folding of chains, by the twistings and turnings of the chains, and by association of subunits into larger groups.

## Transformations

Proteins in solution are not in a static condition. Since the amino acid composition of various portions along the chain differs drastically from that at other portions, there are pressures and counterpressures which provide a tenuous stability to any one form. The best that can be said is that one particular type or form is more favored in any given solution. This great flexibility and mobility of form is the reason given for the participation of proteins as catalysts, as enzymes, in reactions where adjustment in form is part of the catalytic event. It is also the explanation for the sensitivity of the organized structures to changes in environment such as temperature, acidity or alkalinity, or to the presence of surface active agents and a number of other chemicals. It is not unusual for a protein to change its state abruptly with minor changes in the environment. Many of the weak secondary bonds which hold the structure together are broken and reformed when there are changes in structure; the rupture of one bond facilitates the rupture of others. Hence the term cooperative often is employed to express the transformation of proteins.

The entire study of protein chemistry and structure depends on the proposition that it is possible to abstract the protein from its natural environment and put it into a highly artificial one of controlled solvents and temperatures

without altering its structure. Since we are aware of the
sensitivity of protein structure to changes in environment,
we can never be completely sure that some changes do
not take place. There is, however, evidence that many
properties of proteins do remain substantially unaltered
after abstraction from their natural environment. Take
enzymes, for example: these may be isolated from tissues,
animal or plant, and will exhibit their enzymic properties
in the artificial conditions, *in vitro*. This is not only true for
enzymes which are obtained from exudates such as those
from the pancreatic and gastric juices, but also for intracellular enzymes. The evidence of catalytic activity would
seem to suggest that the protein is substantially unaltered;
and this provides confidence that other properties of the
protein are unaltered as well.

Enzymic activity is not the only function that might be
measured: the binding of oxygen by hemoglobin is another
biological property, and so is the polymerization of fibrinogen, or the ability of antibodies to react with antigens. All
are manifestations of biological activity by proteins removed
from their natural environment.

It is possible to alter or destroy biological properties of
proteins by simple means which do not require rupture of
the protein chains, and this enables us to follow transformations of proteins. It is possible to destroy enzymic
activity by heating a protein solution. Besides destroying
biological activity, heat reduces solubility. The coagulation
of egg protein on boiling is an example of such a change.
Changes may also be accomplished by certain chemical
reagents such as urea or detergent solutions, or by subjecting the proteins to strong acid or alkali. In all these
instances, the changes which are observed come about primarily without rupture or cleavage of the chemical bonds
in the proteins. These are transformations of the proteins
and may best be represented as changes in favor of a more
disorganized state.

At first, disorganization involves small changes in the configuration which are reversible if the condition inducing disorganization is not prolonged or too severe. But if such a condition is maintained for sufficiently long periods, then a stage is reached when disorganization may no longer be reversed. Then even primary bonds such as disulfide cross-links may be broken and disorganization is complete. Then the protein behaves more like a random coil, more like most high polymers. There will be less of folding; a greater variety of spacial configurations will be possible. A schematic diagram representing steps in disorganization is given in Fig. 5-4.

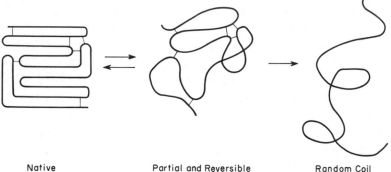

Native                    Partial and Reversible                Random Coil
                              Disorganization

FIG. 5-4. Schematic outline of the course of disorganization of a protein. The lines connecting segments of the chain represent disulfide bond cross links.°

°*Source:* W. Kauzman, "Denaturation of Proteins and Enzymes," in W. D. McElroy & B. Glass (eds.), *The Mechanism of Enzyme Action* (Baltimore, Md.: Johns Hopkins, 1954), p. 70.

There are many consequences of disorganization; the obvious one of course is the loss of biological activity. There are also changes in physical properties, favoring insolubility, higher viscosity, and stickiness. There is a change in susceptibility to action by other enzymes. Many proteins are not digested by proteolytic enzymes until after they have been heated. Chemical availability of reactive groups is more manifest in proteins which have become disorganized; certain reactive groups are not measurable in a native molecule, but become exposed upon transformation. Such groups might be the sulfhydryl of cysteine or some of the other reactive groups on the side chains of the amino acids.

The pathway from amino acids to peptides to protein is one of increasing complexity. But it is not a random complexity—it is a well-ordered complexity. It is not increase in size alone which changes the reactions of amino acids from those which occur in the individual acids to those amino acid residues as they exist in the protein. It is the complex relationship with other amino acids, but this is an ordered complexity.

It is clear now why the chemistry of a protein is not the sum of the chemistry of its individual components, because the reactivity of the components depends in part on their location in the protein, whether they are on the surface or in the interior "protected" from the external environment. This situation can change when the configuration of the protein is altered by heat or by chemical means, and order is changed into randomness.

## SELECTED BIBLIOGRAPHY

Anfinsen, C. B. *The Molecular Basis of Evolution.* New York: Wiley, 1959.
Anson, M. L., K. Bailey, and J. T. Edsall (eds.). *Advances in Protein Chemistry.* New York: Academic (annual).
Anson, M. L. "The Denaturation of Proteins," in R. Stoops (ed.), *Les Protéines.* Brussels: Institut International de Chimie Solvay, 1953
Edsall, J. T., and J. Wyman. "Problems of Protein Structure," *Biophysical Chemistry.* Vol. 1. New York: Academic, 1958, chap. 3, p. 47.
Gross, J. "Collagen," *Sci. Am.,* vol. 204, no. 5 (May 1960), p. 120.
Kauzman, W. "Denaturation of Proteins and Enzymes," in W. D. McElroy and B. Glass (eds.), *The Mechanism of Enzyme Action.* Baltimore, Md.: Johns Hopkins, 1954.
Kendrew, J. C. "The Three-dimensional Structure of a Protein Molecule," *Sci. Am.,* vol. 205, no. 6 (December 1961), p. 96.
Knight, C. A. "The Protein of Tobacco Mosaic Virus," in *Protein Structure and Function,* Report of Symposium held June, 1960, at Brookhaven

National Laboratory, Brookhaven Symposia in Biology, No. 13 (1960).

Linderstrom-Lang, K., and J. A. Schellman. "Protein Structure and Enzyme Activity," in P. D. Boyer et al. (eds.), *The Enzymes.* Vol. 1. New York: Academic, 1959, p. 443.

Low, B. W. "The Use of X-Ray Diffraction in the Determination of Protein Structure," in C. G. Overberger et al. (eds.), "Microstructure of Proteins," Report of a Symposium held September 1960, *J. Polymer Sci.*, vol. 49 (1961), p. 153.

Neurath, H., and K. Bailey (eds.). *The Proteins.* New York: Academic, 1953-54.

Pauling, L. "The Configuration of Polypeptide Chains in Proteins," in R. Stoops (ed.), *Les Protéines.* Brussels: Institut International de Chimie Solvay, 1953, p. 63.

Pedersen, K. O. "The Molecular Weight of Proteins," in R. Stoops (ed.), *Les Protéines.* Brussels: Institut International de Chimie Solvay, 1953, p. 19.

Perutz, M. F. "Structure of Hemoglobin," in *Protein Structure and Function*, Report of Symposium held June 1960 at Brookhaven National Laboratory, Brookhaven Symposia in Biology, No. 13 (1960).

# CHAPTER 6

# *Proteolytic Enzymes and Proteolysis*

ALL KNOWN ENZYMES are proteins. Certain enzymes catalyze the breakdown of proteins; these are called proteolytic enzymes and the process of breakdown is called proteolysis. Enzymes offer numerous facets for study: they may, for example, be studied either as proteins or in terms of their catalytic function. The particular construction which allows a protein to act as an enzyme is receiving considerable attention. Indeed this is one of the exciting fields of enzyme and protein chemistry: the study of the "active center," that portion or configuration of the protein which is responsible for its catalytic function. And when the protein is a particular kind of enzyme, a proteolytic enzyme, an additional aspect is available for study—the action of the protein as an enzyme on protein as a substrate.

But not all proteins are enzymes, least of all proteolytic enzymes. Selection of this class for elaboration in a limited study such as this means that we choose to overlook many other types of enzymes and proteins. We cannot even argue that the ones we choose are typical of enzymes or of proteins; it is well-nigh impossible to find a typical enzyme or protein. Nevertheless, the choice of proteolytic enzymes and proteolysis may be justified because of the emphasis being given in this volume to the role of proteins in foods.

Proteolysis takes place in the digestive tract where ingested proteins are broken down into their constituent amino acids, are absorbed and utilized. The digestive enzymes must be there to act on the proteins but likewise the protein must be available to proteolysis, otherwise it has no value as a foodstuff.

Digestion of proteins as it proceeds *in vivo* is indeed a complex process. Yet some of the events may be reduced to the molecular level of reactions between protein and protein or between protein and protein fragment, because the major proteolytic enzymes of the gastrointestinal tract have been well studied. Pepsin of the stomach was perhaps the first individual enzyme to be recognized—by Spallanzani in 1783. It was the first proteolytic enzyme to be crystallized.

Proteolysis is not limited to the digestive tract. There are intracellular proteases which digest necrotic tissue. The processes of blood clotting and of dissolving of blood clots include proteolysis as a major activity. Plants contain proteolytic enzymes; many bacteria and molds exude proteolytic enzymes into their growth media, and this is one of the ways of producing proteolytic enzymes commercially. The curdling of milk is by proteolysis. Meat is tenderized with a proteolytic enzyme from the papaya fruit. "Black and blue" marks are treated with proteolytic enzymes.

Proteolysis is the fragmentation of a protein by rupture of the peptide bonds between the amino acids making up the protein chain. Fragmentation can be accomplished by boiling in acid or alkali; it can also be accomplished by action of proteases. There is something almost weird about proteolysis, if one looks at it closely. Two unlike proteins collide and then break apart. One, the enzyme, is untouched; the other, the protein substrate, is fragmented. One might well ask: "If a proteolytic enzyme will fragment another protein, why does it not fragment itself?"

Indeed this does happen but at a slower rate than for the substrate.[1] The structure of the protease is such that allows it to act as a catalyst but preserves it from digesting itself at anywhere near the rate with which it fragments other proteins.

## Classification

Proteolytic enzymes have been classified in many ways. It may first be well to categorize the process itself. Proteolysis can go in one of two directions: in one, the end result is fragmentation, complete or partial, depending on the enzyme or enzymes involved; in the other, the proteolysis is a single or small number of events leading to the formation of a new protein with entirely different properties. Prime examples of the first type are the various forms of digestion. But the other is also biologically important: the clotting of blood and the formation of active enzymes from inactive precursors are examples of the second type.

The reason for proteolysis taking one direction or another will become clearer as specific examples are cited, but a partial explanation may be offered at this point. The key lies in the protein substrate, as has been nicely put by Desnuelle (Boyer et al., p. 97). It could be that the protein presents one special portion of its entire surface to the enzyme; it is only here that a rupture in the chain takes place. Let us say that the result is two fragments—one rela-

---

1. The reactions are as follows:
    (1) Protease + protein ⟶ Protease + protein fragments
    (2) Protease + protease ⟶ Protease + protease fragments
Reaction (2) takes place much less frequently than reaction (1). It is possible to modify proteolytic enzymes and bind them chemically on to resins. Then reaction (2) becomes even more infrequent because the protease molecules are hindered from reacting with each other. E. Katchalski, "Water-insoluble Enzyme Derivatives, Their Preparation, Properties and Use in the Study of Native Macromolecules," *Pontifical Acad. Sci.*, vol. 97, no. 22 (1962).

tively small and the other only slightly smaller than the original protein. The structure of this large fragment is so arranged that it no longer presents a surface conducive to further proteolysis. Hence there is, in effect, a new protein. If, contrariwise, when the protein is first acted upon by the proteolytic enzyme the resulting fragments present additional regions for proteolytic enzyme activity, then the rupture of the first bonds makes possible easier rupture of other bonds; the result is a general fragmentation.[2] This explanation reveals that the course of proteolysis is not dominated entirely by the enzyme: the protein substrate is also a directive factor.

The earliest classification of proteolytic enzymes was into one group whose members attack entire proteins, called proteases or proteolytic enzymes, and another group which attacks fragments of proteins (dipeptides, tripeptides, and small peptides), called peptidases. It was thought that those enzymes which attacked proteins could not attack fragments, nor could peptidases attack proteins. Bergmann and his associates showed that the more important determinant of specificity of proteolytic enzymes was the environment around the bond to be ruptured. Some enzymes require basic groups, others aromatic groups in the side chains of the amino acids on one side or the other of the bond to be opened. Some split bonds near the carboxyl end of peptide chains, others near the amino end of the chains; others split only those bonds which are not adjacent either to free amino or carboxyl groups. Hence the observed specificity of proteases as compared to peptidases has been translated into a specificity of environments around the bonds being broken. Specific peptides were synthesized; these could be tested as preferred substrates for the various enzymes; and each enzyme was classified on the basis of its preferred synthetic substrate. Actually the truth lies somewhere in between. Even though enzymes might have well-

2. See page 91.

established specificity on synthetic substrates, this pattern is not followed altogether when the enzyme is acting on intact proteins or on long peptide chains.

There have been other ways of classifying the proteolytic enzyme, by source, or by certain chemical properties (Hartley). For example, some enzymes are inhibited by organophosphorus compounds (nerve gases); it has been proposed that they be called serine proteases because the amino acid serine is the point of attack by this class of inhibitors. Other proteolytic enzymes are sensitive to heavy metals such as mercury. A free sulfhydryl group is required for the action of these enzymes, which have been called thiol proteases. Some enzymes are active only in an acidic medium, such as pepsin and rennin. Some enzymes have been definitely identified as containing intimately bound metals. These have been called metal proteinases and include some members of the older classification of peptidases: carboxypeptidases, aminopeptidase, and dipeptidases.

As the primary structure of more and more protein chains becomes available, it is possible to compare the specificity of various proteases on a natural chain by determining the points of bond rupture. Perhaps the best known peptide chain exposed to a variety of proteolytic enzymes is the oxidized B chain of insulin. The action of various proteolytic enzymes on this chain is shown in Fig. 6-1. Trypsin, perhaps of all the enzymes, retains the selectiveness predicted from studies on synthetic substrates; it only breaks bonds adjacent to either arginine or lysine. But pepsin breaks more bonds on the insulin chain than might have been predicted on the basis of its specificity on small artificial substrates; chymotrypsin occupies an intermediate position.

One of the ways of preserving organization in proteins is by means of disulfide linkages such as exist in ribonuclease and insulin. When these are broken, insulin breaks into two chains and ribonuclease unfolds into one single chain. Another way of unfolding proteins is by subjecting them to strong concentrations of urea or similar reagents, to strong

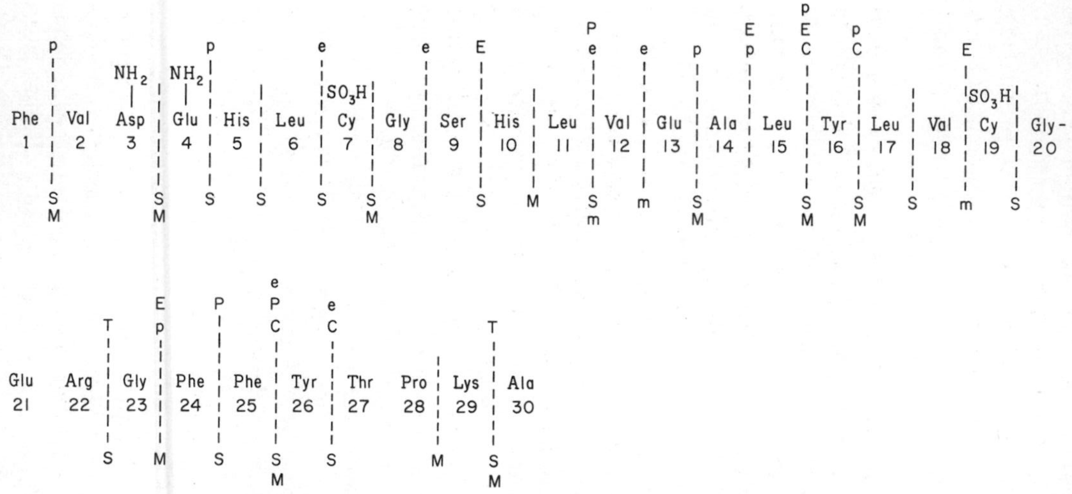

FIG. 6-1. Rupture of Oxidized B Chain of Insulin by Various Proteolytic Enzymes.*

Sequence of the oxidized B chain of insulin, with enzyme cleavage sites (letter codes above each bond, M/m/S markers below):

| No. | Residue | Modification | Markers above | Markers below |
|---|---|---|---|---|
| 1 | Phe | | p | S, M |
| 2 | Val | | | S, M |
| 3 | Asp | NH₂ | | S, M |
| 4 | Glu | NH₂ | p | S |
| 5 | His | | p | S |
| 6 | Leu | | e | S |
| 7 | Cy | SO₃H | e | S, M |
| 8 | Gly | | | S, M |
| 9 | Ser | | e | S |
| 10 | His | | E | S, M |
| 11 | Leu | | | M |
| 12 | Val | | P, e | S, m |
| 13 | Glu | | e | m |
| 14 | Ala | | p | S, M |
| 15 | Leu | | E, p | S, M |
| 16 | Tyr | | E, p, C | S, M |
| 17 | Leu | | p, C | S, M |
| 18 | Val | | E | S |
| 19 | Cy | SO₃H | | m |
| 20 | Gly- | | | S |
| 21 | Glu | | | |
| 22 | Arg | | T | S |
| 23 | Gly | | T, E, p | S, M |
| 24 | Phe | | p | S, M |
| 25 | Phe | | p, P | S, M |
| 26 | Tyr | | e, P, C | S, M |
| 27 | Thr | | C | S |
| 28 | Pro | | | S, M |
| 29 | Lys | | T | S, M |
| 30 | Ala | | | S, M |

*Sources: F. Sanger, "The Structure of Insulin," in D. E. Green (ed.), *Currents in Biochemical Research* (New York: Interscience, 1956); M. A. Naughton and F. Sanger, "The Action of Elastase on the B Chain of Insulin," *Biochem. J.*, vol. 70 (1958) 4 p; P. D. Boyer, H. Lardy and K. Myrbäck (eds.), *The Enzymes*, Vol. 4 (New York: Academic, 1960): pepsin, F. A. Bovey and S. S. Yanari, 6. 77; subtilisin, B. Hagihara, p. 198; mold protease, p. 211.

*Code:* T, trypsin; C, chymotrypsin; S, subtilisin; P, p, pepsin; M, m, mold protease; E, e, elastase. Where noted, the capital letters indicate the major sites of activity. The two chains of insulin were separated by oxidation, hence cysteic acid, CySO₃H, takes the place of cystine.

acid or alkali, or to higher temperatures. And, of course, there is a combination of both rupture of the disulfide bonds and unfolding. Either of these events or their combination makes the protein more susceptible to action by proteolytic enzymes. The strong acidity of the environment in the stomach in which pepsin operates is an important part of the action of this enzyme.

Native trypsin is not attacked by carboxypeptidase, but when it is unfolded by urea and when the disulfide links are ruptured, the carboxyl terminal sequence of amino acids is exposed to proteolysis. Pepsin will only split one bond in the enzyme ribonuclease, but oxidized ribonuclease, i.e., with the disulfide bonds split, is readily digested by this enzyme. Many proteins otherwise immune to breakdown by a specific proteolytic enzyme become susceptible to proteolysis after being coagulated by cooking.

Sometimes the specific coiling of the chain works in the opposite direction. In a short uncoiled chain, the side chains on either side of a bond would be expected to have the most effect in determining susceptibility to proteolysis. In a coiled chain, it is possible to bring to bear on a bond amino acids some distance away on the chain but actually much closer in space because of the twisting and turning and folding of the chains. This may account in part for the change in specificity of pepsin acting on protein chains, as compared to synthetic substances.

## Proteolysis in the Gastrointestinal Tract

In nonruminant animals the general sequence of protein breakdown is first by subjection to strong acids and the enzyme pepsin in the gastric section, followed by digestion by enzymes which operate at neutrality or under slightly alkaline conditions in the intestine. The first enzymes to contact the proteins are the so-called endopeptidases which react with large segments to fragment them into smaller ones. This is followed by digestion with exopeptidases which can react with the smaller fragments, which can split bonds at the end of chains, and split apart dipeptides. There is no line of demarcation where one enzyme ceases to be present and other enzymes take over. There must be areas in the intestine where a maximum variety of enzymes with the most widespread bond-breaking capacity are acting concurrently. It is this cooperative action by numerous proteolytic enzymes which makes possible the efficient digestion of food proteins.

We are indebted to Northrop and his associates for early work in this field. They isolated, purified, and crystallized pepsin, trypsin, chymotrypsin, and carboxypeptidase and studied their properties. These are simple proteins in that they consist solely of amino acid chains; carboxypeptidase, however, requires the presence of a metal ion for activity.

Since proteases digest proteins, there is the problem of confining their activity to the food proteins in the digestive tract. The cells in which they are synthesized must be protected from autodigestion, and these enzymes must be transported from their source of synthesis without damaging normal tissue proteins on the way. Two well-studied phenomena help to explain how this happens: the first is the existence of inactive precursors of the proteolytic enzymes and the second is segregation of the enzymes within the intracellular spaces.

A zymogen is an inactive precursor which can be converted into the enzyme itself by relatively simple means. Pepsin, trypsin, chymotrypsin, and carboxypeptidase are synthesized first in the form of their zymogens. These forms, pepsinogen, trypsinogen, chymotrypsinogen, and procarboxypeptidase, have been isolated and crystallized.

Pepsinogen and trypsinogen are easily converted into their active forms. Acid alone suffices to form pepsin from pepsinogen. Once a small amount of pepsin is formed, this enzyme reacts with more pepsinogen to form more pepsin. This is what is called an autocatalytic process—as more pepsin is formed, the rate of formation of pepsin from the remainder of the pepsinogen increases. Trypsin is activated by a protein present in the intestine called enterokinase by a mode of action not well known; it is presumed to be proteolysis. Here again, once a small amount of trypsin is formed it can react with the remaining trypsinogen molecules to speed up the formation of more trypsin. All other zymogens from the pancreas are activated by trypsin.

Zymogens are activated by a splitting process; one of the fragments has enzymatic activity. This is an example of the formation of a new protein by proteolysis. In some instances only one kind of splitting occurs and, therefore only one kind of enzyme forms from the zymogen. This is true for pepsin and trypsin. Chymotrypsinogen may open up in a number of ways; hence, there exist several forms of the active enzyme. The one which has been most extensively studied is $\alpha$-chymotrypsin. Whereas pepsin and trypsin each consist of a single chain, $\alpha$-chymotrypsin consists of three chains held together by disulfide cross-linkages.

There are some zymogens and enzymes in the digestive tract which have not been as well characterized. Chymotrypsinogen B which occurs in amounts equivalent to chymotrypsinogen A has not been as extensively studied; its activation and the products of activation are not as well characterized. Carboxypeptidase B, originally named protaminase, specifically splits off arginine and lysine when they occur on the carboxyl end of a chain.

Hence, one plausible explanation for the fact that proteolytic enzymes do not damage cells prior to reaching their point of activity is that they are not active until they are in the gastrointestinal tract.

The second part of the story has to do with the synthesis, processing, and transport of the zymogens. This has to do with the architecture of the cell. Even before the electron microscope and in the nineteenth century, Heidenhain noted numerous granules which occupied the apical region of exocrine cells of the pancreas. These granules disappeared shortly after food intake and were replaced with apparently new granules several hours later. Heidenhain concluded that the granules consist of digestive enzyme precursors and he called them "zymogen granules."

A beautiful example of the enrichment in observation made possible by electron microscopy is provided by Palade (Hayaski, p. 64). Besides nuclei, other bodies such as mitochondria and lipid inclusions, the exocrine cells contain an extensive system of vesicles, tubulles, and cisternae interconnected and bounded by membranes. This membrane system has been named the endoplasmic reticulum (Palade, Porter). Another group of scientists describe a somewhat similar category of structures as the "ergastoplasm" (Oberling). Some of the elements of this network have rough surfaces which upon closer examination appear to be a large number of very small granules attached to the outside surfaces of the membranes. These have been identified as particles of ribonucleoprotein (ribosomes); these are presumed to be sites of protein synthesis.

The beginnings of the zymogen granules are first noted in the rough-surfaced elements of the endoplasmic reticulum. Then some of the smooth-surfaced vesicles, or cisternae, appear to be filled with zymogen material. Finally, fully packed, filled vesicles may be seen to congregate at the apical pole. In the last act, the membrane of each zymogen granule becomes continuous with the cell membrane creating an exit through which the contents gain access to the acinar lumen. Hence granules can be produced and discharged without ever being in contact with the cell contents; they are always confined within membranes. An electronmicrograph of a section of the pancreas is shown in Fig. 6-2.

These granules have been isolated and their contents examined. The hypothesis that they are indeed zymogen granules is corroborated by the fact that they were shown to contain trypsinogen, chymotrypsinogen, ribonuclease, procarboxypeptidase, lipase, and amylase. All of these hydrolytic enzymes are separated from the rest of the cell by a membrane barrier clearly visible which measures approximately 70 Angstrom units in thickness.

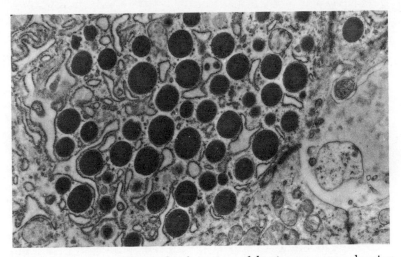

Fig. 6-2. Electronmicrograph of section of bovine pancreas showing portions of acinar cells containing zymogen granules. The granules are the large dark bodies.*

*Reproduced by permission from: L. J. Greene, C. H. W. Hirs, and G. E. Palade, "On the Protein Composition of Bovine Pancreatic Zymogen Granules," *J. Biol. Chem.*, vol. 238 (1963), p. 2054.

## Proteolysis by Microorganisms

Forms of life which do not possess an intestinal tract, digestive organs, or means for ingesting large particles must fragment the proteins in their media into small peptides or amino acids which can be accumulated into the organism This is done for microorganisms by extracellular proteases—proteases expelled from the cell into the medium. Among the better-studied ones are the proteolytic enzymes of *Bacillus subtilis* and from the *Aspergillus* molds. In a suitable medium, *B. subtilis* will produce more than one gram of proteolytic enzyme per liter; hence this becomes a practical way of producing this enzyme. In general, the extracellular enzymes of microorganisms split a wider range of bonds than do proteolytic enzymes of the gastrointestinal tract. As was shown in Fig. 6-1, there are many more points of rupture of the insulin B chain by the enzymes from microorganisms than by any one of the gastrointestinal enzymes.

## Proteolysis in Blood

Proteolysis is a central part of the clotting process and equally essential to the dissolution of clots. Clotting and fibrinolysis are complicated processes involving a number of events, some in series, some in parallel, some in opposing directions; we will deal with this complex phenomenon only in outline form. The essentials of clot formation are the polymerization of fibrinogen to form fibrils which provide the mechanical support for all the elements of the clot; fibrinolysis is the breakdown of fibrin by proteolytic action.

Fibrinogen, a blood protein, is converted under circumstances such as attend injury to a blood vessel into fibrin monomer, a protein which polymerizes spontaneously, i.e., associates with itself many times over. The conversion of fibrinogen is by proteolysis; the products are the monomer and small peptides, and the proteolytic enzyme is called thrombin.

Thrombin, in turn, does not exist as such in blood but as its zymogen, prothrombin. The zymogen is converted into thrombin by a number of agents such as tissue thromboplastin, calcium ion, accelerator globulin, platelet factors, and citrate. Proteolytic enzymes such as trypsin and papain will also activate prothrombin; this, of course, is not the natural pathway. In all of the activations a portion of the protein is split off, thereby unmasking the active thrombin.

But thrombin does not last long in the blood since natural inhibitors combine to neutralize its activity. Hence, its availability for action on fibrinogen is short-lived.

It has been known for many years that blood clots will liquefy spontaneously; and this, too, is the result of proteolysis. Among the many constituents of a clot is the protein plasminogen which under proper stimuli is converted into a proteolytic enzyme plasmin (also called fibrinolysin); this enzyme will dissolve the proteins in clots. The mechanisms for conversion of the zymogen into the enzyme are not clearly known. Urokinase, a protein isolated from urine will activate plasminogen *in vitro,* so will kinases in tissue and in the plasma; proteolytic enzymes such as trypsin, and plasmin itself, will activate the zymogen. Streptokinase is an extracellular bacterial protein produced by actively growing hemolytic streptococci which can initiate activation of plasminogen. There are also inhibitors of the activation process and of the active plasmin.

It has been suggested that plasmin participates in certain metabolic processes such as dissolution of pathologic fibrin deposits, destruction of plasma proteins, resolution of inflammatory processes, and maintenance of fluidity of menstrual blood. There is also the suggestion that impaired fibrinolytic mechanisms may underlie the pathogenesis of atherosclerosis. The zymogen-enzyme conversion already noted for the proteases in the gastrointestinal tract functions differently in the blood. Here the problem is that of hemostasis: the enzymes function only when there is a disturbance of the natural order of blood circulation; once the disturbance is corrected (a clot is formed or a clot is dissolved) there is no further enzyme activity. Normal proteolysis in the blood is on an "event" basis, not continuous.

## Proteolysis in Tissues

Proteolytic enzymes are distributed in many tissues in, probably, a ubiquitous type of proteolysis. The enzymes of this class, cathepsins, are not in the gastrointestinal tract nor in the blood—they are in the tissues themselves. They do not exist as zymogens nor, under ordinary circumstances, do they digest the cellular proteins. They are only active in injured and dead cells or under pathological conditions. De Duve and his associates (Hayashi, p. 128) have presented evidence that cathepsins and other hydrolytic enzymes are present in cells inside subcellular organelles which they have named "lysosomes." As long as the cell is undamaged, the lysosomes remain intact; the enzymes contained within are prevented from reacting with the cellular constituents by the presence of a membrane. When the cell dies or when, for other reasons, the lysosome membrane is ruptured, the enzymes are released and then can react with adjacent cellular tissue. This might be the mechanism by which necrotic tissue is removed and the constituents made available for the synthesis of new cells. This may be one of the means for continuous building and rebuilding of proteins in tissues.

Existence of lysosomes as morphological entities different from mitochondria or microsomes has been inferred from biochemical evidence—the enzymes of the lysosomes may be separated from the enzymes of the mitochondria and microsomal fraction on the basis of differences in density of the particles from which they are obtained. Direct evidence of the identity of these particles by electron microscopy is now beginning to accumulate. No doubt, there will be found a family of lysosomes with individuals differing one from the other in morphology and biochemical expression.

## Other Properties of Proteases

Proteolytic enzymes are members of a larger class of enzymes, hydrolases. These are enzymes which catalyze the rupture of a bond by the interposition of water; they also include esterases and lipases. Esterases catalyze the hydrolysis of ester bonds; one of the more interesting esterases is the one involved in hydrolysis of the important ester acetylcholine. Lipases catalyze the hydrolysis of triglycerides such as natural fats and oils. Indeed many of the proteolytic enzymes—as, for example, trypsin—will also hydrolyze esters as well. Another group of hydrolases are those which catalyze the hydrolysis of carbohydrates such as starch; amylases are members of this group.

In a larger sense, hydrolytic activity is one aspect of a broader activity, a transferase activity. A bond is broken by interposing another compound; this compound may be water, in which instance we are dealing with a hydrolase, or it may be another molecule. Indeed it was found that proteolytic enzymes may catalyze the construction of larger peptide chains from smaller chains. In some instances this takes place by reversal of the process of hydrolysis, but more frequently by transferring the elements of a smaller chain to another so that eventually larger chains are built up. In the latter circumstance, the energy of the chemical bonds is conserved in the exchange. At one time it was thought that reversal of hydrolysis was the mechanism of protein synthesis; it is now known that this is not true, that more complex energy-requiring or energy-conserving mechanisms are involved. But protease reactions which result in an increase in the size of the chains may play some role in the metabolism of proteins.

## General Comments

It would be unwise to extrapolate from the description of proteolysis and proteolytic enzymes to enzymes in general or to proteins in general. There is such a wide variety of reactions catalyzed by enzymes that those performed by hydrolases and transferases are only a small portion of the total; from the description of hydrolases one could hardly be expected to get a notion of the enzymes involved in energy production, in photosynthesis, and synthesis in general. But since all enzymes are proteins, some of the general features of proteins which are exhibited by the proteolytic enzymes are also found in other enzymes.

It is quite evident that there are many gaps left in the information on the proteolytic enzymes. Wherever there has been success in isolating pure members of the group there is where the greatest progress has been made. There is no short-cut to the path of understanding life processes; the participants in these processes must be isolated in as pure a state as possible and then understood in the context of the milieu in which they are found.

And this milieu is not only the soluble materials of a cell but is the entire cellular architecture. The action of enzymes can be studied in many instances in homogenous solutions; but the action of enzymes in real life, *in vivo*, is circumscribed by the structures of the cells and the materials with which the enzyme is in contact. This aspect of biochemistry is a relatively new and important aspect, the realm of cellular biology. The organization of life is on many levels. It is on a molecular level in the enzymes themselves, it is on a subcellular level in granules, vesicles, and other organelles, and on a multicellular organ level. Every one of these levels of organization contributes to the overall organization of living material.

## SELECTED BIBLIOGRAPHY

Balls, A. K., and M. W. Kies. "Proteases," in J. A. Anderson (ed.), *Enzymes and Their Role in Wheat Technology*. New York: Interscience, 1946, p. 231.

Bergmann, M. "A Classification of Proteolytic Enzymes," *Advan. Enzymol.*, vol. 3 (1942), p. 49.

Boyer, P. D., H. Lardy, and K. Myrbäck (eds.). *The Enzymes*. Vol. 4. New York: Academic, 1960.

Bracket, J., et al. "The Living Cell," *Sci. Am.*, vol. 205, no. 3 (September 1961).

de Duve, C. "The Lysosome," *Sci. Am.*, vol. 208, no. 5 (May 1963), p. 64.

Fruton, J. S. "Enzymic Hydrolysis and Synthesis of Peptide Bonds," in Harvey Society of New York, *The Harvey Lectures*, Series 51. New York: Academic, 1957, p. 64.

Hall, C. E., and H. S. Slayton. "The Fibrinogen Molecule: Its Size, Shape and Mode of Polymerization," *J. Biophys. Biochem. Cytol.,* vol. 5 (1959), p. 11.

Hartley, B. S. "Proteolytic Enzymes," *Ann. Rev. Biochem.,* vol. 29 (1960), p. 45.

Hayashi, T. (ed.). *Subcellular Particles.* New York: Ronald, 1959.

Neurath, H. "The Activation of Zymogens," *Adv. Protein Chem.,* vol. 12 (1957), p. 319.

Nielands, J. B., and P. K. Stumpf. *Outline of Enzyme Chemistry.* 2nd ed. New York: Wiley, 1958.

Northrop, J. H. *Crystalline Enzymes.* New York: Columbia U. P., 1939.

Oberling, C. "The Structure of Cytoplasm," in G. H. Bourne and J. F. Danielli (eds.), *International Review of Cytology.* Vol. 8. New York: Academic, 1959, p. 1.

Porter, K. R. "The Submicroscopic Morphology of Protoplasm," in Harvey Society of New York, *The Harvey Lectures,* Series 51. New York: Academic, 1957, p. 175.

Scheraga, H. A. *Protein Structure.* New York: Academic, 1961, p. 129.

Seegers, W. H. "Coagulation of the Blood," *Advan. Enzymol.,* vol. 16 (1955), p. 23.

Sherry, S., A. P. Fletcher, and N. Alkjaersig. "Fibrinolysis and Fibrinolytic Activities of Man," *Physiol. Rev.,* vol. 39 (1959), p. 343.

Smith, E. L. "The Specificity of Certain Peptidases," *Advan. Enzymol.,* vol. 12 (1951), p. 191.

2. Type 1. Fragmentation:

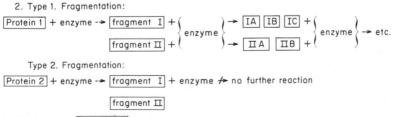

Type 2. Fragmentation:

In this instance fragment I is the new protein.

# III

## PROTEINS
## IN FOOD

# CHAPTER 7

# The
# Protein Requirements
# of Homo Sapiens:

## I

FRANÇOIS MAGENDIE in 1816 recognized the absolute need for protein, a conclusion reached after studying diets poor in nitrogenous substances then being prescribed for the cure and prevention of urinary calculi. His interest led him to feed nitrogen-free diets to dogs. Sugar, olive oil, gum, or butter were each fed to dogs as their sole nutriment, whereupon all the dogs developed severe debility and died within a month. This could be prevented by including protein-containing foods in their diet. We now know that these diets were seriously deficient in certain vitamins and, indeed, Magendie observed peculiar lesions around the eyes—symptoms of vitamin-A deficiency rediscovered a century later. But the major deficiency was of protein; this investigation established the primary role of protein in nutrition.

Actually, for a while thereafter protein was considered the important foodstuff—the only important foodstuff. Foods were rated by Boussingault on the basis of their nitrogen content. Protein was considered by Liebig as the one structural food; the other food principles were required to support respiration. It was only later, toward the end of the century, that the emphasis on proteins was modified by the knowl-

95

edge that fats and carbohydrates were also important and necessary. And only in the twentieth century was full recognition achieved of the role of trace elements and vitamins.

After Magendie there was no longer any question that protein was required in mammalian diets; the problem became that of determining the amount of protein needed. Carl Voit was perhaps the first to attempt a quantitative formulation of protein requirements. From studies of the protein needs of dogs and from surveys of diets of moderately active men, he decided that 118 grams (a little over one quarter of a pound) of protein daily was the desirable allowance for adult man. This Voit standard of 1881 has been disputed since then by many who felt that less protein would be satisfactory; modern standards call for much less. No doubt the early overemphasis on protein which relegated a minor role to the other foodstuffs contributed also to an overstatement of protein needs. Even Voit found a vegetarian who was able to maintain good health at protein intake levels of almost half his recommendation.

Chittenden, after an extensive investigation, concluded that one-half of the 118 grams of protein daily was sufficient to meet all real physiological needs under ordinary conditions of life. He felt very strongly the need for moderation in protein intake. It was his opinion that people (in the United States) consume much more food than is necessary and that this excess is in the long run detrimental to health. His general position is contained in the following quotation:

Physiological economy in nutrition means temperance, and not prohibition. It means full freedom of choice in the selection of food. It is not cereal diet nor vegetarianism but it is the judicious application of scientific truth to the art of living, in which man is called up to apply to himself that same care and judgment in the protection of his bodily machinery that he applies to the mechanical products of his skill and creative power. (p. 475.)

## *Allowances of Food and Nutrition Board (U.S.)*

It is our intention to open the discussion on protein requirements by presenting the recommended allowances of the Food and Nutrition Board of the National Research Council–National Academy of Sciences (U. S.). We will then go back and try to understand how such figures are developed.

In the example of a modern standard (the one of the Food and Nutrition Board), we are listing the recommendations for all of the components of the diet, not merely for protein. This is by way of emphasis, that protein nutrition is not independent of total nutrition. Standards for protein requirements are based upon the assumption of an otherwise adequate nutrition. Previously we had divided foods into two groups: those that provide energy for maintenance of life, and those that provide special nutrients. The energy, derived primarily from fats and carbohydrates is measured as calories,[1] a unit of measure of heat energy; the other foodstuffs are described as specific quantities of the individual components. Since proteins provide the building blocks for construction of body protein and other important constituents, and since it has already been shown that there is an absolute need for protein in the diet, they are listed separately.

The recommended dietary allowances (revised 1958) are shown in the accompanying table (Table 7-1); they are intended for persons normally active in a temperate climate. The amounts of calories and nutrients recommended are believed to be adequate to maintain good nutrition in healthy persons in the United States. But the allowances of

1. A calorie is the amount of energy required to raise the temperature of 1 gram of water 1 degree Centigrade. A kilocalorie is 1,000 calories; it is denoted as "Calorie," the measure generally used in nutrition. Wherever reference is made to *specific* quantities of energy, the capital "C" is used here.

## TABLE 7–1

### Recommended Daily Dietary Allowances[1]

| | Age, yrs. | Weight, lb | Height, in. | Number of Calories | Protein, g | Calcium, g | Iron, mg | Vitamin A, I.U. | Thiamine, mg | Riboflavin, mg | Niacin, mg | Ascorbic Acid, mg | Vitamin D, I.U. |
|---|---|---|---|---|---|---|---|---|---|---|---|---|---|
| Men | 25 | 154 | 69 | 3,200 | 70 | 0.8 | 10 | 5,000 | 1.6 | 1.8 | 21 | 75 | — |
| | 45 | 154 | 69 | 3,000 | 70 | 0.8 | 10 | 5,000 | 1.5 | 1.8 | 20 | 75 | — |
| | 65 | 154 | 69 | 2,550 | 70 | 0.8 | 10 | 5,000 | 1.3 | 1.8 | 18 | 75 | — |
| Women | 25 | 128 | 64 | 2,300 | 58 | 0.8 | 12 | 5,000 | 1.2 | 1.5 | 17 | 70 | — |
| | 45 | 128 | 64 | 2,200 | 58 | 0.8 | 12 | 5,000 | 1.1 | 1.5 | 17 | 70 | — |
| | 65 | 128 | 64 | 1,800 | 58 | 0.8 | 12 | 5,000 | 1.0 | 1.5 | 17 | 70 | — |
| Pregnant (second half) | | | | +300 | +20 | 1.5 | 15 | 6,000 | 1.3 | 2.0 | +3 | 100 | 400 |
| Lactating (28 ounces daily) | | | | +1,000 | +40 | 2.0 | 15 | 8,000 | 1.7 | 2.5 | +2 | 150 | 400 |
| Infants | 2–6 mos. | 13 | 24 | lb × 54.5 | | 0.6 | 5 | 1,500 | 0.4 | 0.5 | 6 | 30 | 400 |
| | 7–12 mos. | 20 | 28 | lb × 45.4 | | 0.8 | 7 | 1,500 | 0.5 | 0.8 | 7 | 30 | 400 |
| Children | 1–3 | 27 | 34 | 1,300 | 40 | 1.0 | 7 | 2,000 | 0.7 | 1.0 | 8 | 35 | 400 |
| | 4–6 | 40 | 43 | 1,700 | 50 | 1.0 | 8 | 2,500 | 0.9 | 1.3 | 11 | 50 | 400 |
| | 7–9 | 60 | 51 | 2,100 | 60 | 1.0 | 10 | 3,500 | 1.1 | 1.5 | 14 | 60 | 400 |
| | 10–12 | 79 | 57 | 2,500 | 70 | 1.2 | 12 | 4,500 | 1.3 | 1.8 | 17 | 75 | 400 |
| Boys | 13–15 | 108 | 64 | 3,100 | 85 | 1.0 | 15 | 5,000 | 1.6 | 2.1 | 21 | 90 | 400 |
| | 16–19 | 139 | 69 | 3,600 | 100 | 1.4 | 15 | 5,000 | 1.8 | 2.5 | 25 | 100 | 400 |
| Girls | 13–15 | 108 | 63 | 2,600 | 80 | 1.3 | 15 | 5,000 | 1.3 | 2.0 | 17 | 80 | 400 |
| | 16–19 | 120 | 64 | 2,400 | 75 | 1.3 | 15 | 5,000 | 1.2 | 1.9 | 16 | 80 | 400 |

*Source:* Food and Nutrition Board, National Academy of Sciences-National Research Council. Designed for maintenance of good nutrition of healthy persons in the United States. Revised 1958.

[1] 145 pounds is equivalent to 70 kilograms; 60 inches is equivalent to 175 centimeters; 1 gram (g) is 1000 milligrams (mg); 454 g is equivalent to one pound; I.U. stands for International Unit of the vitamin. The 1963 revision of the recommended allowances shows a general reduction in calories, reduction in protein for children, and some reduction in the vitamins thiamine, riboflavin, niacin equivalent, and ascorbic acid. For example, men and women age 25 are allowed 2,900 and 2,100 Calories, respectively; boys and girls age 15-18 are allowed 85 and 58 grams of protein, respectively.

nutrients are higher than the least amounts required for health; they are intended to cover the needs of persons who have the highest requirements and hence they provide a margin of safety.

Allowances for adults are given for a reference man and woman. The reference man is described as 25 years old, weighing 70 kilograms (154 lb), living at a mean external temperature of 20°C, and engaged in moderate physical activity, such as light industry or as a deliveryman, painter, or outdoor salesman. The reference woman is described as being 25 years old, 58 kilograms (128 lb), and engaged in moderate activity, examples of which are as a homemaker, saleswoman, or bench worker in a factory. Adults who differ from this norm of modern activity must adjust their calorie intake accordingly. Coal miners, for example, expend up to 4,000 Calories per day, whereas sedentary clerks will use no more than 2,400 Calories in a day. Tables are available for adjustment of calorie allowances by persons who differ in size and age from these reference individuals. For example, calorie allowances for age 45 are 6 percent less than for age 25; and for age 65, 21 percent less than for the reference man.

Notice the high requirements for boys and girls. When a father eats as much as his college-age son, either he is eating too much or his son too little. The same holds true for a mother and her teen-age daughter. Notice also the increased requirements for pregnant and lactating women. Although allowances are not given for protein intake requirements during infancy, it is generally held that intakes of 1.5 grams of protein for each pound of body weight are ample for healthy infants.

A number of nutrients which are recognized as essential were not specified by amount in these recommendations. These include carbohydrates, fat, and water; minerals such as sodium, potassium, phosphorus, magnesium, copper, iodine, cobalt, zinc, manganese, and molybdenum; and the vitamins: folacin, $B_6$, $B_{12}$, pantothenic acid, biotin, E, and

K. In some instances the requirements for these nutrients are not known, but in most instances deficiencies are not likely to occur with the diet ordinarily available. A selection of foods to supply all the recommended nine nutrients will generally supply enough of the other nutrients.

## Food Guides

The United States Department of Agriculture in numerous publications has provided suggestions on how to meet the requirements. Milk or its equivalent is suggested for everyone: three to four cups for children, four or more cups for teen-agers, and two or more cups for adults. Two or more servings of meat, poultry, fish, or eggs daily are recommended, with occasional servings of dry beans, dry peas, and nuts as alternates. Vegetables and fruits furnish much of the vitamin A and nearly all the vitamin C (ascorbic acid). Four or more daily servings of vegetables and fruit are recommended; included are a serving of a citrus fruit or another source of vitamin C and a serving at least every other day of a dark green or deep yellow vegetable to provide vitamin A. Bread and cereal, especially the whole-grain, enriched, and restored kinds, are sources of protein, iron, several of the B vitamins, and food energy (calories).

The same principles follow for all, even those who are trying to lose weight. The following is quoted from recommendations in the 1959 *Yearbook of Agriculture:*

Weight watchers can use the pattern of choices suggested by the daily guide in planning low calorie meals, since they need the same kinds of food for health as everyone else.

To cut down on calories and fat, fluid and dry skim milk and buttermilk can be used in place of whole milk; cheese made from skim milk, as cottage cheese without added cream, can be used instead of whole milk cheese. Fat can be trimmed from meat before eating. Meat can be broiled or roasted rather than fried. Vegetables served plain without cream sauces or seasoned with only a small amount of table or other fat, if any, and fruit without added sugar or cream give fewer calories.

Pies, cakes, and other rich desserts can add many calories to the diet. Jam, jellies, sugar and other sweets used frequently or in generous amounts also mean extra calories.

Tables listing the amount of nutrients in common foods are available from many sources and in many languages. They are mostly for the benefit of nutritionists and dietitians who are best equipped to design diets for general or individual circumstances.

It is noteworthy that surveys conducted in four military training camps in the United States showed that the average of nutrients consumed daily per soldier was 4,265 Calories, 131 grams of protein, 201 grams of fat, and 484 grams of carbohydrates. When we consider that all soldiers proportionately eat better than the average of their counterpart in age in civilian life, we realize that here is yet another "hidden" cost of war and preparation for war.

## Definition of Protein?

Of all the nutrients listed in the table of recommended dietary allowances, only the proteins are not clearly defined. Proteins are described by weight as grams of crude protein (nitrogen multiplied by 6.25). In order for this recommendation to apply generally it is required that all proteins be alike in food value. But is this so? Instinctively we would suspect that proteins would be different, one from the other, if only from visual observations. No one would think of considering hair, wool, silk, or feathers as edible, even though they are almost completely protein. And even edible-appearing proteins differ greatly in their nutritive value: compare egg proteins to gelatin. What then is the meaning of the requirement of 70 grams of protein per day for the adult male in actual practical terms? Actually it does not mean 70 grams of any kind of protein per day; it means 70 grams of the kind of protein generally eaten by Americans. It implies the recognition that more than 50 percent of the protein eaten in the United States is of animal origin. Other things being equal, animal protein is more nutritious than vegetable protein (more about that later). Therefore, it can safely be assumed that the average protein consumed in the United States is of high quality.

But this does not answer our question—it merely provides an answer for a specific, relatively well-defined situation. Is it possible to define protein in such a way for nutritional purposes that it has the same significance anywhere in the world? Is it possible to measure and compare different protein sources for their value nutritionally?

We might also ask how the basis for the recommended allowances was reached. How do these differ from minimum requirements of protein for different individuals? The general approach has been to decide minimum requirements and then to leave a margin of safety so that even those who require much more than the average will have their needs satisfied. But then the question remains: What is a realistic factor of safety? A country with ample food supplies can afford a high factor of safety but the same factors would be unrealistic in a country already with less than enough protein. And there is the question of surfeit: Is there a danger from prescribing too much protein? The term "adequate" is ambiguous. It certainly includes that needed for growth and maintenance of protein equilibrium. But is there also a "hygienic requirement" to provide for stresses of everyday life, not so easily defined or measured?

We bring up these questions because to understand the issues revolving about protein requirements is to understand the art and science of protein nutrition. But above this we raise these questions because there is a certain magic about numbers. To the uninitiated there is a certainty and finality about numbers; unless there is an awareness also of the basis for the quantitative decisions and of their degree of reliability, one is likely to draw inferences far beyond those which are warranted.

## SELECTED BIBLIOGRAPHY

"Army Standard," *Nutr. Rev.*, vol. 18 (1960), p. 203.

Beach, E. F. "Proteins in Nutrition (Historical)," in M. Sahyun (ed.), *Proteins and Amino Acids in Nutrition.* New York: Reinhold, 1948, p. 2.

Chittenden, R. H. *Physiological Economy in Nutrition.* New York: Stokes, 1904.

*Food: The Yearbook of Agriculture, 1959.* Washington, D. C.: U. S. Dept. of Agriculture, 1959.

Maynard, L. A. "An Adequate Diet," *J. Am. Med. Assoc.*, vol. 170 (May 23, 1959), p. 457.

"Nutritive Value of Foods," in *Home and Garden Bulletin No. 72.* Washington, D. C.: U. S. Dept. of Agriculture, 1960.

Page, Louise, and Esther F. Phipard. "Essentials of an Adequate Diet," in *Home Economics Research Report No. 3.* Washington, D. C.: U. S. Dept. of Agriculture, 1957.

Page, Louise, and Lillian J. Fincher. "Food and Your Weight," in *Home and Garden Bulletin No. 74.* Washington, D. C.: U. S. Dept. of Agriculture, 1960.

*Recommended Dietary Allowances,* Publication 589, Food and Nutrition Board. Washington, D. C.: National Academy of Sciences-National Research Council, 1958.

Shank, R. E. "Recommended Dietary Allowances," *Am. J. Public Health*, vol. 49 (1959), p. 1001.

# CHAPTER 8

# *The Nutritive Value of Proteins*

WE MIGHT BEGIN by admitting that proteins differ in their nutritive value, that some are good and some are poor or worthless. We might even admit that we know perhaps the most important reason for the difference: it is their amino acid composition. To introduce this subject, however, it is not necessary to assume anything about the composition of proteins or about the role of amino acids. It is possible to rate proteins in a rank of nutritive value by empirical observations alone, and even to assign numbers to these ratings. It is only when there is a desire to interpret these ratings and project them to new and unusual situations that the need arises to understand the reasons behind difference in nutritive value.

To measure the nutritive value of proteins, it is necessary to devise a regime in experimental animals whereby their performance is made dependent on the amount and kind of protein eaten. Then protein from several sources is substituted in the diet: the relative response of the animal to one protein as compared to another is considered a measure of the quality of the protein.

## Experimental Animals

One of the most popular experimental animals for nutritional research is the white rat. It is small and does not consume much food; hence it can be used in experiments where the food is limited or expensive, as, for example, in vitamin or trace nutrient research. Moreover, it does not take up much space; quite a number of animals may be used in the same experiment to provide sufficient data for statistical analysis. It grows rapidly, is easily handled, and is relatively free from disease. The breeds for experimental purposes are well standardized. Even so, it was not easy to initiate rats into a career of being so important an adjunct to nutritional investigations. McCollum started the first rat colony in 1907 when he was at the University of Wisconsin. He had difficulty in convincing the authorities, who were reluctant to use in experimental tests an animal which was normally considered a pest, and equally reluctant to do any research at an Agricultural Experiment Station on any but farm animals. Nevertheless he persisted and was able to start his colony with a dozen albinos which he bought with his own money from a stock dealer. Shortly afterwards the famous team of Osborne and Mendel established their rat colonies for the purpose of testing the nutritive value of proteins.

Other experimental animals have been used, among them mice, dogs, and chicks, large livestock, and, of course, humans. Most experiments cannot be conducted on humans; we are dependent, therefore, on the considerable similarities in nutritional response among all higher mammals. Yet it is always a comfort when it is possible to repeat some experiments on humans and achieve results comparable to those obtained on animals.

## Methods for Measuring Nutritive Value

The function of dietary protein is twofold: for maintenance, to replace the nitrogen lost daily in metabolism; and for growth, for the elaboration of protein in new tissues. One or the other of these functions may be the principal factor measured depending upon the experimental situation. We might examine three such situations: a growing animal, an adult animal, and a depleted adult animal. In the growing animal, it is the contribution to growth which is measured, although obviously a certain proportion of the ingested nitrogen goes for maintenance; over 80 percent of the nitrogen requirements of a month-old rat are for growth. Only maintenance function is measured on adult animals. And the depleted animal is an artificial one: it is deliberately deprived of nitrogen-containing foods until a well-defined deficiency develops. The rate and completeness of recovery as affected by the kind of nitrogen source in the diet is measured in this type of experiment. While these various methods and their several variations differ widely in experimental procedures, they purport to measure the same thing: the efficacy of a given source of dietary proteins to support protein synthesis in the body of its consumer. The only difference lies in the purpose for which the protein is being synthesized: for growth, or to replace protein that is lost in the ordinary wear and tear of metabolism, or to synthesize protein which has been lost by deliberate depletion or by the kind of depletion which might take place in injury.

GROWTH

Growth is an obvious way for measuring synthesis; this has been one of the first methods devised for measuring nutritive value. Suppose we were to start with young rats and feed them various diets, and suppose that the protein level in the diet is maintained at 10 percent and it is the only known variable—all other nutrients being fed in sufficient quantities and remaining the same in all diets for all the rats in the experiment. Then the gain in weight of a group of rats fed the better proteins would be larger and presumably proportional to the quality of the protein. The *gain in weight* of rats in such an experiment divided by the *amount of protein* which they eat is called the "protein efficiency ratio": the higher the ratio, the better is the protein. Whole eggs have a protein efficiency ratio of 3.8 according to H. H. Mitchell. This means that under well-described experimental conditions one pound of that protein will support an increase in weight of 3.8 pounds in a growing animal. All other proteins have a lower protein efficiency ratio.

## NITROGEN BALANCE

Discussions of this measure are either in terms of dietary nitrogen or as protein (nitrogen $\times$ 6.25). Actually, the former is the way the experiments are conducted: the nitrogen content of the diet is measured and the gain or loss of nitrogen in the experimental subject is observed. This information can then be translated into terms of protein changes.

Even when there is no necessity for growth or when there is no additional requirement of protein needed to repair damaged tissues or to replete tissues which have been depleted of protein, there is still needed a certain minimum amount of protein daily to replace protein lost by metabolism.

We can understand this point better if we realize that any given molecule of protein has a limited life span. A certain percentage of the protein in any tissue is being broken down and replaced with newly synthesized protein. Some tissues are more in a state of flux than others. The blood plasma proteins have a half-life of 14 days. This means that 50 percent of the plasma proteins existing at any given moment are gone after 14 days and replaced by new proteins. The average half-life of overall tissue protein was estimated at 80 days and that of muscle at 158 days.

As the proteins are degraded, the constituents of the proteins, the amino acids, go into a metabolic pool from which are drawn the building blocks for the protein to be synthesized. Not always do the tissues regain in new protein that which they lost in breakdown. There are readjustments—from time to time some tissues gain in proteins as others lose. Nor is the process of addition of endogenous amino acids and their withdrawal from the pool completely balanced; there are losses. A proportion of the amino acids, instead of going back into protein construction, are metabolized for energy, as are fats and carbohydrates. The nitrogen from these proteins eventually finds its way into the nitrogen of the urine. Neither is all of the exogenous protein, that which comes from the food, converted quantitatively into tissue protein. Some of it is metabolized for energy, particularly when there is an excess of protein or when the protein is of lower quality; the nitrogen goes into the urine. Even when no protein is fed, there is a daily loss of nitrogen in the urine and sweat. This is the nitrogen that must be replaced by dietary nitrogen—the nitrogen that is required for maintenance.

The perfect dietary protein must be able to replace *weight for weight* the nitrogen lost by metabolism. An inferior protein would have to be fed in larger amounts to replace the lost protein nitrogen. This then is the principle of the nitrogen balance. Under well-defined experimental conditions it is possible to measure the amount of nitrogen needed to keep an animal in nitrogen balance, i.e., to equate the losses with the gains in nitrogen so that there is no net change. Under those circumstances we define biological value of a protein as the ratio of the retained nitrogen over the absorbed nitrogen multiplied by a hundred. The perfect protein, therefore, will have a biological value of 100. Sometimes, experimental values slightly greater than 100 are obtained, but these have no significance and merely reflect the limitations of the experimental method.

REPLETION

The third method, the repletion method developed by Cannon, substitutes the *weight regained* by a protein-depleted adult rat for the *weight gain* of growing rats. Depletion of rats is accomplished by feeding a protein-free diet until the animals have lost 25 percent of their initial body weight. Then they are fed the protein under test and the rate of repletion is measured. Twelve days have been required by some for depletion and a similar time for repletion. Cannon found a seven-day repletion time adequate. This then is a quick method which provides data similar to the protein efficiency ratio.

All methods of measuring nutritive quality of proteins suffer from the complexity of the consequences of dietary protein: it is not simply a matter of substituting one protein for another. There is a dynamic interchange of the proteins in the various tissues of the animals. There are redistributions of proteins within the individual as his condition varies or as his protein supply changes. No one single measurement, certainly, will provide a clear picture of everything that is going on. Allison provided an interesting example of this complexity. He fed puppies the same amount of protein intake, but one group received egg protein while another was fed wheat gluten. Both groups of puppies gained the same body weight over the feeding period, but the composition of their bodies and their behavior differed markedly. The animals fed egg protein were lean and very active. Those fed wheat gluten were obese, inactive, and the development of their skeletal system was delayed. The puppies fed the egg protein gained twice as much body protein as those fed wheat gluten. In this experiment, gain in weight certainly did not correlate with an optimum balanced growth pattern.

But since it is impossible for the experimenter to measure simultaneously, or even anticipate, all of the changes that take place when quality and amount of protein in a diet are changed, he chooses certain measurements which in his opinion might reflect overall changes, in full view of the limitations of this procedure. It might well be anticipated that there will be improvements on the basic operations of these methods to overcome objections in experimental design, to simplify them, and to take into account the difficulties of obtaining unequivocal measurements of protein growth in so complicated an organism as an animal.

The digestibility of proteins varies. This variation can be taken into account in measuring biological values by introducing the term "net protein utilization" which is defined as biological value multiplied by digestibility. The digestibility of most proteins is over 90 percent; hence, this does not introduce too significant a correction. Bender measured net protein utilization by a shortened technique which involves analysis of total nitrogen content of the rats in the experiment. Allison developed the "nitrogen balance index of nitrogen intake" which has the same significance as net protein value. These and other details should be studied by anyone who is interested in pursuing this matter further; a summary of some of the definitions encountered in estimating nutritional values of proteins is given in Table 8-1.

TABLE 8-1

*Some Common Definitions of Nutritive Value of Proteins*[1]

$$\text{Biological value (BV)} = \frac{\text{retained N}}{\text{absorbed N}} \times 100$$

$$= \frac{\text{food N} - (\text{fecal N} - \text{metabolic N}) - (\text{urine N} - \text{endogenous N})}{\text{food N} - (\text{fecal} - \text{metabolic N})}$$

$$\text{Net protein utilization} \atop (\text{NPU}) = \frac{\text{retained N}}{\text{food N}} \times 100$$

$$\text{True digestibility (D)} = \frac{\text{absorbed N}}{\text{food N}}$$

$$= \frac{\text{food N} - (\text{fecal N} - \text{metabolic N})}{\text{food N}}$$

$$\text{NPU} = \text{BV} \times \text{D}$$

$$\text{Protein efficiency ratio} \atop (\text{PER}) = \frac{(\text{weight increase of animals fed on test protein})}{(\text{weight of protein consumed})}$$

$$\text{Net protein retention} = \frac{(\text{weight increase in experimental animals}) - (\text{weight loss of nonprotein group})}{(\text{weight of protein consumed})}$$

$$\text{Net protein value (NPV)} = \text{BV} \times \text{D} \times (\text{protein content of foodstuff})$$

Source: A. E. Bender, "Biological Methods of Evaluating Protein Quality," *Proc. Nutr. Soc. (Engl. Scot.)*, vol. 17 (1958), p. 85.
[1] N is nitrogen; protein is calculated as nitrogen × 6.25.

## Nutritional Value of Some Food Proteins

Nutritional values of some food proteins are given in Table 8-2. In a broad cooperative experiment, six proteins were

### TABLE 8-2
#### Nutritional Values of Some Food Proteins

| Protein | Biological Value | Net Protein Utilization | Protein Efficiency Ratio | Chemical[1] Score |
|---|---|---|---|---|
| *Animal* | | | | |
| Whole egg | 87–97 | 91–94 | 3.8 | 100 |
| Cow's milk | 85–90 | 86 | 2.8 | 78 |
| Beef muscle | 76 | 71–76 | 3.2 | 83 |
| Dried whole milk | 88 | 75–79 | 1.9–2.3 | |
| Salmon | 72 | 71 | — | |
| Casein | 73 | 60–68 | 2.2 | 80 |
| Gelatin | 25 | 2 | 0 | 0 |
| *Plant* | | | | |
| Wheat (whole) *Triticum aestivum* | 67 | 61 | 1.5 | |

| | | | | |
|---|---|---|---|---|
| Rice (polished) | 75 | 70 | 1.9 | 72 |
| *Oryza sativa* | | | | |
| Soya protein concentrate | 75 | 56–72 | 2.3 | 73 |
| *Glycine max* | | | | |
| Corn (maize) | 60 | 49–55 | 1.2 | 42 |
| *Zea mays* | | | | |
| Potato (whole) | 67 | 60 | 1.5–2.0 | |
| *Salonum tuberosum* | | | | |
| Soya curd (oriental) | 65 | 62 | 1.7 | |
| Cottonseed protein concentrate | 62 | 56–58 | 1.3–2.1 | |
| *Gossypium hirsutum* | | | | |
| Chickpea (cooked) | 59–64 | | 1.3–2.1 | |
| *Cicer arietenum* | | | | |
| Wheat flour (white) | 52 | 52 | 1.0 | 47 |
| Peanuts (groundnuts, roasted) | 56 | 43–54 | 1.7 | |
| *Arachis hypogaea* | | | | |
| Peanut protein concentrate | 46–54 | | 0.8–1.9 | |
| Bean (Navy or kidney, cooked) | 38 | 32 | 1.2 | |
| *Phaseolus vulgaris* | | | | |

*Sources:* R. J. Block and H. H. Mitchell, "The Correlation of Amino Acid Composition of Proteins with Their Nutritive Value," *Nutr. Abstr. Rev.*, vol. 16 (1946-1947), p. 249. S. Kuppuswamy, M. Srinivasan, and V. Subrahmanyan, *Proteins in Foods* (New Delhi: Indian Council of Medical Research, Special Report Series No. 33, 1958). D. S. Miller and A. E. Bender, "The Determination of the Net Utilization of Proteins by a Shortened Method," *Brit. J. Nutr.*, vol. 9 (1955), p. 382. H. H. Mitchell, "The Biological Utilization of Proteins and Protein Requirements," in M. Sahyun, *Proteins and Amino Acids in Nutrition* (New York: Reinhold, 1948). *Protein Requirements* (Rome: Food and Agriculture Organization of the United Nations, FAO Nutritional Studies No. 16, 1957). P. B. Rama Rao, H. W. Norton, and B. C. Johnson, "The Amino Acid Composition and Nutritive Value of Proteins. V. Amino Acid Requirements as a Pattern for Protein Evaluation," *J. Nutr.*, vol. 82 (1964), p. 88.
[1] See Chapter 9.

## TABLE 8-3
### Nutritive Value of Six Selected Proteins [1]

| Test Animal | Egg White | Whole Egg | Beef | Casein | Peanut Flour | Wheat Gluten |
|---|---|---|---|---|---|---|
| *For Growth* | | | | | | |
| Rat | 100 | 95 | 84 | 80 | 31 | 8 |
| Rat | 100 | 90 | 78 | 71 | 56 | 41 |
| *For Maintenance* | | | | | | |
| Rat | 100 | 87 | 73 | 54 | 49 | 69 |
| Dog | 100 | 76 | 68 | 64 | 49 | 39 |
| Man | 100 | 103 | 74 | 74 | 62 | 46 |

*Source:* J. B. Allison, in J. C. Waterlow and J. M. L. Stephen (eds.), *Human Protein Requirements and Their Fulfilment in Practice* (Bristol, England: John Wright and Sons, Ltd., 1957), p. 55. See also: J. B. Allison, "Biological Evaluation of Proteins," *Physiol. Rev.*, vol. 35 (1955), p. 664.
[1] Calculated from observations by various laboratories on six standard sources of protein. Egg white was taken as 100 because it was uniformly the best.

studied by a number of research groups; information was provided from many sources and by varied means on the relative nutritive value of these six proteins; some of the results are listed in Table 8-3.

There are several points worth noting in Tables 8-2 and 8-3. The first is the remarkable parallelism between the various methods of measuring protein values. The best proteins are best by all methods and the worst proteins worst by all methods; there may be some variations in ranking from one method to another, but none significant. This parallelism, therefore, is an indication that something fundamental is being measured—the ability to synthesize protein.

The next point to notice is the wide variation in nutritive value of food proteins. We admitted this at the outset and now have the experimental evidence to demonstrate it. Egg protein has a "protein efficiency ratio" of 3.8 which, as we pointed out, means that one pound of egg protein will bring about an increase in weight of 3.8 pounds in the growing animal under the conditions of the test. On the basis of an estimated 18 percent of the weight of an animal as protein, one pound of egg protein will put on approximately $\frac{4}{5}$ pound of protein on a growing animal. This approaches perfection since some protein is required for maintenance. But wheat flour has a protein efficiency ratio of 1, and corn protein is just about the same. The same sort of calculation would show that five pounds of the grain protein is required to provide for gain of one pound of animal protein.

Examination of the nutritional values of proteins given in the tables show clearly why animal proteins are considered superior to vegetable sources of proteins. Biological values of the animal proteins (excluding gelatin) listed in Table 8-2 ranged from 72 to 97, whereas selected cereal and other vegetable proteins ranged from 46 to 75.

For specific circumstances, nutritional values of proteins may change. For example, in animals which are synthesizing appreciable amounts of hair or feathers, e.g., growing chicks or rats, certain proteins may be superior for that stage than for the adult stage. Proteins which are excellent for growing animals might not be quite so good for adults for other reasons. Casein has a higher nutritive value for young than for older animals.

## Significance of Biological Value

Proteins of lower biological value are less capable of furnishing protein efficiently than those of higher biological value. In the simplest sense, biological value can be interpreted as an inverse measure of the amounts of various proteins required to do the same job. Biological value is determined under rigidly controlled circumstances and holds only for those circumstances. For example, in many instances the nutritive value is determined at a protein level of 10 percent. But the intake of protein by human beings may vary from as low as 6 to as high as 64 percent. Certainly the biological value is not the same over this entire range. In some experiments presented by Allison, the nutritive value of casein (measured as protein efficiency ratio) decreased sharply at levels above about 10 percent, peanut flour after about 20 percent.

Caloric intake has an effect on the biological value of proteins. If insufficient calories are provided by carbohydrates and fats, then some of the protein will be metabolized for energy, even if it is not there in excess. The state of health is another influence on biological value. People who are suffering from diseases such as malaria generally are not able to utilize protein as effectively as healthy individuals; hence, the biological value of proteins for them is lower by approximately ⅔, in some examples cited by Platt.

In a sense the entire discussion of biological value is an artificial one because no one, man or animal, eats pure proteins from a single source. Even if the protein were of adequate quality this would not be a good policy, for such a diet would unquestionably be deficient in other required nutrients. In real life, we eat mixtures of proteins taken from mixtures of foods. What can we say about the biological value of a mixture of protein—can it be predicted from the biological values of the constituents? Some experimental results bearing on this point are given in Table 8-4, which lists the effect of eating bread with cheese and of potato with skim milk. In each instance the biological

### TABLE 8-4

*Protein Mixtures — Effect on Biological Value*

| Protein Source | Biological Value |
|---|---|
| White bread | 52 |
| Cheddar cheese | 76 |
| 1 part cheese + 3.4 parts bread | |
| Given together | 76 |
| Given on alternate days | 67 |
| Expected value if there were no supplementary relationship | 64 |
| Potato . | 71 |
| Skim milk | 89 |
| 1 part liquid skim milk + 1.3 parts potato | |
| Given together | 86 |
| Given on alternate days | 81 |
| Expected value if there were no supplementary relationship | 80 |

*Source:* K. M. Henry and S. K. Kon, "The Nutritive Value of Proteins: General Considerations," *Proc. Nutr. Soc. (Engl. Scot.),* vol. 17 (1957), p. 81.

value of the mixture is much higher than would be expected by merely averaging the biological value of the constituents. Such is very often true, but not universally. For example, a diet with a relatively low level of casein to which is added equivalent amounts of gelatin has a lower biological value than the diet on casein alone.

Another point which becomes evident from this table is that supplementation of protein must take place simultaneously, otherwise there will be no effect; instead, the biological value of such a diet will approximate the average of the two sources.

While it is true that it is not possible to predict the biological value of a mixture from the values for the constituent proteins, some guesses can be made. If a major constituent itself has a high biological value and if adequate protein is fed, the value of the mixture will probably not be much lower, even if the protein of good quality represents no more than ⅓ of the total. This point is well illustrated in Table 8-4; this is the reason for confidence in diets which contain substantial amounts of animal protein. Only when none of the constituents possess a high biological value is it difficult to guess the value for the mixture.

That proteins do supplement each other means that something else is required in their description besides a number called biological value or its equivalent. But this is as far as we can go with the empirical treatment. Further understanding requires that we learn the basis for the differences in biological values of proteins; this leads us to a study of the role of the amino acids.

## SELECTED BIBLIOGRAPHY

Allison, J. B. "Biological Evaluation of Proteins," *Physiol. Rev.*, vol. 35 (1955), p. 664.

Frost, D. V. "Methods of Measuring the Nutritive Value of Proteins . . . ," in A. A. Albanese (ed.), *Protein and Amino Acid Nutrition*. New York: Academic, 1959, p. 225.

McCollum, E. V. "The Beginnings of Essential Nutrition," *Nutr. Rev.*, vol. 14 (1956), p. 256.

Miller, D. S., and A. E. Bender. "The Determination of the Net Utilization of Proteins by a Shortened Method," *Brit. J. Nutr.*, vol. 14 (1956), p. 257.

Mitchell, H. H. "The Biological Utilization of Proteins and Protein Requirements," in M. Sahyun (ed.), *Proteins and Amino Acids in Nutrition*. New York: Reinhold, 1948, p. 46.

"The Nutritive Value of Proteins: A Symposium," in *Proc. Nutr. Soc.*, vol. 17 (1957), p. 78.

# CHAPTER 9

# *The Role of the Amino Acid Composition*

WHEN PROTEINS ARE EATEN they are fragmented in the digestive tract by proteolytic enzymes and finally broken down into their constituent amino acids. That these amino acids are absorbed from the digestive tract into the blood stream may be demonstrated by direct analysis at short time intervals after the proteins are eaten: there will be a temporary increase in the concentration of amino acids in the circulating blood. Proteins, then, are essentially a source of amino acids; if we are looking for differences between proteins, the first place to look is at their composition of amino acids. No two proteins have the same amino acid composition; it might be reasonably expected that certain proteins will have a more desirable amino acid composition from the point of view of nutrition than others.

Proteins may be eliminated entirely from the diet and replaced with synthetic diets composed of sources of energy,

117

vitamins, and other trace materials, and selected quantities of chemically pure amino acids. This became possible when Rose discovered threonine, the last amino acid needed to form a complete synthetic mixture which would be the equivalent of protein sources. Rose was able to maintain young men and animals in nitrogen balance with such mixtures. In recent years, Greenstein and his associates were able to raise generations of rats on synthetic water-soluble mixtures of pure amino acids and other necessary nonprotein dietary constituents.

## Essential Amino Acids

With his mixture of amino acids, Rose initiated experiments to determine whether all were equally necessary. Osborne and Mendel had already proposed the concept of essential amino acids; in experiments with rats he confirmed and expanded this idea. Amino acids could be divided into two groups: those that were essential, whose withdrawal from the diet would stop growth or reduce it to a low level, and those that were nonessential—whose withdrawal and substitution with other sources of nitrogen would not seriously affect growth. With young men as volunteer subjects, he found that eight amino acids were required to maintain nitrogen balance in the young adult. These are isoleucine, leucine, lysine, methionine, phenylalanine, threonine, tryptophan, and valine. Histidine is a dietary essential for the human infant. All of the essential amino acids must be presented at the same time for any synthesis of protein to occur. Even when only one of these is missing or supplied several hours later than the others, protein synthesis will either cease or decrease to a very low level. We have already noted this time effect in supplementation of one protein with another.

The construction of a protein from its constituent building blocks is an "all-or-none" process. This is not surprising if we consider an analogy with the construction of a building where eight different structural materials are needed in various proportions and interlocking arrangements. When one of these materials is missing, all construction ceases, since none of the other materials can be put into their proper places.

Animal species differ in their requirements for essential amino acids. The rat and chick also require histidine and arginine, and the chick needs glycine for maximum growth. The rat does not require arginine for maintenance, but needs it for growth. Certain nonessential amino acids spare the essential ones: cystine can partially replace methionine, tyrosine can partially replace phenylalanine, and serine can spare glycine for the chick. We know that the proteins of animal tissue contain all of the 20 amino acids. If they need not all be furnished as such, then we must conclude that the nonessential amino acids are manufactured by the animal from other sources of nitrogen and from other metabolites. Indeed, it has been found that fragments of carbohydrates are built into nonessential amino acids but not into the essential amino acids of the body protein.

We may summarize amino acid requirements by stating that certain amino acids cannot be synthesized at all or, at most, very slowly by the animal organism; hence they are required in the diet for optimum growth. Certain nonspecific sources of nitrogen are required to provide for the nonessential amino acids since these can be synthesized rapidly enough from other constituents of the diet.

Does the nature of the nonspecific sources of nitrogen matter? It seems that it does. Greenstein and his associates found that rats grew better on some sources of nonessential amino acids than on others, even though the amount of essential amino acids was the same in all instances. For example, if the nonessential amino acids were the same as those in casein, better growth was achieved than if other sources of nonessential amino acids were present. Simple nitrogen-containing compounds such as urea and ammonium citrate are also utilized, but not so effectively as the amino acids.

## Requirements for Essential Amino Acids

By providing a source of nonessential nitrogen for satisfactory performance, it is possible to withdraw the essential amino acids one by one and add back increments to measure the amount of each required for optimum performance. Considerable work of this sort was done with human subjects—mostly infants under one year of age and young adults (college students). Although there may be some disagreement among investigators as to the detailed outcome of these experiments, one conclusion is clear: not all of the essential amino acids are required in the same amount. Actually there is a wide spread between their requirements: 250 milligrams of tryptophan are required daily by adults but 1,100 of leucine are needed. Rose and his associates found a large variation in the requirements among the experimental subjects; for some amino acids this was over 100 percent. Rose chose in every instance the highest value of the range as the minimum requirement. Thus for tryptophan which showed a range of requirements of 150 to 250 milligrams daily, he chose 250; for leucine the range was 500 to 1,100 milligrams daily, he chose 1,100 milligrams.

Some of the published values for average minimum requirements are given in Table 9-1. You will notice that the sum of methionine plus cystine is listed; this is the total of

*The Role of Amino Acid Composition*

## TABLE 9-1

### Some Average Minimal Daily Requirements of Humans for Amino Acids

| Amino Acid | Infants | | | Men[2] | Adults | | |
|---|---|---|---|---|---|---|---|
| | | | | | Men[1] Mg/ | Men[1] Mg/ | Women[1] Mg/ |
| | Mg/Kg[1] | Mg/Kg[2] | Mg/Kg[3] | Mg/Kg | Day | Day | Day |
| L-Histidine | 32 | | 34 | | | | |
| L-Isoleucine | 90 | 90 | 126 | 10.4 | 730 | 700 | 45 |
| L-Leucine | 150 | | 150 | 9.9 | 690 | 1100 | 620 |
| L-Lysine | 105 | 90 | 103 | 8.8 | 615 | 800 | 500 |
| L-Methionine | 85[5] | 85 | 45[6] | | | 200[7] | |
| L-Methionine & L-Cystine | | | | 13.1 | 925 | 1100 | 550 |
| L-Phenylalanine | 90 | 90[8] | 90[8] | 13.3 | 935 | 300[9] | |
| L-Phenylalanine & L-Tyrosine | | | | | | 1100 | 1120 |
| L-Threonine | 60 | 60 | 87 | 6.5 | 455 | 500 | 305 |
| L-Tryptophan | 22 | 30 | 22 | 2.9 | 203 | 250 | 157 |
| L-Valine | 93 | 85 | 104 | 8.8 | 615 | 800 | 650 |

[1] *Evaluation of Protein Nutrition,* Publication 711 (Washington, D. C.: National Academy of Sciences-National Research Council, 1959).

[2] *Protein Requirements,* Nutritional Studies No. 16 (Rome, Italy: Food and Agriculture Organization of the United Nations, 1957).

[3] L. E. Holt, Jr., P. Gyorgy, E. L. Pratt, S. E. Snyderman, and W. M. Wallace, *Protein and Amino Acid Requirements in Early Life* (New York: New York U. P., 1960). The requirements for histidine were later found to be less, closer to 23 mg/kg.

[4] Calculated from data in column to the left for a man weighing 70 kg.

[5] No cystine was given. With cystine present at 50 mg/kg, the methionine requirement was 65 mg/kg.

[6] In the presence of cystine.

[7] 810 mg/day of cystine were given.

[8] Tyrosine was given.

[9] 1100 mg/day of tyrosine were given.

sulfur-containing amino acids. Since cystine can spare part of the methionine requirements, the sum of the two is listed rather than methionine alone. Similarly for the aromatic amino acids, phenylalanine and tyrosine; since tyrosine spares the other, the sum is listed. The requirements for infants are listed in terms of body weight; the correlation between weight of adults and requirements was poor, hence some investigators chose to list their requirements in terms of milligrams of amino acid per day.

In Rose's experiments 3.5 grams of nitrogen per day supplied as amino acids were sufficient to maintain nitrogen balance in adults. This amount of nitrogen is approximately equivalent to 22 grams (3.5 × 6.25) of protein daily. Of the total amount of nitrogen required, 1.5 grams represented that furnished by the essential amino acids and the remainder came principally from the amino acid glycine. Rose estimated that the nitrogen needed for the synthesis of the nonessential amino acids probably lies between 2.3 and 2.5 grams daily. Swendseid et al. found that the total essential nitrogen requirements for young women ranged from 0.65 to 0.85 grams per day and, for young men, from 1.0 to 1.3 grams per day.

## The Ideal Aminogram

We may now elaborate on our definition of essential amino acids: a certain amount of each essential amino acid is required for maintenance; additional nitrogen supplied by a miscellaneous group of materials is required for synthesis of the nonessential amino acids. One of these essential amino acids, tryptophan, is required in the least amount by humans; its concentration in the diet may be set arbitrarily at one and the others listed in terms of their proportion to tryptophan.[1] This constitutes a proportionality pattern of amounts of the essential amino acids needed for best performance (sometimes called "aminogram"); any serious deviation from this pattern will reduce the nutritional value of the mixture. The FAO provisional pattern is shown in Fig. 9-1.

1. It is, of course, equally possible to arbitrarily set any other amino acid as unity. Allison prefers to set threonine as unity.

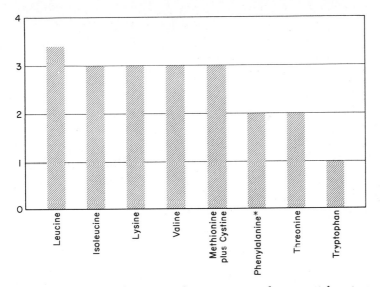

Fig. 9-1. Provisional pattern of requirements for essential amino acids expressed in relation to tryptophan.°

°Assumes a ratio of tyrosine to tryptophan of about 2.
   *Source: Protein Requirements,* Nutritional Studies No. 16 (Rome, Italy: Food and Agriculture Organization of the United Nations, 1957).

Such might be considered the pattern of the ideal food protein. Such a protein, i.e., a protein which provides upon digestion each of the essential amino acids in the correct amount and sufficient nitrogen for synthesis of the other amino acids, would have, by definition, a biological value of 100.

There are other ways of estimating the essential amino acid pattern. It is possible to measure the minimum amount of various proteins needed for nitrogen balance and determine from their analysis the minimum intake of each essential amino acid that will satisfy the requirement. An example of such a calculation is shown in Table 9-2. Let us examine this table more closely because it tells many things about

## TABLE 9–2

### Amount of Essential Amino Acids Supplied by Different Protein Sources Fed in Sufficient Quantity to Maintain Nitrogen Equilibrium in Normal Adult Man

| Protein Intake, g/kg of Body Weight | Egg Albumin 0.40 | Milk 0.50 | Beef 0.60 | Casein 0.59 | Peanut Flour 0.74 | Wheat Gluten 1.00 | Minimum Value 0.40 |
|---|---|---|---|---|---|---|---|
| | | | $Mg^1$ per Kg of Body Weight | | | | |
| Leucine | 25.8 [2] | 32.6 | 31.0 | 37.2 | 28.0 | 45.6 | 25.8 |
| Isoleucine | 35.0 | 78.0 | 47.0 | 58.5 | 49.0 | 71.8 | 35.0 |
| Lysine | 28.8 | 60.6 | 51.6 | 47.5 | 25.4 | 20.2 | 20.2 |
| Phenylalanine | 23.7 | 24.7 | 23.4 | 31.4 | 34.4 | 50.2 | 23.7 |
| Tyrosine | 13.3 | 26.0 | 17.8 | 30.2 | 20.2 | 27.8 | 13.3 |
| Total Aromatic | 37.0 | 50.7 | 51.2 | 61.6 | 54.4 | 78.0 | 37.0 |
| Methionine | 16.5 | 12.5 | 16.3 | 19.2 | 5.9 | 16.6 | 5.9 |
| Cystine | 11.9 | 4.5 | 8.7 | 2.3 | 8.1 | 23.7 | 8.1 |
| Total Sulfur | 28.4 | 17.0 | 35.0 | 21.5 | 14.0 | 40.5 | 14.0 |
| Threonine | 19.5 | 23.5 | 26.7 | 26.4 | 19.5 | 28.0 | 19.5 |
| Tryptophan | 4.7 | 7.2 | 6.0 | 5.6 | 5.5 | 7.7 | 4.7 |
| Valine | 29.8 | 35.0 | 31.0 | 43.0 | 31.8 | 42.5 | 29.8 |

Source: J. B. Allison, "Amino Acid Requirements," Feedstuffs (December 6, 1958), p. 5–7, Food Technol, vol. 13 (1959), p. 597.

[1] One gram (g) equals 1000 milligrams (mg).

[2] The boldface underlined numbers are those taken as minimum values of proteins and amino acids.

food proteins. You will notice that these are the same proteins previously listed in Table 8-3 as differing in biological value. Egg albumin has the highest biological value; it is required in the smallest amount to maintain nitrogen balance, as is shown in the top row. Notice also the variation in amino acid composition among the proteins; egg albumin has 3½ times as much lysine as wheat gluten and almost four times as many sulfur amino acids as peanut flour; milk protein is highest in leucine and lysine.

The lowest value of a given protein which will satisfy the requirements for nitrogen balance is listed as the minimum value; and so are the values for each amino acid. With only six proteins to select from, the estimate of minimum requirements for amino acids is only a rough guess. If a larger number of proteins with equivalent information on nitrogen balance were compared, the estimate would become more representative and accurate.

Are there natural proteins which have the perfect "pattern" of amino acids? You might expect from Table 9-2 that egg albumin comes closest to this pattern. Actually there is an opinion that egg protein contains more than enough of the essential amino acids of the proper pattern and may be diluted by 15 percent with nonessential amino acids and still retain its high biological value.

## Chemical Score

Let us consider what would happen to a protein or to a mixture of amino acids if it were to deviate from the so-called optimum pattern by the concentration of one amino acid. Suppose that all of the amino acids except lysine were present in a mixture of essential amino acids in exactly the proper pattern, but that the quantity of lysine were only 60 percent as much as required. And let us assume that there is sufficient additional nitrogen to satisfy the requirements for synthesis of the nonessential amino acids. Then if one were to eat sufficient quantities to satisfy the need for tryptophan, all other requirements but that of lysine would be met. Almost twice as much of this mixture (1.7 times as much) would need be consumed to satisfy the lysine requirement.

This point may be illustrated by superimposing this new pattern on the ideal pattern given in Fig. 9-1. If only that part of the amino acid mixture which conforms to the pattern is usable, we must make a new pattern by reducing all the other amino acids to 60 percent so that now they all are in line with the lysine content. This is shown in Fig. 9-2. The obvious result is that only 60 percent of the mixture has any protein nutritional value—i.e., can be used as a source of amino acids to support protein growth. The remainder serves only for energy in the same manner as carbohydrate. In this artificial case we have one deficit,

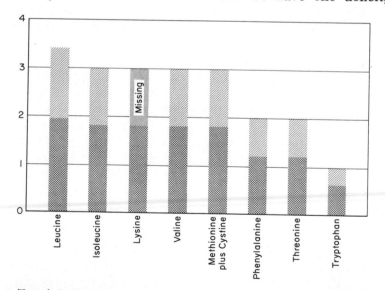

Fig. 9-2. Pattern as compared to provisional pattern when the amount of one of the essential amino acids is only 60 percent of the minimum.

one limiting amino acid, lysine. The fraction of protein or amino acid mixture available for protein synthesis is that determined by the percentage deficit of the limiting amino acid. This is an example of the "law of the minimum," of the saying that, "a chain is no stronger than the weakest link."

Let us go further and suppose that we had four such mixtures, all with the proper pattern of amino acids but deficient to a different degree in the amino acid lysine. Then the four mixtures (they could just as well be proteins) could be rated in order of biological value by the percentage deficit. The one which had its full complement of lysine would have a biological value of 100; the others would have lower biological values directly proportional to the percentage deficit in lysine. On this basis we should be able to rate food proteins for nutritional value by analyzing their amino acid composition, determining their amino acid pattern, and calculating the percentage deficit of the first limiting amino acid. A protein may be deficient in several amino acids as compared to the ideal pattern, but the one in which it is most deficient is the first limiting amino acid; the percentage deficit of this amino acid defines the maximum deviation from the normal pattern. This type of rating has been called the "chemical score" of a protein by Mitchell and Block. These two compared the amino acid patterns of a number of food proteins to that of egg protein, which they considered the ideal food protein, as a basis for calculating a chemical score. The chemical score of egg protein, of course, was set at 100; the others were lower by the percentage deficit in the limiting amino acids.

## The Concept of Reference Protein

It is not necessary to refer to a natural food protein as the standard; the standard might as well be a hypothetical amino acid mixture containing the essential amino acids in the proper amount and pattern. Such was the basis of scoring proteins by the Food and Agriculture Organization and by the National Research Council (U. S.); the groups differed slightly in their concept of the ideal amino acid pattern.

The reader will remember that we have already rated food sources of protein on the basis of their nutritional value by empirical measurements designed to determine biological value or a related parameter. We have now shown that proteins may be rated on the basis of their amino acid compositions by comparison to a reference amino acid composition. It turns out that there is remarkable similarity between these two ratings, as shown by examples in Table 8-2. That the biologically determined values and the chemical scores are not identical would be expected from the fact that there is no general agreement on all of the factors affecting the biological value, nor is there general agreement on what might be considered the ideal amino acid pattern. Bender has made some suggestions for modifying the calculation of the chemical score to improve the correlation.

But the principle has been established: an explanation, an almost quantitative explanation, of the reason for biological value can be presented. An explanation is available for the variation in biological value of proteins on the basis of the conformation of each protein to an amino acid pattern. We now not only know that some proteins are better than other proteins as sources for nutrition, but, in a general way, why they are better. If we know this much, then we should be able to predict what would happen when two proteins of different biological values are mixed.

## Amino Acid Patterns of Mixtures

The ideal kind of mixing of two proteins is such that the amino acid pattern of the second protein complements and makes up the deficiencies of the amino acid pattern of the first, thereby resulting in a mixture which has a higher biological value because the combined amino acid pattern more closely approximates the ideal one. For example, as little as 10 percent cottonseed flour when added to wheat flour increases the tryptophan content by 36 percent, the lysine by 79 percent, and the methionine plus cystine by 33 percent; there is an overall improvement of the pattern. Milk has more than enough lysine and wheat flour has more than enough methionine plus cystine. One cup of milk and two slices of bread provide an adequate pattern of tryptophan, lysine, and methionine.

All food proteins contain enough extra amino acids to take care of the synthesis of the nonessential amino acids; hence the only problem is that of supplying the essential amino acids, and the only consideration in mixing is that of improving the amount and pattern of essential amino acids.

If the proteins in a person's food supply have a biological value of 100, then he requires the minimum amount of protein. If the biological value is less, the same end is accomplished by eating more protein. Here is an example taken from the National Research Council publication: Milk protein is slightly deficient in total sulfur amino acids. Whereas 17.7 grams of milk protein daily will supply the 250 milligrams of tryptophan required, 28.4 grams of the milk protein is required to meet the requirements for sulfur amino acids. When this amount is taken, it is the equivalent of a smaller amount of the ideal protein.

Compensation for lower quality by consumption of a larger quantity is effective up to a point. It is generally considered that such an adjustment is effective for proteins of biological value of 60 and higher. Proteins with lower biological value can be too far out of balance: the excesses of some of the more abundant amino acids brought about by taking in enough protein to furnish a sufficient amount of the deficient amino acid may not be easily tolerated or handled by the organism; indeed, they may be toxic.

The correction of problems caused by proteins of low

biological value is to create a new mixture by supplementation with other proteins with a resultant improvement in the amino acid pattern and an increase of the biological value of the mixture to above 60 percent. Then the remainder of of deficiency may be corrected by a higher intake.

There is a third approach which arises entirely from modern synthetic organic chemistry and from fermentation science. In recent years, it has become possible to synthesize amino acids or produce them by fermentation in quantities and at prices reasonable enough to consider them seriously as sources of food. For example, methionine is included in many diets for poultry based on a mixture of corn and soybean meal which is limited in methionine. It has been found profitable in many instances to add the small quantities of methionine that are needed to balance the amino acid pattern. There has been considerable interest in the supplementation of wheat flour, which is limited in lysine, with synthetic lysine even though this is relatively expensive. It is estimated that the prices of these amino acids could be reduced considerably by large-scale demands.

The entire idea of being able to improve proteins by adding small amounts of synthetic material produced from nonagricultural raw materials or from fermentation of wastes offers an exciting new possibility for increasing the available food supplies. It is not necessary to grow more of any given protein in order to increase the world's supply of that source of protein, if the biological value of protein itself can be improved. And if this can be done by supplementation with amino acids, this is, in essence, the same as increasing overall production of food proteins.

There has been some hesitancy to supplement human diets with amino acids even though this has been done successfully for animals. The Food and Nutrition Board of the National Research Council (U. S.) concluded that there is no evidence of the need of amino acids supplementation for an individual eating an average mixed diet in the United States; hence it has not encouraged such supplementation of American diets. The Food and Agriculture Organization of the United Nations in its report on Protein Requirements made the following statement:

The use of amino acids as supplementation would in all circumstances call for careful expert study and control.

The reason for this hesitation is that there is a possibility of imbalance if too much of an amino acid is added. A new pattern, now out of balance because of excessive supplementation, would be equally as bad as the original pattern which it was intended to improve.

We must be mindful, also, that the pattern of proportions is an abstraction of the actual amounts of amino acids in the reference protein. If the proportion is right but the total amounts of amino acid are insufficient, then the protein will still be deficient in quality. As pointed out in a report of the Food and Nutrition Board (Publication 711), the supplementation of wheat proteins with lysine brings the amino acid proportions of whole wheat almost in line with those of egg proteins; but wheat proteins contain about one-third less of the essential amino acids. When both are fed at equal levels, whole wheat even supplemented with lysine is still inferior despite the excellent amino acid pattern.

But the idea of being able to add to our agricultural production by such means and the eventual relative simplicity and reasonable cost of amino acid supplementation will act as a powerful force to stimulate research leading to an understanding of how such supplementation may be effected safely, practically, and cheaply.

### S E L E C T E D   B I B L I O G R A P H Y

Albanese, A. A. (ed.). *Protein and Amino Acid Nutrition.* New York: Academic, 1959.

Allison, J. B. "The Ideal Aminogram," *Federation Proc.,* vol. 20, no. 3, part III, suppl. 7 (1961), p. 66.

Banks, W. L., Allison, J. B., and Wannemacher, R. W., Jr. "Supplementation of Wheat Gluten Protein," *J. Nutr.,* vol. 82 (1964), p. 61.

Block, R. J., and H. H. Mitchell. "The Correlation of the Amino Acid Composition of Proteins with Their Nutritive Value," *Nutr. Abstr. Rev.*, vol. 16 (1946-47), p. 249.

Bender, A. E. "Correlation of Amino Acid Composition with Nutritive Value of Proteins," *Clin. Chim. Acta*, vol. 5 (1960), p. 1.

"Evaluation of the FAO Amino Acid Reference Pattern," *Nutr. Rev.*, vol. 21 (1963), p. 101.

*Evaluation of Protein Nutrition.* Publication 711. Washington, D. C.: National Academy of Sciences-National Research Council, 1959.

*Protein Requirements.* Nutritional Studies No. 16. Rome, Italy: Food and Agriculture Organization of the United Nations, 1957.

Rose, W. C. "The Amino Acid Requirements of Adult Man," *Nutr. Abstr. Rev.*, vol. 27 (1957), p. 631.

Swendseid, M. E., C. L. Harris, and S. G. Tuttle. "An Evaluation of the FAO Amino Acid Reference Pattern in Human Nutrition: II, Studies with Young Women," *J. Nutr.*, vol. 77 (1962), p. 391.

"Unessential Nitrogen, an Essential Dietary Factor," *Nutr. Rev.*, vol. 21, no. 3 (1963), p. 68.

Waddell, J. "Supplementation of Plant Proteins with Amino Acids," in A. M. Altschul (ed.), *Processed Plant Protein Foodstuffs.* New York: Academic, 1958.

Winitz, M., S. M. Birnbaum, T. Sugimura, and M. C. Otey. "Quantitative Nutritional and *In Vivo* Metabolic Studies with Water-soluble, Chemically Defined Diets," in J. T. Edsall (ed.), *Amino Acids, Proteins and Cancer Biochemistry — Jesse P. Greenstein Memorial Symposium.* New York: Academic, 1960. See also J. P. Greenstein, S. M. Birnbaum, M. Winitz, and M. C. Otey, "Quantitative Nutritional Studies with Water-soluble Chemically Defined Diets, I-V," *Arch. Biochem. Biophys.*, vol. 72 (1957), pp. 396-456.

# CHAPTER 10

# *The Protein Requirements of Homo Sapiens:*

## II

IT IS CLEAR from the foregoing that the prescription of protein requirements for man or animals without definition of the protein has no general meaning. Protein means one thing to North Americans, another thing to Chinese, and an entirely different thing to residents of Central America. Since proteins do differ chemically and nutritionally, the problem must be approached by setting up a reference protein to which all other food proteins may be related. Then the measure of protein would approach more nearly in definition that of other nutrients; any group or nation could relate its own average type of protein to this standard, and make suitable adjustments in recommended allowances to take this difference into account.

### Nature of Reference Protein

The simplest approach is to select as a standard a natural protein of high nutritive value. This was done by Block and Mitchell when they compared all proteins to egg protein to which they assigned a biological value of 100. Another approach, as was suggested by Terroine (in Waterlow and Stephen), was to take cow's milk as the basic protein food in establishing the protein requirements of babies, children, and pregnant women. Even though milk protein does not have as high a biological value as egg protein, it is of high quality and is a common source of protein, hence a practical choice for a standard protein.

There are many who prefer a reference from among natural proteins. Such a selection has the advantage of dealing with a concrete protein and does not require any profound theoretical basis.

But we now have a reference protein in terms of minimum amounts and a pattern of essential amino acids. When we talk about the ideal protein with optimum nutritive value, we are talking about this reference protein. This kind of a reference protein, although an abstraction, has definite relationship to reality; this is a protein which can be compared to real-life proteins by comparison of amino acid content and pattern; information and requirements developed on the basis of the reference protein can be translated into terms of existing food proteins. We know that egg proteins come close to or exceed the reference protein in quality; we know that many animal proteins such as milk and meat proteins approach this reference protein in nutritive value; therefore, we have the basis for visualizing in a practical way the properties of the reference protein. With the concept of reference protein, it is now possible to attempt to describe the minimum protein requirements in more precise terms.

## Minimum Protein Requirements

In a sense, the determination of the nutritional value of a variety of proteins for any given animal and the determination of the minimum requirements of the same animal for a reference protein are two sides of the same coin: the same techniques are followed, only the questions differ. If it is nutritive value, we take as our measure a standard of biological performance by which to compare various sources of proteins. Such a standard may be growth, nitrogen balance, adequate protein plasma regeneration, or any number of the other factors mentioned earlier. On the basis of such performance, proteins are related according to their ability to replace tissue proteins or to produce new tissue proteins. This is their nutritive value.

To determine minimum protein requirements, again we must first decide upon a measure of good biological performance. But this time we start with a protein of known high biological value such as egg protein, and determine the minimum amount of this protein required to achieve the performance standard. Or we may take as our source of protein a mixture of amino acids having the composition of the reference protein. There is no need to review the various methods employed to measure the minimum protein requirement; these have been discussed in previous chapters. There is one significant experimental difference between the problem of measuring biological value of proteins and the problem of measuring minimum requirements of proteins for man. Whereas, in the first instance, it is allowable to use experimental animals, and these data generally are transferrable to man, no such possibility exists in determining protein requirements. Man is the slowest-growing of the animals whose nutritive requirements are ordinarily measured, his needs are different, his maintenance requirements are different; no experiments but those on man would have any validity in establishing minimum protein requirements for man. That we use information on biological value of proteins as determined on animals as a basis for evaluating these proteins for man is justified by the fact that this approximation provides a built-in factor of safety. Since the experimental animals are more rapid growers than man, they are more sensitive in their need for proteins; hence the factor of safety. Large differences in the biological value of proteins for rats would generally become smaller differences when applied to man.

It is an interesting commentary on the comparative growth rates of various mammalian species that in the course of evolution the content of nutrients in the milks reflected these differences. Particularly noticeable is the correlation between protein content and the number of days required to double birthweight (Bernhart). In general, the calorie value of the milk of the faster-growing animal is also higher.

The limitations of humans as experimental animals cuts deeply into the amount of experimental evidence which may be obtained. Rose based his amino acid requirements for humans on a relatively small number of experiments. Hence, it is difficult to arrive at a consensus which will have a broad basis. One has only to read the discussions on protein requirements in the monograph *Human Protein Requirements and Their Fulfilment and Practice* to realize the differences in opinion between competent experimenters on this subject.

## Theoretical Approach to Minimum Requirements

It is possible to develop a theoretical approach to the protein requirements of humans as was done by Hegsted. He estimated the amount of protein required for maintenance and for growth from other physiological data and made additional corrections to take care of incomplete digestibility and other protein losses. His argument is as follows:

The protein which is lost daily is part of the metabolism of nitrogen incident with basal metabolism. We can calculate this protein component from the basal metabolism. For example, if an animal is fed a restricted amount of high-quality protein (much less than it requires), the urinary nitrogen excretion decreases and usually approaches the value of 12.5 milligrams of protein per basal Calorie, that is, per Calorie of basal metabolism. Hence, an adult human with a basal metabolic rate of 1500 Calories per day would require 1500 × 12.5 milligrams or 18.7 grams of the reference protein per day to replace such losses. An additional 10 percent of protein, that is, an additional 10 percent of this 18.7 grams, is estimated as required to replace losses of protein in the feces. Moreover, some of the protein is not digested; but for nearly all proteins, at least 90 percent is digested. Hence, an additional correction of 10 percent is estimated to allow for protein of high quality which is not quite completely digested. These add up to a total of a little over 20 grams per day of protein of biological value 100 required to balance natural daily losses of protein. Compare this value to the 22 grams required as calculated from Rose's data based on feeding pure amino acids (see Chap. 9).

For children we have the additional requirement for growth. When a child gains a pound of weight, 18 percent of this gain is estimated as gain in protein. It is only necessary to use figures for average weight gain of children to calculate average protein gain at the various age levels. The reference protein by definition will support the gain in protein, pound for pound. The increment of protein needed to support growth is added to the estimated protein needs for maintenance and other losses; this is the basis for estimating the minimum protein requirements of growing humans.

The beauty of this approach is that it does not depend on experimental evidence dealing directly with proteins. Instead, it draws from data on basal metabolism and weight growth, both of which are types of information easier to obtain than nitrogen balance. And because it deals with other types of measurements, it provides an independent check on the direct experimental basis for defining minimum protein requirements.

The result of such calculations for bigger than average boys (90 percentile) is shown in Fig. 10-1 as a plot of protein requirements per kilogram of body weight for vari-

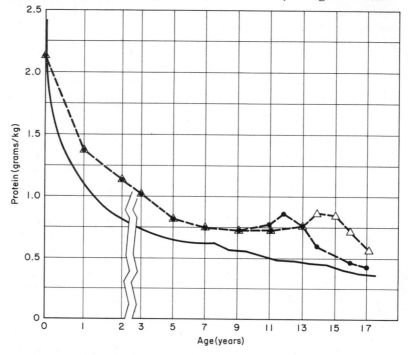

FIG. 10-1. Minimal requirements for reference protein.*
*Solid line is theoretical estimates of minimal protein requirements for boys. *Source:* D. M. Hegsted, *Federation Proc.,* vol. 18 (1959), p. 1131.
Dotted lines are average minimum protein requirements. *Source: Protein Requirements,* Nutrition Studies No. 16 (Rome, Italy: Food and Agriculture Organization of the United Nations, 1957).
Δ———Δ, Boys.
●———●, Girls.

ous ages. On the same figure is superimposed the curve proposed by the Committee of FAO based upon actual experiments with proteins.

The curve based on Hegsted's calculations and the FAO curve have about the same shape; the highest requirements are for the infant. Adults no longer have requirements for growth (except for tissue repair, as a result of illness, surgery, or injury). Therefore they require protein only for maintenance. Although the curves are similar, there are divergencies in amounts and also in the shape. The one proposed by FAO has higher minimum requirements for adolescents based on the thesis that this age group is more susceptible to infection by disease and reinfection by tuberculosis if insufficient quantities of protein are consumed during these critical years.

## Percentage of Protein Calories

The concentration of protein in a food or diet may be expressed in relation to the total caloric value. This may be as weight of protein per 100 Calories of food or as percentage of protein calories. In the latter instance the caloric value of proteins, which is equal to that of carbohydrates, is the basis for calculating the fraction of the total food calories contributed by proteins. This calculation does not attempt to assess the amount of protein serving as a source of calories (as against a source of amino acids) in any particular feeding situation nor should it be so construed; it is simply a convenient way of expressing two numbers at once: the amount of protein and its proportion to the total calories.

A normal animal ingests only the amount of food necessary to satisfy caloric requirements; therefore, optimum satisfaction of food requirements will occur only if this intake contains, as well, an adequate amount of protein and all other essential nutrients. If the percentage of protein is too high, then the excess protein will be metabolized as a source of calories instead of being incorporated into new proteins. If the protein content is too low and a person ingests just enough food to satisfy caloric requirements, he will not get enough protein. If he eats more food so as to satisfy the protein requirements, the result will be an imbalance, which can have dangerous consequences. In the extreme case when the percentage of proteins in the diet is very low, this type of regime results in severe protein deficiency disease.

We would define an ideal food as so constituted that when an individual eats enough of it to satisfy his calorie requirements, he will automatically eat enough of all other food requirements. The ideal protein-calorie relationship is the one wherein the ratio of protein to total calories is such that protein needs are satisfied with calorie needs.

On the basis of the minimum protein and calorie requirements proposed by FAO and other groups, the following would represent ideal reference protein-calorie ratios: nine-month-old infant, 4.5 percent; five-year-old child, 3.7 percent; fourteen-year-old adolescent, 5.5 percent; and normal adult, 3.1 percent.

Analyses have been made of diets consumed by humans and livestock; the percentage of calories represented by protein is given in Table 10-1. The protein is presumably good protein but is not reference protein. Nor are these necessarily minimum values.

## TABLE 10-1

### Percentage of Calories Represented by Protein

| Man | Age Group | Percent Protein Calories |
|---|---|---|
| Infant | 0–1 | 13–16 |
| Toddler | 1–3 | 9–17 |
| Child | 4–9 | 14–16 |
| Boys | 10–15 | 12.5 |
| Girls | 10–15 | 12–13.4 |
| Boys | 16–18 | 10.6 |
| Girls | 16–18 | 12.6 |
| Adults | 20–30 | 2.4–8.8 |
| Poultry | | |
| Chickens | Starter | 20 |
| | Grower | 16 |
| | Egg production | 15 |
| Turkey | Starter | 28 |
| | Grower | 20 |

| Swine | Prestarter | |
|---|---|---|
| | (up to 12 lb) | 24 |
| | Starter | |
| | 12–25 lb) | 18 |
| | Grower | 16 |
| Dairy Cattle | Calves | 15 |
| | Heifers | 12 |
| | Lactating cows | 14 |

Source: J. C. Waterlow and J. M. L. Stephen (eds.), *Human Requirements and Their Fulfilment in Practice* (Bristol, England: John Wright and Sons, Ltd., 1957); A. A. Albanese, *Protein and Amino Acid Nutrition* (New York: Academic, 1959).

## Safe Protein Allowances

We have thus far been discussing the *minimum* protein allowances. The next problem is to translate these figures into recommendations for practical nutrition. Obviously, there are variations among people; we cited above the variations in leucine and tryptophan requirements reported by Rose. That these are greater than is commonly realized was emphasized by Williams, who provided examples of ranges of 400 to 1,600 milligrams per day for lysine requirements and 103 to 500 milligrams per day for threonine.

Aside from individual variations, there are other factors, yet unknown. It is possible, for example, to maintain nitrogen balance at a number of levels of protein intake. At higher levels some of the excess proteins go into a reserve (Shapiro and Fisher). The nature of these reserves is not clearly known, but there is a feeling among some investigators that certain of the proteins in the mammalian body are more accessible than others to fill emergency protein needs. For example, the quantity of blood-plasma albumin reflects the state of protein nutrition. Protein depletion effects the protein content of the liver, muscle, and kidney, has less effect on the heart and spleen proteins, and none on the brain protein. The more labile proteins in the body (plasma albumin and the cytoplasm of the liver and gut) might well be considered as sort of reserves; they reflect a biological heirarchy—the proteins of higher priority being maintained at the expense of other proteins. (See also Patwardhan and Holt et al. (1960), p. 9.)

Some investigators believe that resistance to stress depends upon the size of these reserves and on the general adequacy of protein content at any given time, a figure which cannot be easily measured. Terroine said that it would not be wise to fix the adult protein requirement at the minimum level necessary to maintain nitrogen balance. He said: "To build up a certain capital of labile proteins might perhaps be regarded as a kind of insurance, enabling the organism to put up a better resistance against infections and stresses of various kinds. But here we are treading on unexplored ground, for we have no scientific facts which enable us to fix this minimum for health on such a level which is distinctly higher than the physiological minimum, and might even be regarded as the physiological optimum" (Waterlow and Stephen, p. 119). Holt et al. (1962) challenge the idea that there may be a relationship between protein intake and resistance to protein deprivation.

Rose arbitrarily doubled his highest experimental values of minimum amino acid requirements to arrive at a figure for safe amino acid intakes. The FAO committee suggested an arbitrary increment of 50 percent over the average minimum requirements in order to cover the needs of individuals whose requirements exceed the average minimum requirement. The National Research Council (U. S.) made more liberal allowances. (See Chap. 7.) Obviously it is impossible to compensate for individual differences by any general formula; in the last analysis each individual must try to find out for himself where in the spectrum of individuality he belongs. But the general allowances provide a point of departure; further research and discussion will provide a sounder basis for establishing a consensus (Pearson and Darby).

Platt and his associates calculated the safe percentage of protein calories in a diet by combining the recommended

Calorie allowances for human subjects per kilogram per day with the protein allowances on the same basis. Taking figures submitted by committees of the Food and Agriculture Organization, they arrived at results shown in Table 10-2. These data emphasize the importance of protein

TABLE 10-2

*Calorie and Protein Allowances for Various Age Groups* [1]

| Subject | Age, Years | Calories per Day | Reference Protein, Grams per Day | Reference Protein Calories, Percent |
|---------|------------|------------------|----------------------------------|-------------------------------------|
| Infant | 0–1 | | | 8.0 |
| Toddler | 1–2 | 1,230 | 24 | 7.8 |
| Child | 4–9 | 1,970 | 29 | 5.9 |
| Adolescent | | 3,050 | 61 | 8.0 |
| Adult | | 2,960 | 34 | 4.6 |
| Lactating mother | | 3,200 | 76 | 9.5 |

*Source:* B. S. Platt, D. S. Miller, and P. R. Payne, "Protein Values of Human Food," in J. F. Brock (ed.), *Recent Advances in Human Nutrition* (London: Churchill, 1961). See also M. Autret and R. Jacquot, "Valeur protéique de l'alimentation dans les pays tropicaux et subtropicaux," *Federation Proc.*, vol. 20, no. 1, part III, supp. 7 (1961), p. 89.

[1] The data for requirements of calories and proteins are taken from publications of the Food and Agriculture Organization of the United Nations: *Calorie Requirements*, FAO Nutritional Studies no. 15 (1957), *Protein Requirements*, FAO Nutritional Studies No. 16, FAO (Rome, Italy: Food and Agriculture Organization of the United Nations, 1957).
Calculations were made as follows:

$$\text{Reference protein} \times 4 = \text{reference protein Calories}$$

$$\frac{\text{Reference protein per day} \times 4}{\text{Calories per day}} = \% \text{ reference protein Calories}$$

nutrition to the lactating mother; on this basis, her minimum requirement is even higher than the need for the infant. Notice again the importance given to protein in the diet for adolescents and the comparatively low requirement for adults.

The values of percentage of protein calories in Table 10-2 are for reference protein, fully available. Platt et al. have constructed a nomogram to facilitate calculation of percentage reference protein calories from actual intake. Two factors must be considered: the biological value of the protein source and the percentage of protein in the diet. There is a correction for biological value of less than 100, and there is a second correction to take into account reduction in biological value of a protein as its concentration in the diet is increased. In general, as we pointed out in an earlier chapter, a protein fed as 10 percent of the calories is utilized more efficiently than the same protein fed at the level of 20 percent of the calories.

Examples of Platt's calculations are the following:

A meal of egg, bacon, and beans having a net protein utlization (NPU) value of 78 and fed at a level of 22 percent protein calories calculates as 11 percent reference protein calories; wheat protein with an NPU value of 47 fed at a level of 11 percent protein calories comes out to be 5 percent reference protein calories; a mixture of wheat, beans, and sesame with an NPU value of 70 fed at a level of 15 percent protein calories becomes 8.2 percent reference protein calories.

## Adequacy of National Diets

It is possible to rate the protein component of a national diet by analysis of the food supplies, to get some notion of its adequacy, and even to suggest how it may be improved most economically. But first it is necessary to convert minimum requirements for reference protein into minimum requirements for real-life food proteins. There is no standard operating procedure. The simplest way is to increase the requirements of food protein in the diet by multiplying the minimum requirements for reference protein by the ratio of 100 over the actual biological value (BV) or net protein utilization (NPU). Thus the requirements for the dietary protein with BV of 60 will be 1.7 times the requirements for the reference protein (BV = 100). This is the method of calculation of requirements for milk protein given in Chap. 9, and is also the basis for calculating chemical scores in the hypothetical example of lysine deficiency (Fig. 9-2). Hegsted considers that the decrease in biological value of a protein is more than the above-mentioned ratios would indicate because its amount in the diet is raised. His correction is an additional 30 percent. Platt, as we mentioned earlier, has a more complicated formula and nomogram to provide this adjustment.

In its report the FAO Committee provides an example of their treatment; the simplest correction procedure was chosen as the basis for the calculations and appraisal of three different national diets. Compared were the food supplies in three countries: the first, Country A, provided 3200 Calories and 95 grams of protein per person, with more than 60 percent of the total protein coming from animal sources; the second, Country B, provided 1900 Calories and 47 grams of protein per person of which 12 percent came from animal sources, 27 percent from legumes, and 58 percent from cereals, which include rice and wheat; and the third, Country C, provided 2030 Calories and 57 grams of protein per person, 32 percent of which was obtained from animal sources, 14 percent from legumes, and 51 percent from cereals, chiefly corn. For all three countries, the food supply was deficient in tryptophan and in sulfur-containing amino acids. On this basis the protein source for the first country was calculated to have a chemical score of 81; for Country B, it was 76; and for Country C, 62. The low score of Country C was the result of high tryptophan deficiency because the staple was corn rather than rice or wheat. The safe practical allowances for each country are the average minimum requirements for the reference protein multiplied by 1.5, the arbitrary FAO increment to take into account individual variations in protein requirements, and then multiplied by the factor relating the protein quality to that of the reference protein. A summary of these allowances is given in Table 10-3.

### TABLE 10–3

#### Estimation of Safe Practical Allowances for Three Hypothetical Countries

| Age of Subject | Average Minimum Requirement of Reference Protein | Safe Practical Allowances | | |
|---|---|---|---|---|
| | | Country A | Country B | Country C |
| | | Col. 2 × 1.5[1] × 1.25[2] | Col. 2 × 1.5[1] × 1.3[2] | Col. 2 × 1.5[1] × 1.6[2] |
| | Grams per Kilogram | | | |
| 9 months | 1.4 | 2.6 | 2.7 | 3.4 |
| 2 years | 1.1 | 2.1 | 2.15 | 2.6 |
| 5 years | 0.8 | 1.5 | 1.6 | 1.9 |
| 9 years | 0.7 | 1.3 | 1.4 | 1.7 |
| Adolescent | 0.8 | 1.5 | 1.6 | 1.9 |
| Adult | 0.35 | 0.7 | 0.7 | 0.8 |

Source: *Protein Requirements*, FAO Nutritional Studies No. 16 (Rome, Italy: Food and Agriculture Organization of the United Nations, 1957).

[1] Coefficient to allow for individual variations in protein requirements.
[2] Coefficient to allow for differences in protein quality (100/BV).

A more practical way of improving the protein nutrition of Country C might be to raise the amount and quality of the proteins by supplementation. The total amount of protein available per day may be raised from 57 to 63 grams by supplementing with one egg per person per day; this will also raise the protein score from 62 to 68. The intake can also be raised from 57 to 74 grams per day and the quality of protein from a score of 62 to 72 by the addition of 50 grams of sesame which is high in tryptophan and in sulfur-containing amino acids.

It is interesting to consider the status of wheat. It contains about 6 percent of the calories as protein calculated as reference protein; a child raised on a diet based on wheat as a staple is likely to attain its protein requirements. As a matter of fact, according to Platt, it would be difficult to devise a diet consisting mainly of wheat which did not contain 8 percent of reference protein calories. Such is not possible with corn and rice as staple foods; this underlines the importance of wheat and may account for the fact that cases of malnutrition are rare in wheat-raising areas. (See, however, Chap. 14.)

## SELECTED BIBLIOGRAPHY

"Advances in Human Nutrition," Proceedings of the Heinz International Symposium on Nutrition, *Federation Proc.*, vol. 18, no. 2, part II, supp. 3 (1959).

Bernhart, F. W. "Correlation between Growth Rate of the Suckling of Various Species and the Percentage of Total Calories from Protein in Milk," *Nature*, vol. 191 (1961), p. 358.

*Calorie Requirements*. FAO Nutritional Studies No. 15. Rome, Italy: Food and Agriculture Organization of the United Nations, 1957.

Hegsted, D. M. "Theoretical Estimates of the Protein Requirements in Children," *J. Am. Dietet. Assoc.*, vol. 33 (1957), p. 225.

Holt, L. E., Jr., E. Halac, Jr., and C. N. Kajdi. "The Concept of Protein Stores and Its Implication in the Diet," *J. Am. Med. Assn.*, vol. 181, no. 8 (1962), p. 699.

Holt, L. E., Jr., P. Gyorgy, E. L. Pratt, Selma E. Snyderman, and W. M. Wallace. *Protein and Amino Acid Requirements in Early Life.* New York: New York University Press, 1960.

Patwardhan, V. N. "Biochemistry of Human Protein Metabolism," *Federation Proc.*, vol. 20, no. 1, part III, supp. 7 (1961), p. 73.

Pearson, W. N., and W. J. Darby. "Protein Nutrition," *Ann. Rev. Biochem.*, vol. 30 (1961), p. 325.

Platt, B. S., D. S. Miller, and P. R. Payne. "Protein Values of Human Foods," in J. F. Brock (ed.), *Recent Advances in Human Nutrition.* London: Churchill, 1961. See also D. S. Miller and P. R. Payne, "Problems in the Prediction of Protein Values of Diets: Calorie Restriction," *J. Nutr.*, vol. 75 (1961), p. 225.

"Protein Nutrition," *Ann N. Y. Acad. Sci.*, vol. 69 (1958), p. 885.

*Protein Requirements.* FAO Nutritional Studies No. 16. Rome, Italy: Food and Agriculture Organization of the United Nations, 1957. A revised statement is being prepared by an expert committee and will be issued shortly.

Shapiro, R., and H. Fisher. "Protein Reserves: Relationship of Dietary Essential and Nonessential Amino Acids to Formation and Maintenance of Fowl," *J. Nutr.*, vol. 76 (1962), p. 106.

"Symposium on Protein Requirements and Its Assessment in Man," *Federation Proc.*, vol. 18 (1959), p. 1125.

Waterlow, J. C., and J. M. L. Stephen. *Human Protein Requirements and Their Fulfilment in Practice,* Report of a Conference at Princeton, N. J., in 1955. Bristol, England: John Wright and Sons, Ltd., 1957.

Williams, R. J. "Individuality of Amino Acid Needs," in A. A. Albanese (ed.), *Protein and Amino Acid Nutrition.* New York: Academic, 1959, p. 45.

# CHAPTER 11

# *The Effect of Heat on Food Proteins*

HEAT ON FOODSTUFFS is a two-edged sword; no discussion of protein in foods would be complete nor accurate without mention of the role of heat during cooking and processing, and its effects, good and bad.

Heat-preparation of foods is as old as fire itself. The beneficence of Prometheus which enabled man to live in all climates also provided him with the choice of a wider range of foodstuffs than any other living creature. Paleolithic man only knew of roasting the flesh of wild animals. With the Neolithic revolution, when food production began, man had at his disposal the basic foods which could be prepared together by cooking. Porridges were made of cereals, biscuits were prepared, and, finally, leavened bread was developed. Often heat was employed as a preservative and as an aid to agriculture. Smoking of animal flesh and fish was known to prehistoric inhabitants of Europe. Cereals were roasted slightly to aid in threshing and to improve storage quality.

Nutritive value was not the first consideration in cooking and in other heat applications. Even if it did not happen as Charles Lamb portrayed it, flavor and palatability were involved first in cooking. It was the warmth of the prepared food which made it more savory and more delectable. It was the odor carried up by steam which awakened the appetite. Even the simple job of soaking with water was made easier; hard grains like rice were softened by cooking in water. There is no limit to the pleasurability of foods cooked in the hands of a competent chef, who can blend tastes, odors, and flavors together in a warm, tasty, and appetizing dish. Indeed, if any nutritional benefits were also derived, their recognition must have come much later.

## Chemical and Physical Changes

All cooks, in a sense, are chemists. This is actually what happens when a foodstuff is heated: chemical and physical changes take place. Some are easily noticed—changes in color and texture when meat is broiled or cooked, the softening of spaghetti, the hardening of an egg. There are also subtle changes such as production of new volatile compounds with characteristic odors which are responsible for the many and varied odors and flavors in cooked foods. It is only in recent years, with the sharpening of analytical tools to measure such evanescent materials, that it becomes possible to explore the chemical nature of the odors. Soon, perhaps, they will be made synthetically and then it will be possible to obtain the same odors without actually having to cook.

Certainly no other promoter compares with heat as the producer of physical and chemical changes which have so profoundly influenced man's food habits. We might consider the cooking of foods as one of the major characteristic differences between man and animals.

Although not as obvious as changes which play on the culinary sensibilities, we might expect that heat also produces changes in the nutritive quality of the foods as well. Some of these effects are mostly physical: cellular organization is destroyed or disrupted, and food materials become more available to digestion. This is probably the major effect of cooking of rice, for example, in promoting the availability of rich starch to digestion. Digestibility is a property often acquired by cooking. The tough materials in muscles are changed in such a manner as to promote better grinding. But there are changes also in the proteins themselves. Raw proteins are less digestible than cooked or denatured proteins.

## Destruction of Toxic Materials

Aside from the direct effect of cooking on the foodstuffs, indirect effects no less important come by destruction of toxic or interfering materials. Raw eggs, for example, contain a protein, avidin, which combines with and renders useless the vitamin, biotin. Hence, those who eat excessive quantities of raw eggs may suffer from biotin deficiency. But this protein is destroyed by heat; it cannot function as a vitamin inhibitor in the cooked egg. There are inhibitors in various kinds of legumes which interfere with their utilization. Some are trypsin inhibitors; these have been implicated as interfering with the natural digestive action. But there are other inhibitors which interfere in a yet unknown way. The trypsin inhibitors and some of the others are proteins which are inactivated by cooking. Raw fish contains an enzyme that catalyzes the destruction of the vitamin, thiamine; cooking inactivates the enzyme and prevents the destruction of this vitamin in diets rich in fish foods.

Thus cooking engenders nutritional benefits in two ways: by improving the digestibility of the food itself and by destroying interfering materials, this in addition to promoting a more tasty dish. Leonardo da Vinci included cooking in his prescription of good health habits:

If you would keep healthy, follow this regimen: Do not eat unless you feel inclined, and sup lightly; chew well, and let what you take be well cooked and simple.

## Losses in Cooking

Not all of the results of cooking are beneficial, however. There are losses and destruction of nutrients on cooking. Major losses are among the vitamins, most of which are heat-labile, hence destroyed to varying extents during cooking. For example, one of the B vitamins, thiamine, is unstable in all processes of heating muscle meat. The least damaging are broiling and frying, the most damaging are boiling and brazing, and canning. Perhaps the most vulnerable of the B vitamins in foods of animal origin are vitamin $B_6$ and pantothenic acid. Choline is entirely stable and so is biotin. Ascorbic acid is the most sensitive to heat destruction of all the nutrients investigated in foods of vegetable origin; whereas carotene is quite stable under the same circumstances. Under certain conditions fats, as in deep-fat frying, may become oxidized and liable to destroy portions of the fat-soluble vitamins (A, D, K, E, and essential fatty acids) and even some of the water-soluble vitamins in the fried food.

Protein may be rendered less suitable as a result of heat. In some instances some of the amino acids in the proteins are actually destroyed by overheating and cannot be recovered by any means. In many instances amino acids are not destroyed but are bound or changed in such a way that they are rendered indigestible, or much less (or more slowly) digestible. It is certainly possible to lower the biological value of a protein by certain types of heat.

This, then, is why heat is a two-edged sword. Heat promotes beneficial effects but also destroys nutrients; the virtue is that the good usually comes first. While it is rarely possible to attain improvements through cooking without destruction of nutrients, it is practically possible to work out a compromise between the favorable results and the nutrient losses, predominantly in favor of the benefits. Only by overcooking or overheating is the damage so preponderant that it overshadows any of the advantages of heat. Our inquiries into the effect of heat on proteins in food are fundamentally investigations into the nature of the compromise.

In order to understand the nature of heat effects, it is best to start with relatively simple systems: pure proteins and simple mixtures of proteins and other compounds.

## Effect on Proteins

Heat causes profound changes in the physical characteristics of proteins. Prolonged heating many introduce chemical changes as well, but the first effects are the transformations described in Chap. 5. In much of the early literature, these changes are referred to as "denaturation." Such transformations change (mostly reduce) solubility of proteins, render them more digestible, and destroy biological activity of enzymes and of toxic proteins.

### THE MAILLARD, OR "BROWNING," REACTION

Heating of the type which produces only the physical changes associated with early stages of denaturation should not be expected to reduce the biological value of a pure protein as a food. On the contrary, denaturation should favor digestibility. And often the concomitant destruction in a natural mixture of toxic or interfering proteins improves the biological value of the mixture. But excessive heating might destroy some of the amino acids or render them unavailable to digestion.

It is possible to render amino acids unavailable as nutrients even though they are not destroyed chemically. Suppose that a portion of an amino acid on a protein chain forms a chemical bond with a portion of a second amino acid located somewhere else along the chain or on a neighboring chain. Each of the two amino acids is changed thereby; whereas they might have been normally released from the protein chain by the digestive enzymes, the new bond introduces a degree of "confusion" which either slows down or prevents the release of these amino acids.

This new chemical bond need not be a strong one; it usually is disrupted by boiling in strong acids. It need only be strong enough to withstand rupture in the environment of the digestive tract. Here, then, is an instance in which amino acids are not destroyed, because they can be recovered from proteins by treatment with strong acids, but they are nevertheless unavailable to 'digestion.

The reaction between portions of amino acids in protein chains with each other is not so easy to come by; a more likely reaction which produces the same effect is that between portions of amino acids and reducing sugars such as glucose. This reaction was first noted by Louis Maillard and bears his name. In the early stages a bond is formed between the sugar and the amino acid (lysine is most frequently involved) which interferes with the action of proteolytic enzymes but which is ruptured by boiling in acid. If the reaction is continued, more reaction products are formed. These polymerize to yield brownish-colored products; hence, another name for this reaction is the "Browning" reaction. The crust of bread, the "golden" color of most breakfast foods, the color of roasted peanuts, are examples of this reaction. In the last stages, when browning has become extensive, amino acids are actually destroyed.

Chemical destruction of amino acids is an extension of the Maillard reaction between amino acids and sugars. It even may come about as an extension of "internal" reactions between two portions of amino acids in the same protein, but this is less likely. Actual destruction of amino acids by simple heat without postulating either of the above-mentioned reactions would require drastic conditions which lead to charring; these are unlikely in ordinary food processing.

We should also recognize the central role of moisture content. Experiments with simple systems of amino acids and sugars have shown that a moisture content of 30 percent is most favorable for the Maillard reaction. Moisture contents above or below this level are less favorable for protein damage; and the extremes of bone dry or soaking wet are least favorable. Under comparable conditions of temperature and length of exposure to heat, cooking and toasting should promote less damage to protein quality than drying or baking. In the latter circumstances, the moisture content is reduced from a high value to a relatively low one, passing, on the way, through the range of moisture content of maximum sensitivity to protein damage. This is not to say that cooking or toasting are totally innocuous treatments. It is possible to reduce protein quality by autoclaving, as in canning, and by toasting, but more severe heat treatments are required to accomplish the same ends, achieved more easily at intermediate moisture contents.

## HEAT AND BIOLOGICAL VALUE

With the introduction of heat as an important and ubiquitous variable in the preparation of foods, we must qualify our previous statements on the relationship between biological value and amino acid composition. It is not the amino acid composition in the uneaten food protein that counts; it is the amino acid composition of the digested protein as it is presented for assimilation by the animal that is important. There may be a great disparity between the two. This disparity, which will vary from product to product and with the complex circumstances of food gathering and processing, accounts in part for the lack of better correlation between amino acid content of foods and their biological value. But more than this: the disparity presents a problem to the consumer of food proteins (and all of us are consumers) who must learn how to cope with this additional complication superimposed upon natural differences. It means that foods which are heat-treated are artifacts, are new products modified from their original state by heat.

## Practical Consequences of Heating Foods

### AT HOME

At the home level there is little danger of extensive heat damage to proteins, although, as was mentioned earlier, there is the opportunity for considerable destruction and loss of other nutrients, particularly vitamins. The meats (animal, fish, or fowl) contain relatively small quantities of carbohydrates. Beef muscle, for example, contains 1.3 percent soluble carbohydrate and 55 percent protein on a moisture-free basis. When meats are cooked in an excess of water, the conditions are minimal for damage; there is even evidence of improvement to some degree in digestibility. Ordinary canning procedures do not damage meat protein; a decrease in nutritive value is shown only in those samples receiving the most extensive treatment. Even when meats are broiled, there is insufficient carbohydrate to support extensive Maillard reaction. Losses in protein quality on heating whole milk or whole eggs are small. There is relatively little information on the effect of home cooking on the proteins of vegetables, but under conditions of excess moisture the damage should not amount to much.

### FOODS THAT ENTER THE HOME

But many foods enter the home after having been exposed to extensive heating. This is not a modern development; we have already noted the ancient practice of drying foods for preservation; Marco Polo observed the preparation of dried milk in Asia in the thirteenth century. More and more in modern life foods are being modified from their original condition into forms which are more convenient to handle and transport, are more stable, and are more tasty. Water confers a bulkiness to a foodstuff; it confers an instability to the product, be it to chemical deterioration or to biological change from endogenous enzymes or exogenous microorganisms. And water is the common solvent. It can be taken away and added back to a foodstuff with least prejudice to local tastes. Even the individual flavor of the neighborhood water is an asset; water may be removed from a food in one part of the world and returned to it in another part. When the dried food is rehydrated with local water it will taste more like a local product than had it been shipped intact from its original source.

Although dehydration is the major basis for heat during processing, there are numerous examples of heating to introduce desirable flavors or textures, or to facilitate removal of components, such as fats and oils in the processing of oilseeds. Hence there are many opportunities for heat damage to proteins; actually the facts of heat damage to food proteins came first and prompted the explanations which came later.

Dried skim milk was distributed in untold millions of pounds to hungry children in the years following World War II by UNICEF and other agencies from stores of surplus milk made available by the United States government. These could never have been exported as fluid milk, and, in most areas, could never have been kept unspoiled before being incorporated into food. And there are many solid food products containing milk powder; by being put into a dried form, the opportunities for incorporation of the valuable nutrients of milk have been extended to foods other than drinks. In the United States approximately 1.7 billion pounds of nonfat dried milk are produced annually.

Milk contains approximately 3.5 percent protein and 5 percent lactose. Fluid milk may be autoclaved, as is done in the production of evaporated milk, without loss in protein quality. It may even be dried in such a way as not to lose protein quality. But it is equally possible to produce a dry milk with low protein quality. Samples of roller-dried milks had NPU values ranging from 57 to 81, whereas raw liquid skim milk had an NPU value of 86 (Fairbanks and Mitchell). Once a dry powder is produced, it may deteriorate on prolonged storage even at low moisture conditions; the Maillard reaction takes place, albeit slowly, in dry products at ambient temperatures.

Reduction in protein quality of milk has been traced to the reduction in lysine availability. There are instances of actual destruction of lysine, particularly among the roller-dried milks. But the reduction in availability is far greater. And for a wide range of values of lysine availability there is a linear relationship between this value and protein efficiency; four roller-dried milks which had values for lysine availability of 28, 37, 54, and 66 percent, when fed to rats had protein efficiency ratios of 0.6, 1.2, 2.2, and 3, respectively. Mauron and his colleagues concluded: ". . . We must emphasize that the extent of lysine deterioration in the same type of milk may somewhat vary as the manufacturing conditions differ from one factory to another. But, even so, we feel justified in considering the processing of evaporated and roller-dried milk as it is usually performed to be more injurious to lysine than that of sweetened condensed and spray-dried milk."

The drying of eggs is also an ancient practice. Its modern development into a large industry (25 million pounds annually in the U. S.) has permitted storage of eggs for longer periods, has reduced cost of transportation, and encouraged their incorporation into a number of new products. But dried eggs which have not been stored properly deteriorate in flavor, physical properties, and protein quality.

Bread is a most convenient and tasty form for obtaining the nutritional benefits of wheat flour. The extensive utilization of wheat flour as a major source of food would not have been possible if baked forms were not available. Yet there is a loss in available lysine of from 10 to 30 percent on baking of bread and a little larger loss when the bread is toasted. Most of the loss is in the crust.

There is a large industry for conversion of cereal grains into appetizing ready-to-eat breakfast foods. Cereal grains are cooked and toasted or "exploded," with or without added sugar for sweetening. These are now part of a standard pattern of the breakfast diet in the United States; close to 5 pounds per capita are consumed annually. Yet it is quite clear that a major reaction in the formation of these products is the Maillard reaction. In one series of investigations it was shown that if raw oat dough were rated as 100 percent in protein efficiency and cooked dough 99 percent, toasted flakes and puffed oats would rate 72 percent and 23 percent, respectively, on the same scale. Several of these breakfast cereals have a protein efficiency rating of zero; taken even with milk they are not considered a good dietary source of protein (Campbell and Chapman).

More and more premixes are being marketed as a convenience food to aid the housewife in preparing cakes and other baked materials. Entire meals are being marketed in a premix form. Aside from the losses in protein value through the Browning reaction during the preparation of the dried materials, there is the additional possibility of destruction of protein value during long storage of dried ingredients, such as eggs or milk. And more vegetables are being dehydrated either for incorporation into such premixes or as more stable and convenient products in their own right.

The commercial preparation of protein concentrates from plant and animal sources involves drying under conditions favoring the Browning reaction. Such are the conditions in the production of millions of tons of soybean, cottonseed, or peanut protein concentrates for human and animal consumption; such is the preparation of dried fish products for consumption by man and animal; and such is the preparation of dried blood products for animals. Duckworth et al. found that the Gross Protein Value (a measure of nutritive value) of fish protein concentrates available on the British market ranged from 92 to 119, milk powders from 65 to 102, and soybean protein concentrates from 59 to 93.

Even the medical profession, aside from its interest in nutrition, becomes involved in the Browning reaction when using protein hydrolyzates. Proteins are hydrolyzed in acid to provide amino acid concentrates which can serve as intravenous alimentation. Here again is a danger of destruction of some of the amino acids by Browning reaction during sterilization in the presence of glucose, added to the mixture to provide more calories for the patient.

In recent years there have appeared formulations to facilitate reduction in calorie intake without engendering insufficiency of other nutrients. These reducing diets provide adequate protein even with a total daily intake of approximately 900 Calories. Major sources of protein are dried milk and vegetable protein concentrates from soybean. When the protein sources have been properly handled, there is adequacy of amount and quality of the proteins. But certainly these products are sensitive to improper processing and to heat damage to the protein constituents.

This is but a partial listing of products which enter modern homes after having already been subjected to heat processing of one type or another. We can anticipate that their number will increase and their distribution become more widespread in the future. As we will discuss in later chapters, any consideration of means for increasing world protein supplies leads to need for development of new products, particularly from plant sources. Such new foods will be produced most efficiently in industrial-type operations which will in most instances include a heating step, be it for drying or for destruction of toxic factors. Heat, then, is a basic part of our food culture; heat damage is one of the facts of food preparation. Society must learn to cope with the heat effect, but first it must recognize that it exists.

Just as we have shown that there is no such thing as protein "in general," that proteins differ in biological value depending upon their amino acid composition, so must it be emphasized that heating changes protein value drastically. The heated and unheated protein are not the same in nutritive value, even though the name is the same.

## The General Problem of Heat Injury

Scientists, as they became aware of the possibility of heat injury, expressed a concern over its economic and nutritional implications. The National Research Council (U. S.) has issued a pamphlet entitled *The Problem of Heat Injury to Dietary Protein* for the purpose of summarizing the information existing on this subject and particularly to call public attention to the problem. In this pamphlet P. R. Cannon, Chairman of the N.R.C. Committee, has this to say about some of the foods:

It is fortunate that, by the methods now in use, there seems to be but little damage to such important protein foods as meat and milk. Nonetheless it may be possible to improve still further some of the methods employed so that even slight injury may be eliminated.

Although current methods of processing of the ready-to-eat breakfast foods lead in several instances to a marked deterioration of the protein value, the gravity of the situation is lessened somewhat by the fact that these foods are commonly eaten with milk, and this tends to make up for amino acid deficiencies to the cereal proteins brought about by heat injury. However, the fact should not be overlooked that diversion of lysine from milk in order to atone for lysine injury in the cereal may render ineffectual the nutritive value of the remaining amino acids of milk. Moreover, it should not be forgotten that several of the toasted cereals now on the market have good protein values, proving that depreciation of the protein value of some of the cereals by the drastic methods now employed is not altogether necessary. This needless waste of protein may seem unimportant now, but the time may come again when the folly of such useless waste will not be looked upon so complacently as it is today. (pp. 3–4.)

The industries involved in processing of protein foods are aware of this problem, and, by and large, try to minimize the effects when they can recognize and control them. There is no question about the fact that the nutritive value in heat-damaged foods is lowered; the performance of experimental animals fed such foods is proof enough. But the problem is to measure quickly and easily the proper stopping point—the point where the benefits of heating have been attained before the liabilities of overheating become serious. There are no simple chemical tests that predict the extent of lowering of biological value of a protein. While for specific instances in dried milk, in dried fish flour, and in soybean and cottonseed products there are some chemical measurements to guide the processor, these are by no means completely reliable. This is an area which is bound to improve with further research. As more chemical methods become available to measure and recognize heat damage, research will accelerate on processing itself, to improve it to develop procedures which achieve the same beneficial results without the damage.

But the greatest incentive to minimize heat damage will come when the consumer recognizes the problem and insists on the highest quality protein. This has been slow in coming. Among the first to react to the variability in protein value of processed foodstuffs were some of the better-informed livestock feeders who incorporate protein concentrates from plant and animal sources in their rations. This is particularly important in the feeding of monogastric animals such as poultry or swine. These feeders have learned to select among the processed products those which have been damaged least. They decide on the basis of practical experience, or biological tests of the various sources, or by judicious application of the available chemical tests.

Among many of the feeders, however (and this holds for the general public) there is yet to be found the recognition that protein is more than nitrogen multiplied by 6.25, that just as there are differences in biological value of proteins from different sources, so are there variations in proteins from the same source ascribed to heat damage. The ultimate will be specifications for processed protein products which will include a section on heat damage and a measure for it. There are indications of trends in this direction.

In the meantime there are some simple principles which should be of general value in the industry and home. These have been stated clearly and succinctly by S. Lepkovsky:

> Heat must be applied cautiously and intelligently in the processing of foods. Those foods containing toxic proteins must be heated sufficiently to destroy their toxic properties, but they must not be overheated because excess heat decreases the biological value of nontoxic and detoxified proteins. Frequently, there is little difference between just enough and just too much heat, so that careful control must be exercised in the heat processing of foods. (p. 122.)

If the housewife is truly interested in the kind of protein she serves her family, she, too, has a stake in the heat-injury problem. She does not have facilities for biological testing of foodstuffs nor is she able easily to judge the food value of her diet by observing her own family. (It is so much easier to follow the progress of livestock.) But awareness of this problem is a big step forward. Her willingness to insist on high quality products and to pay for better protein would encourage strict attention to heat damage among food processors and purveyors.

It is no exaggeration to state that the equivalent of millions of tons of additional satisfactory protein-rich foods could be made available for humans and animals were the present knowledge of the effects of heat on protein applied and heeded. In a protein-hungry world, this is something to think about.

## SELECTED BIBLIOGRAPHY

Campbell, J. A., and D. G. Chapman. "Evaluation of Protein in Foods — Criteria for Describing Protein Value," *J. Can. Dietetic Assn.*, vol. 21 (1959), p. 51.

Duckworth, J., A. A. Woodham, and I. McDonald. "The Assessment of Nutritive Value in Protein Concentrates by the Gross Protein Value Method," *J. Sci. Food Agr.*, no. 5 (1961), p. 407.

Ellis, G. P. "The Maillard Reaction," in W. W. Pigman (ed.), *Advances in Carbohydrate Chemistry*. Vol. 14. New York: Academic, 1959.

Fairbanks, B. W., and H. H. Mitchell. "The Nutritive Value of Skim-Milk Powders with Special Reference to the Sensitivity of Milk Proteins to Heat," *J. Agr. Research*, vol. 51 (1935), p. 1107.

Feldberg, C. "Adequacy of Processed Cereals," in S. A. Matz (ed.), *The Chemistry and Technology of Cereals as Food*. Westport, Conn.: Avi, 1959.

Frost, D. V. "Methods of Measuring the Nutritive Value of Protein Hydrolyzates and Amino Acid Mixtures: The Rat Repletion Method," in A. A. Albanese (ed.), *Protein and Amino Acid Requirements of Mammals*. New York: Academic, 1960.

Harris, R. S., and H. von Loesecke (eds.). *Nutritional Evaluation of Food Processing*. New York: Wiley, 1960.

Hodge, J. E. "Chemistry of Browning Reactions in Model Systems," *J. Agr. Food Chem.*, vol. 1 (1953), p. 928.

Lamb, Charles. *A Dissertation upon Roast Pig and Other Favorite Essays*. Mount Vernon, N. Y.: Peter Pauper Press (n.d.).

Liener, I. E. "Effect of Heat on Plant Proteins," in A. M. Altschul (ed.), *Processed Plant Protein Foodstuffs*. New York: Academic, 1958.

Lepkovsky, S. "Nutritional Stress Factors and Food Processing," in E. M. Mrak and George F. Stewart (eds.), *Advances in Food Research*. Vol. 4. New York: Academic, 1953.

MacCurdy, E. (ed. and translator). *The Notebooks of Leonardo da Vinci*. New York: Garden City, 1941–42.

Mauron, J. "La lysine, facteur limitant de nutrition; sa détérioration lors de la preparation des ailments," *Médicine et Hygiène* (Geneva), vol. 17 (June 30, 1959), p. 59.

Mauron, J., F. Mottu, E. Bujard, and R. H. Egli. "The Availability of Lysine, Methionine, and Tryptophan in Condensed Milk and Milk Powder, *in Vitro* Digestion Studies," *Arch. Biochem. Biophys.*, vol. 59 (1955), p. 433.

National Research Council. *The Problem of Heat Injury to Dietary Protein*. Reprint and Circular Series No. 131. Washington, D. C.: National Academy of Sciences, 1950.

Rice, E. E., and J. F. Benk. "The Effects of Heat upon the Nutritive Value of Protein," in E. M. Mrak and George F. Stewart (eds.), *Advances in Food Research.* Vol. 4. New York: Academic, 1953.

Singer, C., E. J. Holinyard, and A. R. Hall (eds.). *A History of Technology.* Vol. 1. London: Oxford U. P., 1954, chaps. 5, 10, 11.

# CHAPTER 12

# *Proteins in Food — Some Things to Think About*

WE HAVE TRIED to compress into a few brief chapters the elements of proteins in food. We have emphasized that the word protein has multiple meaning in foods: proteins differ in their nutritive value; protein requirements vary with species, age, and state of health; heat-treated proteins are artifacts which may bear no relationship to the original raw material.

Differences in protein values of foods can be measured. In general, proteins from animal sources are superior to proteins from vegetable sources. Since proteins are a source of amino acids, the reason for differences in their food value is attributed primarily to their amino acid composition. Hence, it is possible by blending several proteins which complement each other's amino acid composition to achieve mixtures of good protein quality. An abstract reference protein is defined as totally available to the human being with the best possible amount and pattern of essential amino acids and with sufficient additional nitrogen to support synthesis of the nonessential amino acids.

Regardless of the initial amino acid content of a protein food, it is the amino acid composition as delivered to the digestive tract which counts. Hence, proteins which are not completely digestible are less nutritious than would be predicted from their compositional data alone. And proteins which have been modified by heat-treatment might be either better or worse than the original material. Heat, therefore, is an opportunity as well as a hazard.

The minimum protein requirements for various age groups of the human species have been set down. Although there are differences in opinion among the investigators on the details, the general agreement is of a relatively high need for infants, pregnant women, and lactating mothers, possibly a higher than normal need for adolescents, and the lowest needs for adults. With the information on minimum requirements it is possible to decide, even if only arbitrarily, on what may be the safe allowances. And with a formula for transferring from the ideal protein to real life protein and to a complete food mixture, it is possible to make allowances for the quality of protein as it actually is presented in the food. Hence, one may, in a semiquantitative way at least, survey a national dietary and decide on its adequacy in amount and quality, and point to directions for its improvement.

Failure to meet the protein requirements of an individual has serious consequences in terms of growth, resistance to disease, and general well-being. Chronic protein malnutrition is one of the most formidable problems facing humanity. Since we plan to devote an entire section to this subject, we will pass it up for the moment and devote the remainder of this chapter to certain questions involving those who have enough protein supply. Are there certain sensitive segments of the population whose protein needs are not met, even though there are adequate supplies? Is it possible to consume too much protein? There are no definitive answers, but there are some suggestions, some things to think about.

We know the critical elements of the population: the infants and toddlers, the adolescents, the pregnant and nursing women. Under ordinary circumstances, when there is enough food, they get enough. But they bear watching.

Another segment of the population whose protein nutrition is critical are the ill, particularly convalescents from illness, surgery, or injury. And often this point is not sufficiently appreciated. Wounds heal with difficulty, resistance to infection is lowered, and the liver becomes vulnerable to toxic agents when there is protein deficiency or a disturbed protein metabolism. Even if the patient might not have been originally in a state of protein deficiency, the illness itself could induce such a state. There may be interference with protein metabolism, mechanical loss through burns or exudates, interference with digestion or absorption, or decreased protein intake from loss of appetite. Trauma may increase the basal metabolic rate and hence the food requirements. As stated by Pollack and Halpern, "A vicious cycle may thus be produced, the disease causing a disturbance of protein metabolism and the disturbance of protein metabolism making the disease more serious."

There is recognition that increased attention be given the nutrition of the hospital patient. Protein therapy is an important part of improved nutrition of the patient; the proteins must be of high biological value in addition to being sufficient in quantity. These should be administered together with a regime which is adequate in calories, water, minerals, vitamins, and other accessory factors. The amounts must be determined individually for each patient. Of course, nutrition is only a part of the treatment of a patient; it is one of the many factors considered by the physician.

There is no evidence that the protein requirements of the aged differ significantly from those of other adults. In general, the amino acid and protein requirements for normal adults are constant regardless of age, weight, or activity. But the caloric requirements of the aged are less than for younger adults. This means that although they eat less, they require as much protein as the others. Hence the percentage of protein calories in their diet might well be higher. It might be safe to say that elderly people require a higher concentration of good quality protein in their diets than do younger adults.

Now we come to the normal adult who has the least protein requirements of all. Of this category we may properly ask whether there are times where more than enough is eaten. And here again, the conclusive results are yet to come. But there are many who think that there is such a thing as an optimum amount of protein in a diet, that a person can eat more protein than is good for him. Certainly it is known that general overeating is harmful; obesity, indeed, is a serious illness in some countries.

Protein surfeit would be generally associated with an increase in the animal protein components of the diet. And this is often reflected in a concomitant increase in the percentage of fat in the diet. In Table 12-1 is given the percentage of calories contributed by fat in a number of

TABLE 12–1

*Percentage of Calories Derived from Fats*
*in Some Typical Foodstuffs*

| *Foodstuff* | *Percentage of Calories Contributed by Fat* |
|---|---|
| Milk | 52 |
| Cheddar cheese | 76 |
| Eggs | 65 |
| Hamburger | 82 |
| Frankfurter | 65 |
| Peanut butter | 72 |
| Canned salmon | 71 |
| Dried chipped beef | 30 |

Source: *The Role of Dietary Fat in Human Health,* Publication 575 (Washington, D. C.: National Academy of Sciences–National Research Council, 1958).

common foods. Fat contributes a remarkably high percentage of the calories in the foods listed. We cannot divorce protein nutrition from overall nutrition. Far be it for us to take a position on the difficult and controversial question in-

volving fats in the diet. Suffice to remind the reader that
the role of fats in food in relation to health is being seriously and critically investigated and debated.

There is the general feeling among experts in nutrition
that overindulgence in food is detrimental to good health.
Passmore, for example, suggests that, if foods do not provide 20 percent of the calories in the form of fat, people
may be expected to complain; if more than 30 percent are
fat, luxuries are being supplied. In 1936, Professor Terroine presented a report to the League of Nations on "The
Protein Components in the Human Diet." We present several lengthy excerpts from this report as a clear statement
of some of the issues—not necessarily the final statement:

> ...A reduction in the consumption of vegetable products
> and a correlative increase in that of meat is undoubtedly one
> of the most salient features of improving standards of life.
> Poor families regard the restrictions they have to place upon
> their consumption of meat as one of the greatest privations
> inflicted on them by fate; they are jealous of families in better
> circumstances who can make abundant use of this food. We
> have here a deplorable state of mind, against which all those
> who are called upon to advise working-class and peasant
> families should be forewarned. If, as has frequently been
> written, "meat is the rich man's food," one might almost retort,
> "so much the worse for him!," for an abundance of meat
> in the diet yields no physiological advantage. Quite the
> contrary. . . .

Terroine's prescription of a reasonable diet for humans
is the following:

> In the first place and above all, make certain that energy
> requirements are amply covered and, to that end, advise
> recourse to the most suitable natural products — namely, those
> richest in carbohydrates; this means to say that cereals,
> legumes, and potatoes form the basis of nutrition and will
> occupy a predominant place in the diet. Finally, in considera-

tion of the superior quality of their proteins, of the exigencies
of taste and of the advantage to be derived from the consumption of the excellent foods, such as fish, which are provided
by Nature, and in order, moreover, to use animals as means
of converting into comestible foods substances not in themselves fit for human consumption, associate with the basic
vegetable food a quantity, in all cases small, of animal foods,
among which pure or skim milk should occupy a privileged
position. After this, very little will be needed to convert such
a scheme into an excellent diet by adding a little fresh fruit
and raw green vegetables, which will make up total vitamin
requirements.

In this connection, it is a melancholy reflection, that, as
physiological knowledge advances, the dietary practice of
civilized man tends to become more and more irrational; the
more so, the higher the standard of living. Could anything
be more absurd than the type of meal which consists of
hors d'oeuvre to begin with (in which meat, tinned fish, pork,
butcher's wares, etc., predominate), of a large slice of grilled
meat with just a potato or two and a few leaves of undressed
salad, which are mere trimming and not to be eaten; and
finally, of a further supply of protein in the form of cheese;
the whole accompanied by a small slice of bread, a food
which seems to have been deliberately condemned for some
considerable time past? The diner is lucky if dessert consists
of fresh or stewed fruit, and not of some pastry or sweet
containing an abundance of milk and eggs.

The old dietary practice of the working and agricultural
laboring classes was infinitely more reasonable and much
more in accord with physiological facts: there was bread,
the basic food; the milk foods; and stews of all kinds in
which meat, in small quantities played the part of a condiment,
of an appetizer, satisfying the palate, but in which vegetables
(beans, lentils, peas, potatoes, rice, flour in the form of
dumplings) formed the bulk of the dish, hotch-potch or soups
in which a small piece of salt meat lent savour to the mixed
array of vegetables.

And the best advice that can be derived from the teachings
of physiology is that the luxurious habits which lead people
into the stupid practice of increasing the animal protein, and,
especially, the meat, content of their diet should be abandoned;

that we should return to the simpler forms of mixed diet in which meat is used to awaken appetite, but in which the substantial part of the food intake is of vegetable origin.

If we follow this advice, we shall be conforming to the teaching of physiology, and we shall be, at the same time, providing an excellent diet in the most economical way.

General warning against high protein intake is echoed by many nutritionists. Pearson and Darby suggest that the current protein allowances of the National Research Council (see Chap. 7) are liberal. Brock states that "Perhaps the cult of moderation in eating (not to mention other pleasures) may have material advantages in health and longevity which outweigh its alleged penalty of smugness." Holt et al. suggest that protein enrichment of diets ought to be critically evaluated, particularly from its long-term consequences; they suggest that it would be safer to call a halt to further enrichment of American diets until such long-term consequences can be better evaluated.

Attention has been called to long-term experiments on rats which may be suggestive of similar effects in humans. When the intake of food was restricted, there was an expansion of life expectancy and a delay in the onset of major diseases including neoplasms. This was not at the expense of retardation of skeletal growth or sexual maturity. With similar types of restriction there was also a reduction in the incidence of cardiac, renal, and vascular lesions. When the intake of food was restricted there were comparatively small differences resulting from variation in the protein and carbohydrate content. But when the same diets were fed on a nonrestricted basis, rats which received a diet low in protein but high in carbohydrate, restricted their own intake and, therefore, their total intake of protein; they had the longest life span.

A few pertinent quotations from papers on this subject follow:

Cataracts, chronic eczema of the extremities, coarse, sparse, discolored hair, scaly dry skin, obesity, sluggish attitudes, etc., characterize the appearance of rats maintained on a commercial diet after their 18th month of life. On the other hand, at 30 months of age the experimental rats whose intake of casein or of sugar was low, and especially when intakes of both casein and of sugar were low, were clean, had fine hair with thick coats, were active and showed no external sign of disease. Their size and general appearance and attitude gave the impression that these rats were considerably younger than their chronological age indicated. (Ross, 1959.)

The present experiments demonstrate that a single factor, namely food intake, can effect the onset of the major degenerative diseases in the rat. Though the nature of the metabolic mechanism involved in this phenomenon is obscure, it is evident that *ad libitum* feeding accelerates the development of lesions, whereas food restriction at a level that provides for good nutrition and prevents the storage of excess body fat has a delaying effect. (Berg and Simms, 1961.)

The question of "adequacy" must be re-examined in view of the possibility that nutritional requirements as they change with advancing age, may make it necessary not only to continuously alter dietary components quantitatively but also to alter them qualitatively in order to attain maximum life expectancy. (Ross, 1961.)

There is no comparable data on the long-term effects of diet on humans. We can only, at the moment, speculate on the possible relationship.

After reviewing the existing status of nutrition and nutrition information, the Committee on Amino Acids of the Food and Nutrition Board (National Research Council, U. S., Publication No. 711) concluded: "No evidence is available that the recommended allowance value of 1 gm. (of protein) per kg. (of weight of normal adult) is out of order or excessive."

The same committee had this to say about protein standards and minimum requirements.

...Such values are only useful as a guide for practical nutrition and are not, or should not be, considered as standards. Practical nutrition requires art as well as science, since individuals as well as population groups are subject to physiologically changing requirements and pathological stresses that demand a flexibility that is not inherent in a set of minimum values.

It is clear that this is a complex problem. It would be so nice to be able to offer simple solutions, but neither is there enough information nor is the problem simple enough despite the number of solutions designed for popular appeal which appear regularly. Therefore, it would seem obvious that no one person or group of people should undertake any serious changes in their diet without the advice of competent medical authorities.

Many hold to the maxim that, "if a little is good, more is better." A better position concerning food intakes might be: "sufficient is good, neither more nor less is as good."

## SELECTED BIBLIOGRAPHY

Allison, J. B., and W. H. Fitzpatrick. *Dietary Proteins in Health and Disease.* Springfield, Ill.: Thomas, 1960.

Berg, B. N., and H. S. Simms. "Nutrition and Longevity in the Rat. III. Food Restriction beyond 800 Days," *J. Nutr.*, vol. 74 (1961), p. 23.

Brock, J. F. (ed.). *Recent Advances in Human Nutrition.* London: Churchill, 1961.

Cannon, P. R. *Some Pathologic Consequences of Protein and Amino Acid Deficiencies.* Springfield, Ill.: Thomas, 1948.

*Evaluation of Protein Nutrition.* Publication 711, Food and Nutrition Board. Washington, D. C.: National Academy of Sciences–National Research Council, 1959.

Holt, L. E., Jr., P. Gyorgy, E. L. Pratt, Selma E. Snyderman, and W. M. Wallace. *Protein and Amino Acid Requirements in Early Life.* New York: New York University Press, 1960.

"The Nutritional Ages of Man," *Proceedings of the Borden Centennial Symposium on Nutrition.* New York: The Borden Foundation, 1958.

Olson, R. E. "Diet and Coronary Artery Diseases," *Circulation,* vol. 22, no. 3 (September 1960), p. 29.

Passmore, R. "Estimation of Food Requirements," *J. Roy. Statistical Soc.,* vol. 125, part 3, series A (1962), p. 387.

Pearson, W. N., and W. J. Darby. "Protein Nutrition," *Ann. Rev. Biochem.*, vol. 30 (1961), p. 325.

Pollack, H., and S. L. Halpern. "The Relation of Protein Metabolism to Disease," *Advan. Protein Chem.*, vol. 6 (1951), p. 383.

Ross, M. H. "Proteins, Calories, and Life Expectancy," *Federation Proc.*, vol. 18 (1959), p. 1190.

Ross, M. H. "Length of Life and Nutrition in the Rat," *J. Nutr.*, vol. 75 (1961), p. 197.

Terroine, E. F. "The Protein Component of the Human Diet," *Quarterly Bulletin of the Health Organization of the League of Nations*, vol. 5 (1936), p. 427.

# IV

# PROTEIN FOOD SUPPLY

And God said: ". . . Behold, I have given you every herb yielding seed, which is upon the face of all the earth, and every tree, in which is the fruit of tree yielding seed — to you it shall be for food; and to every beast of the earth, and to every fowl of the air, and to everything that creepeth upon the earth, wherein there is a living soul, I have given every green herb for food." And it was so. . . .

*Genesis* 1:29

# CHAPTER 13

# The Protein Food Problem I: A General Discussion

## Introduction

Food deficiency is generally a complex phenomenon; only in rare instances is it clearly and completely a lack of one particular nutrient. More likely it is a combination of deficiencies, although it is quite possible that one nutrient is the most limiting factor and may be the first cause of the clinical manifestation. Clearly one could be accused of "protein myopia" if the impression were given that all nutritional ills came from protein deficiency. One might actually question whether it is even proper, or theoretically possible, to consider the problems of food deficiency in terms of one component such as protein. Yet if one maintains the proper perspective and recognizes the complexity of the phenomenon, there is value to be gained to considering particularly the role of protein; it makes for better understanding of the entire problem, and points to serious practical considerations.

The most important point to remember about chronic

food deficiency is that, as a rule, the quality of the diet becomes lowered more rapidly than does the quantity; the percentage loss in nutrition is greater than the percentage lowering of food intake. This comes about for two general reasons: there is a selectivity of reduction in food items, and the tolerance of the human to changes in food intake varies with the nutrients.

When a food budget is cut, the first items to be removed are the expensive items, among which are fruits and products of animal origin. And when a food budget is chronically inadequate, there is a history—and sometimes even a tradition—of abstinence from eating the more expensive food items which contain more than their proportionate share of vitamins and good protein. Unless there is compensation by proper blending of less expensive food items (and this is seldom done), the result is that the quality of the diet is lower proportionately more than the quantity.

Even if there were uniform reduction in all constituents, there would still be a lowering in nutritional quality over and above the reduction in quantity. The relative requirements for the various nutrients change as the total intake is reduced. It is possible to survive a serious reduction in calories more easily than in protein or vitamins. A diet which may be in perfect balance when there is adequacy, may be seriously unbalanced when there is less of everything. There is an interrelationship between nutrients: calories spare protein, some amino acids spare vitamins, and some vitamins are needed for proper metabolism of carbohydrates. A general lowering of all nutrients disturbs this relationship; when there is a dearth of calories, part of the protein supply will be drafted to fill the caloric need rather than support protein synthesis.

The quality of the protein in a diet is generally reduced as the total intake of protein is lowered because the protein withdrawn is primarily of animal origin. If we take total calories as a measure of food intake, it is generally true that as the amount of calories in a people's diet is reduced, so are the total proteins in the diet, but, more precisely, so is the protein quality in the diet. And while it may be possible sometimes to bring back the caloric intake by increasing availability of high-caloric foods, this may not necessarily solve the total problem if there is no concomitant increase in the amount and quality of other ingredients.

We will deal in this chapter with the general protein problem, with statistics and projections, and with a general description of consequences which can be related to protein malnutrition.

## *Availability of Calories and Protein*

There are vast differences among the diet patterns of nations and this is reflected in the availability of protein supplies. It is difficult, except on a small, completely controlled scale, to measure the average individual food intake of a nation. Waste is unaccounted for, nor is distribution within the family group necessarily on the basis of need. The best that can be done on a large scale is to estimate the *available* food supplies and average these over a nation or area. This average will come closer to being a *maximum* intake. Many will be below the average and some age groups will fare worse than others. Nevertheless, the information so obtained reveals a sensitivity to national wealth and to other factors which affect food supply; certainly it can be a first approximation to the real situation.

Studies of the calorie and protein supply for a number of nations taken from information prepared by a UN agency show that the total available protein varies from over 100 grams per capita per day to less than 50. And, with the level of protein content, so goes the percentage of animal protein. For the nation with the highest amount of total protein available, the animal protein supply is 70 grams; some nations have only 5 to 8 grams of animal protein. Over half of the world population receives less than 15 grams of animal protein per day, and another fourth gets less than 30 grams. Total food intake, as measured by availability of food calories, parallels the protein availability; it might better be put that protein intake parallels total food supply. The nations with the highest protein supply have available over 3,000 Calories per capita per day, and those with low protein supplies have available less than 2,000 Calories.

## Animal Protein in Diet

The percentage of animal protein in a national diet closely follows its per capita income. An interesting analysis of this situation was made years ago by Bennett; a more recent analysis shows the same parallel; both are included in Table 13-1. Nations ranked on the basis of national wealth were grouped into five categories. The wealthiest had the smallest percentage of carbohydrate and the highest percentage of fat in their diet. The total availability of protein as percent of calories was constant, but the animal protein content decreased with lowered wealth.

It is possible to calculate the protein quality of a national diet if the major protein sources are known; an example was given in Chapter 10; this is the preferred type of approach. It is much simpler, however, to assume that a diet which contains 30 grams per day of protein from animal sources (milk, eggs, meat, fish, etc.) will be of adequate quality regardless of the source of the remainder of the protein. Thirty grams is considered by some as the break-even point. An average of less than 30 grams per day may be of questionable quality especially for the sensitive elements of the population, and less than 15 grams of animal protein per day poses almost the certainty of protein malnutrition for part of the population. Certainly one may design an adequate diet containing less than 15 grams of animal protein per day, but this requires skill in blending proteins from various sources to achieve the desired quality. It will not come about naturally nor easily. Uncomplicated

# TABLE 13-1

## Composition of National Diets in Groups of Nations Arrayed According to Income

| Group | Per Capita National Income (1939), U.S. Dollars | Per Capita National Product (1950-54), U.S. Dollars | Average Percentage of Total Calories Derived from (1934-38): | | | | | Per Capita Calories (1954-57), per Day | Per Capita Animal Protein (1954-57), Grams per Day |
| | | | Carbo-hydrates, Percent | Fat, Percent | Protein | | | | |
| | | | | | All, Percent | Animal, Percent | Vegetable, Percent | | |
|---|---|---|---|---|---|---|---|---|---|
| I | 389–554 | 1,000–1,870 | 53.4 | 34.9 | 11.7 | 6.8 | 4.9 | 3,120–3,390 | 52–71 |
| II | 188–338 | 750–950 | 58.2 | 29.8 | 11.9 | 5.8 | 6.1 | 2,980–3,340 | 43–56 |
| III | 109–184 | 500–740 | 66.7 | 21.3 | 12.0 | 3.5 | 8.5 | 2,980–3,230 | 43–58 |
| IV | 63–98 | 250–460 | 73.5 | 15.2 | 11.3 | 3.0 | 8.3 | 2,560–2,900 | 24–56 |
| V | 22–61 | 60–230 | 73.6 | 14.8 | 11.6 | 3.3 | 8.3 | 1,880–2,660 | 6–23 |

Source: M. K. Bennett, The World's Food (New York: Harper, 1954); "World Food Supply," Population Bulletin, vol. 15, no. 1 (February 1959), p. 3.

and unplanned diets low in animal protein are most likely
to be poor in quality; the burden of evidence lies in proving otherwise; hence, the general preoccupation with the
animal protein content of diets.

## Kwashiorkor

It is not enough to present statistics which make it appear
that protein supplies are inadequate for large population
groups; it is also necessary to demonstrate that protein malnutrition actually occurs as a clinically identifiable disease.
One would look for such evidence amongst the most sensitive elements of the population; for these, protein malnutrition could develop where supplies are inadequate and
social customs fail to compensate for their extra requirements. This is actually what happens to numerous children;
this is the story of kwashiorkor.

"Kwashiorkor" is a term of the Ga dialect of the Gold
Coast of Africa (Trowell et al.). It means "first" and "second"; it refers to the weanling displaced from the breast
by pregnancy or by the next sibling. Even before it is displaced, this child may be ill-fed for lack of sufficient quantity or quality of breast milk. But when he becomes displaced and there is no replacement of protein from other
sources, then he is prone to serious and often fatal diseases
of malnutrition. Although there are many synonyms and
vernacular expressions for this disease, kwashiorkor is the
most widely accepted one; this is the name given by Williams in her pioneering clinical descriptions of cases observed in the Gold Coast. It is perhaps fortunate that this
disease is not given a medical term but is rather a description of a state of affairs, because the consequences and
expressions of this malady may take several directions.

### KWASHIORKOR AND MARASMUS

Two extremes of malnutrition of children are generally
recognized; at one end is clear kwashiorkor, a case of severe

protein malnutrition with absence of serious calorie deficiency; and at the other end is severe general malnutrition of both calories and protein. The latter syndrome is named marasmus. In between are variations on the theme of severe malnutrition. One graphic representation of the two types of malnutrition is shown in Fig. 13-1 adapted from Scrim-

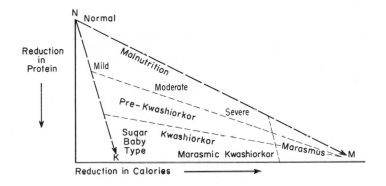

FIG. 13-1. Types of protein malnutrition in children. Decrease in calories is plotted horizontally at the base; decrease in protein is plotted vertically at the left. If both the amount of protein and calories decrease at about the same rate, as along the line N —— M, the child passes through stages of malnutrition finally leading to marasmus. If the decrease in protein is much more rapid than the decrease in calories, as along the line N —— K, a clear-cut case of kwashiorkor develops.°

°See N. S. Scrimshaw and M. Béhar, "Protein Malnutrition in Young Children," *Science*, vol. 133 (1961), p. 2039.

shaw and Béhar. The normal child is represented at the apex of the triangle to the left. Such a child when starved would lose weight rapidly, become malnourished and show clinical symptoms of marasmus. When a normal child is deprived of protein but given sufficient calories, there will be some loss of weight, and the child will move rapidly toward kwashiorkor. Photographs of children suffering from each of these two extremes of malnutrition are given in Fig. 13-2.

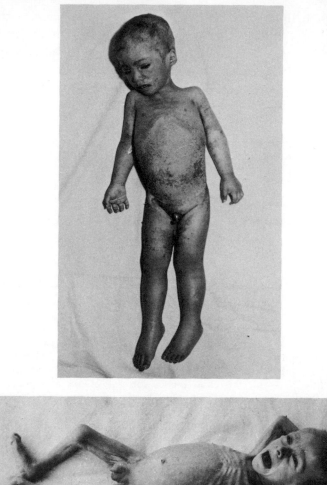

FIG. 13-2. Examples of protein malnutrition in children. The child above is suffering from kwashiorkor; the one below, from marasmus.*

*Photographs courtesy of Drs. Moisés Béhar, Fernando Viteri, and Nevin S. Scrimshaw.

Kwashiorkor is characterized by edema, abrasions of the skin, hair changes, apathy, aneroxia, enlarged fatty liver, and low serum protein. When the diet is deficient also in calories, the affected children often show a considerable degree of tissue wasting, reduction in stature and in weight, marked enation, absence of subcutaneous fat, and a much greater degree of muscular wasting.

Aside from the direct effect of the disease, there are the secondary effects, principally lowered resistance to infection. This is not a cause-and-effect relationship; there is an interdependence of infection and nutrition. The lowered nutritional status makes the child more susceptible to infection; the infection reduces the capacity of the child to be nourished and enhances the malnourished condition. Scrimshaw and his associates have stated: "Kwashiorkor can originate in dietary deficiency alone, but in most cases is the result of synergism between infection and protein malnutrition." Often, the infection, which may cause diarrhea, aggravates the original condition because of the response of society. In many countries the reaction of mothers to diarrhea in children is to put the baby on a reduced diet of gruel and starchy foods. And if this continues for a sufficiently long time, the already undernourished infant becomes further deprived.

The mortality of hospitalized kwashiorkor patients is 10 to 30 percent (Waterlow et al.). Whereas the mortality rates of children one to four years of age in countries where kwashiorkor is rare range from 1 to 3.8 per 1,000 population, mortality in countries where kwashiorkor is prevalent ranges from 12 to 60 for the same age group (Scrimshaw and Béhar).

Children who have recuperated from kwashiorkor show less development of bone structure than normal children. Compared with bones of healthy children, the bones of children with a history of protein malnutrition were smaller and less calcified. The degree of retardation was much greater than could be accounted for by the known length of the illness; the growth retardation was a record of the entire longer period of malnutrition of which the final extreme form was the end result.

The primary evidence that kwashiorkor and marasmus are diseases of dietary origin comes from the history of the children who are so affected: they all have a history of undernourishment. Additional evidence comes from the nature of the successful treatment: the basic treatment is dietary. Children with kwashiorkor are given a high protein diet combined with a sufficiently high caloric intake to ensure good protein utilization. Successful treatments have included supplementation with dried skim milk, a protein hydrolyzate, and a vegetable protein mixture.

### DISTRIBUTION OF KWASHIORKOR

The geographical distribution of kwashiorkor is shown in Fig. 13-3. The areas of prevalence of this disease coincide with known areas of low protein supply.

////// Geographical Distribution of Kwashiorkor

FIG. 13-3. The geographical distribution of kwashiorkor.[*]

[*]See B. R. Sen, *The Basic Freedom—Freedom from Hunger* (Rome: Food and Agriculture Organization of the United Nations, 1960).

## Protein Malnutrition in Adults

We can consider this question from two points of view. First there is the prospect of permanent damage to organs in those adults who had a bout with protein malnutrition as children. Those organs which bore the brunt of protein malnutrition in infancy will probably show abnormalities later on. Secondly, there may either be permanent or transient periods of protein malnutrition in the adult which would not have the same serious effect as in children, but which would nonetheless influence life habits and activities. Protein malnutrition in adults may occur when a diet which is already low in protein is rendered less adequate by any number of causes such as extra physical exertion, fever, illness, or pregnancy. If there has already been damage from previous attacks in childhood, then these extra stresses assume a greater importance. We might say that the adult who does finally show evidences of protein malnutrition has for a long time been on the brink of it.

Protein malnutrition in adults is not as easily detected as in children, and yet it may be as far reaching in effect. What can we say, for example, about the implications of an inferior physique both on the ability to perform sustained physical work as well as to be at the peak of mental activity? How much of this is the result of dietary background and what portion is the consequence of other cultural factors remains to be discovered. There are an unexpectedly large number of deaths in adult life from ordinary infectious diseases which are much less to be feared in countries where there is adequate nutrition.

## The Protein Supply Problem

Clearly there is a problem of protein supply. There is no question that areas exist where there are inadequate protein supplies to support the *present* population. The consequences are manifested by acute clinical symptoms, particularly among children, but are not confined to children. Moreover, even where the children survive the deficiency, the aftermath leaves its mark on adulthood and renders the adults more susceptible to further debilitations when exposed to protein deprivation, or when exposed to diseases which normally would be thrown off by people with a history of good nourishment.

This is the problem facing the world today. In 1960 it was estimated that the total world population was close to 3 billion; the projection for the year 2000 is for over 6 billion people. Largest increases in population are expected to be in those regions which now have a prevailing food shortage; hence, in those areas already suffering from insufficiency of food the population is increasing faster than food production. Given the present trends, it can be expected that the food problem will increase in severity with time under the existing patterns of food procurement and distribution.

## SELECTED BIBLIOGRAPHY

Bennett, M. K. *The World's Food.* New York: Harper, 1954.

Jelliffe, D. B. "Protein — Calorie Malnutrition in Tropical Pre-school Children," *J. Pediat.*, vol. 54 (1959), p. 227.

"Protein Nutrition," *Ann. N. Y. Acad. Sci.*, vol. 69, no. 5 (1958), p. 855. (See particularly articles by J. Senecal, M. Béhar et al., and F. Gomez et al.)

Scrimshaw, N. S., and M. Béhar. "Protein Malnutrition in Young Children," *Science*, vol. 133 (1961), p. 2039.

Sen, B. R. *The Basic Freedom — Freedom from Hunger.* Rome, Italy: Food and Agriculture Organization of the United Nations, 1960.

Trowell, H. C., J. N. P. Davis, and R. F. A. Dean. *Kwashiorkor.* London: Arnold, 1954.

Waterlow, J. C., J. Cravioto, and Joan M. L. Stephen. "Protein Malnutrition in Man," *Advan. Protein Chem.*, vol. 15 (1960), p. 131.

Williams, Cicely D. "Kwashiorkor: A Nutritional Disease of Children Associated with a Maize Diet," *Lancet*, vol. 2 (1935), p. 1151.

# CHAPTER 14

# *The Protein Food Problem II: Some Details*

## *Introduction*

How is it that children become victims of protein starvation? Ignorance, poverty, large families, poor sanitation, inadequate and unbalanced food supplies all contribute their share. So many diverse factors combine to create this situation and they are so deeply ingrained that the problem cannot be solved or disposed of by proclamation, by well-wishing, or even by money and gifts. It is difficult for anyone in modern society to comprehend the levels of poverty and ignorance that are involved. It is difficult for city dwellers to appreciate the state and the problems of their countrymen just a few miles beyond the city limits or even in the slum areas of the cities themselves.

The problem of weaning an infant is solved when there is available cow's milk or other milk to replace the human milk. Where such conditions are satisfied, the transition from breast feeding to conventional feeding takes place successfully. When there are insufficient supplies or no milk at all, then it is necessary to get along with less milk, or none, and to find milk substitutes to satisfy the deficiency. The various degrees of success achieved in this endeavor determine whether or not a child will successfully weather the transition in the ages of one to three years—ages sensitive to protein-deficiency disease. The common objective of all feeding programs for children in this transitional period is to develop a liquid diet to substitute and take over for the mother's milk. But often this liquid diet is totally inadequate nutritionally, as, for example, the sugar waters of Jamaica, the tapioca or plantain gruels of Africa, or the corn *atoles* of Central America.

In a larger sense it is the lack of animal protein which is at the core of the problem. There is no milk, but neither are there eggs, meat, or fish in noticeable quantities. The difficulty is aptly put in the following quotation: "When the parents are poor, the infant cannot get the proper substitute for its mother's milk and so gets the sickness." (Quoted in Trowell et al.)

Case histories of malnutrition are available for practically every part of the world. We shall select several of these to illustrate the generalizations already made.

## Examples of the Protein Problem

INDIA

A survey under the auspices of the World Health Organization was conducted in four states of South India among families with a monthly income of less than 100 rupees (approx. 25 U. S. dollars), an income level typical of 85 percent of the population (Rao et al.). Eighty percent of the population live in villages where agriculture is the main occupation. Whether they own their own land or are landless laborers, the output is insufficient to maintain their families at adequate levels of nutrition. Nor is the situation much better for those living in urban areas.

The principal food crops of the region are rice and millet. (Millet is a general term for species of small grains including *Pennisetum, Eleusine, Setaria, Panicum,* and *Paspalum* species.) Next to these in quantity are the pulses, legumes, of which the following species are popular: *Cicer arietinum* (Bengal gram), *Cajanus cajan* (red gram), *Phaseolus mungo* (black gram), and *Phaseolus radiatus* (green gram). Large quantities of groundnuts (peanuts) are grown, but most are processed for edible oil and only 8 percent or so are available directly for food. Available Calories per day average 1,842, of which 1,335 are from cereals. Of the total of 45 grams of protein available, 32 are from cereals, 7.5 from pulses and plants, and only 5 from animal sources.

Two to three meals a day are consumed, and these consist mainly of cooked cereals. Rice is the preferred cereal, but is replaced frequently in lean months by millets. The food is cooked once or twice a day, with a minimum number of ingredients. Millets are broken or ground into flour and then cooked with water to make either a porridge or balls. In some areas, unleavened bread *(roti)* is made of millet flour. The rice and millets are consumed with a spiced soup in which various quantities of pulses are included. In some instances, legumes are added to the rice to make a sort of cake which is a breakfast item, but this is an occasional feature. Vegetables are either added to the soup or cooked into curries and consumed with the rice, but these are of small quantity and available but infrequently.

Very few of the families interrogated had religious or sentimental objections to flesh foods except for beef, but in practice none of them consumed these foods with any regularity. The frequency of consumption of animal foods varies from once a week to once or twice a year, and on these occasions the quantities are from half a pound to a pound for the entire family. Very little poultry and eggs are consumed; the consumption of milk is unsatisfactory as well. Even though some milk is produced, the yield is low and most of it is sold in towns, very little being retained by the producers themselves. The most popular beverages are tea and coffee.

The dietary needs of the vulnerable group such as preg-

nant or lactating women do not receive any special attention. Infants and young children are weaned straight onto
the adult foods and all members of the family share the
common dishes in quantities which are probably determined
by their availability. As a rule, the wage earner has prefer-
ence over the rest.

Breast feeding is the rule; at the age of six months 92 percent of the children were at the breast and over 50 percent
continued breast-feeding to the age of 18 months. In the
majority of cases, pregnancy was the factor responsible for
cessation of breast feeding the first and second years of
the child's life. In the group as a whole, one woman in every
five became pregnant again within a year after delivery.

Cereal products or some animal milk are the main foods
given as supplementary feeding to infants. Fifty to 90 percent of the children received rice, 10 to 50 percent of the
children milk, and up to 10 percent of the children tapioca,
banana, coffee, or tea. The cereal foods given the infants
are those usually consumed by adults and are given mixed
with soup or cooked vegetables. If the children refuse
food because of its hot, spicy taste they are given plain rice
only, and these supplements are discontinued temporarily
whenever the child develops diarrhea, fever, or other ailments.

Analysis of samples of children's diets indicated that in
the first six months of life, mother's milk alone would seem
to satisfy the protein and calorie needs. In the next six
months the supplementary foods given were not sufficient
to make up the protein deficit. And as the breast milk output declined and the quantity of supplementary foods increased, the two together were still considerably short of
supplying the protein allowances for children up to three
years of age. Only after the child reached the age of three
years, would it seem that the observed intake came close
to recommended levels.

It is of interest to compare the growth of these and
African children to the standards for well-fed children; this
is given in Fig. 14-1. Such comparisons are interpreted by

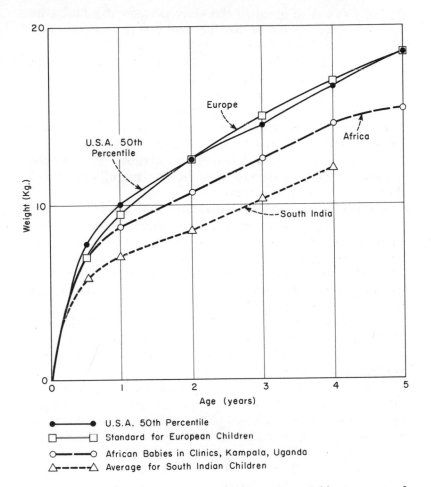

Fig. 14-1. Weight of African and South Indian children compared to children from Europe and the United States.*

*Source: J. F. Brock and M. Autret, *Kwashiorkor in Africa*, FAO Nutritional Studies No. 8 (Rome, Italy: Food and Agriculture Organization of the United Nations, 1952); K. S. Rao, M. C. Swaminathan, S. Swarup, and V. N. Patwardhan, "Protein Malnutrition in South India," *Bull. World Health Organ.*, vol. 20 (1959), p. 603.

Rao et al. and Brock and Autret to indicate a retardation of growth of the Indian and African children as compared to children who are well fed in the early stages of life. Retardation was not so great in the early periods of infancy, but became more apparent as the child was switched over gradually to mixed feeding.

The authors of this survey attempted to calculate the number of children suffering from protein malnutrition in this area of India. In 1951 the total number of children in this region under the age of five years was estimated to be The various degrees of success achieved in this endeavor 14 million. Even if the lowest incidence recorded for that level of income is the basis of calculation, the probable number of frank cases of kwashiorkor might exceed 120 thousand at any given time.

According to calculations from the 1951 census for southern India, 20 percent of children under five years died as compared to a mortality rate of 3 percent in better-developed countries. There is no information on the causes of death, but for all ages, diarrheas and dysenteries which usually precede malnutrition syndromes are second only to fevers as causes of death.

It had been felt that protein malnutrition would be more likely to occur in rice-eating areas, but would not be found in predominantly wheat-eating areas because of the higher protein content of wheat. This point is challenged by Manchanda and Gupta who relate cases of malnutrition, including protein deficiency, in the wheat-growing area of the Punjab. The history of the children examined revealed that their diet was inadequate in calories, proteins, vitamins, and minerals in varying proportions. In some instances the total calories were one-quarter to one-third of the recommendations for that age, and in the vast majority hardly averaged half of the minimum requirements. Total quantity of proteins for the children approximated five to seven grams per day and less, and these were derived mostly from pieces of loaf made of maize or wheat. The liquid diet was more in the form of tea; milk was a luxury article. Most families bought hardly one-half to two pounds of milk per day to be shared among the entire family unit of 8 to 12 members. It was beyond the means of the income group studied to purchase food containing animal proteins.

Mothers, both during pregnancy and lactation, subsisted on a definitely subnutritional diet consisting of *dahl* (legumes), *roti* of maize or wheat, rice, cheap vegetables, onions, and chillies. Tea with one to two ounces of milk was taken by over half the mothers.

The authors conclude that malnutrition in its various forms is not uncommon in the Punjab. The various causal factors are widespread poverty, large families, lack of suitable foods, ignorance about dietetics, superstition, food taboos, and myriads of infections. They support the generalization of Patwardhan that amongst the various problems arising from malnutrition perhaps the most pressing in India is that resulting from protein deficiency.

Patwardhan has described the peculiarities of the diet of poor Indians as consisting of a preponderance of cereals and being deficient in protective foodstuffs. Relative figures for animal protein consumption are not generally available. The best estimate is that an average of 9 percent of the total protein in the diet is animal protein. This is probably an optimistic estimate as judged by the general pattern of the diet which contains extremely small quantities of milk and meat products. The amount of animal protein eaten is, of course, directly related to income. In Bengal, 23 ounces of rice were consumed per unit per day among the poor Indians as compared to 10 ounces in the middle-class group. The greatest difference between the diet of the middle-class and the poor group was in the amount of milk, meat, fish, and eggs consumed.

Problems arising from poverty and inability to obtain animal protein are compounded and confounded by cultural blocks (Jelliffe, 1957). In West Bengal, for example, there is the rice-feeding ceremony normally held at six months of age for male babies and seven months for females. This is the ceremonial introduction to mixed feeding; if it is not done on schedule—and this often happens—the child will be deprived for several months of many types of supplementary foods. In general, there is a reluctance by mothers to introduce mixed feeding in the second six months of life,even after the ceremony of *mukhe bhat*. The mothers may feel that the child cannot digest the solid food; more likely it is the actual additional trouble of feeding the infant with solid foods which makes the mother reluctant to try. And there are only limited amounts of liquid foods: milk, sago, and barley gruels.

Then there is the custom of withdrawing most added foods from the child's diet at the first sign of illness. Since the village child suffers extensively from one illness or another and since the mother is reluctant, even under normal circumstances, to introduce new foods into the child's diet, the further dietary restrictions applied for even minor illnesses predispose the child to nutritional marasmus or kwashiorkor.

According to Jelliffe, the problem of apparent resistance to mixed feeding in the second semester is an outstanding infant feeding problem, is widespread, and lays the basis for much malnutrition in the second and third years of life.

AFRICA

Throughout most of Africa cow's milk is available only in insignificant amounts. In the few exceptions where it is available, there is no evidence of malnutrition among children. Supplementary feeding takes the form of starchy gruels. In some places children are given soft bananas or yams which have been masticated by the mother. The infant is given the kind of food which the parent thinks is easiest to digest, but digestion is confused with entrance of food into the stomach. Therefore, efforts are made to make the food soft, but the treatment which they receive may often reduce their nutritive value, which, initially, is not high.

During the period of weaning, the infant begins fairly quickly to consume the ordinary food of the family, but for a long time after this stage is reached it does not succeed in sharing fully in that food. When it begins to compete for its food with others around the family dish, it does not secure the best portions. It is the privilege of the adult man to help himself first and take the pieces of meat or fish which the dish contains. This is not evidence of negligence on the part of the parents, but is the general custom among all poor people, and not only in Africa, to allow the breadwinner to obtain the best of whatever food is available. Since there is insufficient food, the young child is likely to secure only such parts of the dish of which it often is prone to waste a large portion. Later, children are able to get more and better food, both by obtaining a more adequate share of family meals and by seeking food to supplement their diet in the fields and forest.

In tropical Africa, pregnant and nursing women do not receive any special kind of diet. In rare circumstances, mothers during the first three months after childbirth are given what is considered the best portions of family food, resuming work in the fields only when the baby has reached six months of age. In other regions there is a tendency for the amount of food consumed by pregnant and lactating women to be increased in quantity, but this really means an increase in intake of starchy foods.

Whereas in India the predominant source of calories comes from cereals, there exist sections in Africa where tubers, yams, and plantains are the major source of calories. There is a root crop zone in the tropical-forest region of the Congo Basin, which extends westward along the Guinea coast. This is surrounded by a cereal zone in the areas of savanna and dry forest. Manioc is the predominant food crop in the root crop zone. In the Guinea coast this is superseded often by yams and occasionally by taro *(Colocasia esculentum)* or malanga *(Xanthosoma sagittifolium).* The banana is especially important in parts of the Congo

Basin and in southern Uganda, and the sweet potato is usually present in most of the root crop area. Only maize and rice penetrate the tropical forest area to a significant extent.

The introduction of root crops, or perhaps more accurately of noncereals, as a major source of carbohydrate poses a serious problem in protein nutrition. Brock and Autret have tabulated the protein content of many of the major

TABLE 14-1

*Protein Content of Isocaloric Portions of Foods*

| Food | Proteins per 100 Calories, Grams |
|---|---|
| Beef (thin) | 9.6 |
| Pork | 2.6 |
| Fish, fresh, fatty | 11.4 |
| Fish, dried | 15.3 |
| Milk, whole, fluid, 3.5% fat | 5.4 |
| Milk, skim, dried | 10.0 |
| Wheat flour, medium extraction | 3.3 |
| Millet *(Eleusine coracana)* | 2.0 |
| Millet *(Setaria italica)* | 2.9 |
| Millet *(Pennisetum glaucum)* | 3.4 |
| Sorghum *(Sorghum vulgare)* | 2.9 |
| Maize, whole meal | 2.6 |
| Rice, home pounded | 2.0 |
| Rice, milled white | 1.7 |
| Cassava, manioc *(Manihot utïoissíma)* | |
| fresh | 0.8 |
| meal and flour | 0.4 |
| Yams *(Discorea sp.)* | 2.3 |
| Taro *(Colocasia esculentum)* | 1.7 |
| Sweet potatoes | 1.1 |
| Plantains, fresh | 1.0 |
| Beans and Peas, different species | 6.4 |
| Soybeans, whole seeds, dry | 11.3 |
| Voandzou, bambarra nuts *(Voandzeia subterranea)* | 5.7 |
| Groundnuts | 4.7 |

*Source:* J. F. Brock and M. Autret, *Kwashiorkor in Africa*, FAO Nutritional Studies No. 8 (Rome, Italy: Food and Agriculture Organization of the United Nations, 1952), p. 49; see also R. F. A. Dean, "Use of Processed Plant Proteins as Human Food," in A. M. Altschul (ed.), *Processed Plant Protein Foodstuffs* (New York, Academic, 1958), p. 221.

sources of energy, as well as some of the higher-protein-content foods; these are given in Table 14-1. The percentage of proteins in manioc, yams, taros, sweet potatoes, and plantains ranges from 0.4 to 2.3 grams per 100 Calories as against a range of 1.7 to 3.4 grams of proteins per 100 Calories for the cereal grains. It is obvious that any population which bases its calorie supply on noncereals will be putting an additional stress on its protein procurement. If the deficit is not met by supplementation with high-protein foods, surely the result will be protein malnutrition for young and old. Brock and Autret noted that in some parts of the Congo where manioc is the staple and often almost the only food infants of three months of age were literally stuffed with manioc flour in the form of a fermented paste, *luku.*

An example of a dietary based on noncereals is that of the Baganda in Uganda (Welbourn). Their staple food is green bananas which are cooked by wrapping the peeled bananas in leaves and steaming them for several hours until they are about the consistency of a mashed potato. Sweet potatoes and occasionally cassava (manioc) are also used. The banana or potato is eaten with a small quantity of relish made from groundnuts, beans, or green vegetables. The food, traditionally, is cooked twice daily, at midday and at night. If the husband is out at work, the wife may not bother to cook food at midday, but she and the children will have tea and scraps from the previous day's meal. The husband may come in late at night, so that the main meal of the day is often at 9:00 to 10:00 P. M. If the children are asleep, they may be awakened and fed. Tea, with or without milk and sugar, is taken extensively between meals.

A study of intake in selected homes showed that children under three years of age received over nine ounces of cooked plantains a day; this by far was the largest intake of any foodstuff. They averaged only six ounces of fluid milk, and 0.4 ounce of meat. There were 2.4 ounces of potatoes, 6 ounces of sauces from peanuts and other sources, no dried beans, no fish or eggs, and a very small amount of cereals, bread, and sugar. In homes of higher income, there was a drastic decrease in the amount of plantains eaten to an average of 3 ounces compared to 9.3, an increase in the amount of fluid milk and meat, a large increase in the amount of potatoes, and now a significant amount, close to 3 ounces, of cereals, and 4.5 ounces of sugar. There was a decrease in the sauces to about less than 3 ounces, and a drastic increase in fruit consumed and in the amount of dried beans.

Clearly, the noncereal cannot possibly serve as a major source of carbohydrate without causing a drastic derangement of the protein supply. And often the prevalence of large amounts of root and tuber foods is the difference between kwashiorkor and general malnutrition or marasmus. For example, in the northern region of Ghana, the staple foods are bulrush, millet, and sorghum. In most years this area is subjected to a period of acute and often dramatic food shortage, and the storage of food is practically nonexistent. If the rains fail, the only food may be wild leaves and other bush foods. In the south, the staple foods are corn, manioc, with supplements of plantains, yams, eggplants, onions, and palm nuts. Peas and beans are relatively rare components of the diet, and fish is available only in certain seasons. Meat is expensive and eggs are only occasionally eaten. In this region, where calories are abundant but where the major source of calories is from tubers which have a low protein content, kwashiorkor is the prevalent form of malnutrition. In the northern region, where calories as well as proteins are likely to be in short supply, marasmus dominates the picture.

## CENTRAL AND SOUTH AMERICA

In Central and South America we return to a situation in which the major source of calories is cereals; wherever the indigenous population predominates, the major cereal is

## TABLE 14–2

### Examples of Menus in Costa Rica and Panama

| | COSTA RICA[1] | | PANAMA[2] | |
|---|---|---|---|---|
| | *Urban* | *Rural* | *Panama City* | *La Concepción* |
| *Breakfast* | Coffee<br>Bread with butter, cheese or cream[3] | Coffee or sweet water<br>Rice and beans<br>*Tortilla* (corn cake) | Black coffee with sugar<br>Bread with butter | Oats with milk sweetened with syrup<br>Fried green plantains |
| *Noon* | Salad of cabbage or lettuce, sometimes with tomato or beet<br>White rice and beans<br>Ripe plaintain, fried or baked<br>Fruit (orange, banana, or pineapple)<br>*Tortilla* or bread<br>Coffee | White rice<br>Beans and banana<br>Egg<br>Coffee or sweet water<br>*Tortilla* | Vegetable soup | Stew of chiricanos beans with rice and beef |
| *Evening* | Soup of meat and vegetables[4]<br>Omelette (based on one vegetable with meat and egg)<br>Rice<br>Beans<br>Dessert<br>Bread, Coffee | Meat stew<br>Pumpkin or vegetable<br>Pears<br>Fried rice<br>Beans<br>Coffee or sweet water<br>*Tortilla* | Rice with fat<br>Fish (Bacalo)<br>Fried slices of plantain | Fried rice<br>Fried meat with egg<br>Oat shake with syrup<br>Mangos |

[1] Lia G. de Brenes, Superoisora de Education para el Hogar, personal communication, July 1959. (Translated by Ernest Reich.)

[2] Bertha Q. de Moseote, Director, Escuela Profesional Isabel Herrera Obaldia, September 1959. (Translated by Ernest Reich.)

[3] This is practical in families of higher economic level.

[4] The consumption of meat is generally low.

## TABLE 14-3

*Average Food Consumption and Intake of Calories and Protein
in Rural and Urban Central America and Panama*

INTAKE PER PERSON PER DAY, GRAMS

| Food Groups | Guatemala R | U | El Salvador R | U | Honduras R | U | Nicaragua R | U | Costa Rica R | U | Panama R | U |
|---|---|---|---|---|---|---|---|---|---|---|---|---|
| Dairy products[1] | 10 | 129 | 46 | 118 | 136 | 231 | 316 | 378 | 114 | 200 | 47 | 75 |
| Eggs | 4 | 6 | 5 | 21 | 5 | 4 | 4 | 2 | 4 | 6 | 8 | 1 |
| Meat and Fish | 34 | 45 | 21 | 66 | 49 | 59 | 32 | 71 | 20 | 50 | 83 | 87 |
| Pulses | 58 | 64 | 60 | 48 | 56 | 47 | 85 | 45 | 64 | 68 | 54 | 20 |
| Fresh vegetables | 61 | 46 | 32 | 82 | 127 | 82 | 214 | 31 | 82 | 82 | 6 | 30 |
| Fruits | 23 | 33 | 1 | 34 | 30 | 33 | 8 | 16 | 49 | 22 | 36 | 26 |
| Musaceaes[2] | 2 | 16 | 27 | 44 | 18 | 24 | 16 | 58 | 51 | 52 | 36 | 67 |
| Starchy roots | 5 | 9 | 5 | 14 | 9 | 32 | 7 | 15 | 24 | 80 | 35 | 29 |
| Cereals | 494 | 290 | 326 | 244 | 367 | 264 | 182 | 231 | 250 | 240 | 189 | 183 |
| Sugars | 47 | 40 | 32 | 32 | 40 | 33 | 33 | 54 | 122 | 112 | 53 | 43 |
| Fats | 1 | 7 | 6 | 23 | 5 | 21 | 12 | 22 | 7 | 17 | 35 | 26 |
| Calories | 2,243 | 1,727 | 1,666 | 1,723 | 1,964 | 1,740 | 1,623 | 1,843 | 1,822 | 2,049 | 1,927 | 1,454 |
| Total protein, grams | 66 | 53 | 48 | 52 | 59 | 54 | 55 | 60 | 40 | 53 | 55 | 44 |
| Animal protein, percent | 11 | 24 | 12 | 35 | 24 | 35 | 31 | 45 | 20 | 30 | 36 | 50 |

*Source:* Marina Flores, "Food Patterns in Central America and Panama," in
*Tradition, Science, and Practice in Dietetics: Proceedings of the Third International
Congress of Dietetics* (Bradford, England: Wm. Byles & Sons, Ltd., 1961).
[1] In terms of liquid milk.
[2] Bananas.

maize. In Table 14-2 are given some examples of menus in Costa Rica and Panama; a summary of average food consumption in Central America is given in Table 14-3 (Flores). It will be noted that generally there is more animal protein eaten in the urban areas. The rural area of Guatemala with its predominantly Indian population has the highest calorie intake and the highest intake of cereals, mostly maize. In general, there is a lack of milk products, hence the problem of weaning children is similar to that encountered in other areas where there is a shortage of milk.

A study was made of the relative nutritional satisfaction of entire families and of the children in these families in the village of Amatitlan in Guatemala (INCAP). While the total protein intake was apparently equal to the requirements for the adults, the fact that this protein was predominantly corn was attested by the low amount of vitamin A and riboflavin in the diet; these ordinarily would come from animal products. In general, there was sufficient calcium because the corn is eaten as *masa* which has been soaked in lime, but even this treatment did not provide sufficient calcium for the adults in Amatitlan. The children, however, received less of their protein requirements than of calories, and considerably less of the other nutrients. As in other cases, the children were given adult foods when they were weaned, but as soon as they developed digestive disturbances, the only supplement that they were given was a drink of ground corn, *atole*.

## Conclusion

We have taken but a brief sample of a few places in the world where protein malnutrition can exist and where problems of weaning children do exist. We have emphasized children because their nutritional deficiencies are most obvious, but certainly similar phenomena are observable in all elements of the population. Even from this sample it is clear that malnutrition is a serious social problem and that it is possible to identify predominantly protein aspects of this problem. If it were possible to satisfy the protein needs, there might still exist deficiencies of other nutrients, but at least many existing problems would be solved. And this might extend beyond the nutritional aspect. For we cannot state with exactness where in the ecological balance of man nutrition plays a role as compared to medical progress, sanitation, and other cultural patterns of survival. Actually the various forces are interrelated. Resistance to disease is clearly a function of nutritional state, and convalescence from disease is in part related to nutritional adequacy.

## SELECTED BIBLIOGRAPHY

Autret, M., and M. Behar. *Sindrome Policareucial Infantil (Kwashiorkor) and Its Prevention in Central America.* FAO Nutritional Studies No. 13. Rome, Italy: Food and Agriculture Organization of the United Nations, 1952.

Brock, J. F., and M. Autret. *Kwashiorkor in Africa.* FAO Nutritional Studies No. 8. Rome, Italy: Food and Agriculture Organization of the United Nations, 1952.

Chiroboga, C. C., I. M. Franklin, Y. B. de Rueda, A. Castellanos, C. C. de Fuentes, A. Rocy, and R. B. Bradfield. "La Alimentation y el Estado de Nutrition en el Peru." *Anales de la Facultad de Medicina,* Lima, vol. 43, no. 1 (March 1960).

Flores, M. "Food Patterns in Central America and Panama," in *Tradition, Science, and Practice in Dietetics: Proceedings of the Third International Congress of Dietetics.* Bradford, England: Wm. Byles & Sons, 1961.

"Foodstuffs and Diet," in *Human Environments in Middle Africa: Final Report.* Washington, D. C.: National Academy of Sciences–National Research Council, February 1961.

Jelliffe, D. B. "Cultural Blocks and Protein Malnutrition in Early Childhood in Rural West Bengal," *Pediatrics,* vol. 20 (1957), p. 128.

Jelliffe, D. B., B. E. R. Symonds, and E. F. P. Jelliffe. "The Pattern of Malnutrition in Early Childhood in Southern Trinidad." *J. Pediat.,* vol. 57 (1960), p. 922.

Manchanda, S. S., and H. L. Gupta. "Malnutrition in the Punjab, with Particular Reference to Protein Deficiency," *Indian J. of Child Health,* vol. 7 (1958), p. 386.

"Mezclas Vegetales como Fuentes de Proteina en la Alimentacion Humana: Desarrolo de la Incaparina," *Rev. Col. Med. Guatemala,* vol. 12, no. 1 (March 1961).

"Nutritional Problems in Ghana," *Nutr. Rev.*, vol. 17 (1959), p. 193.

Patwardhan, V. N. *Nutrition in India,* Bombay: Indian Journal Medical Science, 1952.

Trowell, H. C., J. N. P. Davies, and R. F. A. Dean. *Kwashiorkor.* London: Arnold, 1954.

Rao, K. S., M. C. Swaminathan, S. Swarup, and V. N. Patwardhan. "Protein Malnutrition in South India," *Bull. World Health Organ.*, vol. 20 (1959), p. 603.

Waterlow, J., and A. Vergara. *Protein Malnutrition in Brazil.* FAO Nutritional Studies No. 14. Rome, Italy: Food and Agriculture Organization of the United Nations, 1956.

Welbourn, H. F. "The Danger Period during Weaning (Part II), *J. Pediat.*, vol. 1 (1955), p. 98.

# CHAPTER 15

# Examples of Partial Solutions to the Protein Problem

WE MUST NOT LEAVE this subject with the impression of the inevitability of malnutrition when animal proteins are scarce. Obviously all is not failure. The population of the world is increasing rapidly; growth is even more rapid in those particular areas where protein malnutrition exists. Surely rapid growth has nothing to do with malnutrition; it happens despite insufficiency of food. But most children do survive, become adults, and reproduce. Most people manage to eat enough to exist, at least at a minimum level of activity and energy. It might be of interest, therefore, to review some of the reasons for success.

## Breast Feeding

First, and foremost, is the widespread practice of nursing children for as long a period as is usually practiced. As a result, the child suffers no malnutrition during the first six months of life, and gets a good start. The breakdown comes when breast feeding is stopped too early before the child is capable of taking on the available supplementary foods,

208

or when the nursing is prolonged to such an extent without supplementation that the child finally obtains very little nourishment from that source.

Whenever breast feeding is the major source of nutrition of the infant, the nutritional state of the child depends almost exclusively on the mother. The well-nourished mother during pregnancy will have more probability of giving birth to a well-nourished child and of nursing sufficiently. During the first months of life the nutritional state of the child will be affected by the quantity and quality of the milk offered by the mother. Even after weaning, when there is no direct biological relationship between the child and the mother, the child depends for its nutritional health on the food which the mother buys, prepares, and offers. This marked relationship between the mother and the child is indispensable in considering the malnutrition of both as a single problem. In the more technically developed countries, where a greater variety of foods is available, and where the process of weaning is not so difficult, this relationship is less critical.

Ethnic groups differ in their practice of breast feeding. Within each group, the wealthier class is less apt to prolong breast feeding. In Singapore, for example, at the age of six months 62 percent of the children of poor Chinese were either wholly or partly breastfed, compared to 26 percent for wealthier Chinese, 75 percent for poor Malays, and 41 percent for poor Indians (Millis). Compensation for a shortened breast-feeding period among the wealthier Chinese comes from availability of a more varied weaning diet and from failure to observe all the food taboos so universal, particularly among poorer peoples.

It is no wonder that pediatricians look with dismay at trends which come with greater industrialization, where there are greater opportunities for the mother to find outside employment. Weaning is attempted at an earlier age, yet there is inadequate replacement with either milk or other sources of animal protein.

The following is quoted from a statement by Jelliffe et al. on the situation in southern Trinidad:

> In the temperate zone, the last few decades have been characterized by a spectacular fall in incidence of breast feeding. More recently, this trend, following in the wake of technologic sophistication and urbanization, has commenced to invade the tropics, especially the towns, as shown by reports from West Bengal, India; Lagos, Nigeria; and Kampala, Uganda. This unfortunate trend, which initially always involves the more sophisticated Westernized well-to-do segment of the population, in Trinidad has also come to affect at least some of the relatively lower socio-economic group village dwellers, as has also been reported from Panama.

Mothers in Trinidad are going out to work more often; this interferes with the breast feeding and also leaves the preparation and administration of the infant's food to an older sibling. The infants still do not receive much dried milk as a substitute for the breast milk, and what milk is given is diluted with, or mixed with arrowroot flour *(Maranta arundinacea)* which is almost pure starch and can be considered particularly "kwashiorkorogenic." These changes in the breast feeding habits have been reflected in a lower age at which children exhibit symptoms of kwashiorkor. In the various Caribbean islands, and in Panama City, the average age of children with kwashiorkor ranges from seven to thirteen months. This is lower than the one- to three-year period usually reported for this disease.

## Substitutes for Major Cereals

In addition to the basic principle of optimum breast feeding, there are other instances of beneficial food and agricultural practices which have minimized the difficulty caused by shortage of animal protein. In Ethiopia, for example, the major cereal is teff *(Eragrostis abyssinica)*. The seed of this cereal is very small, half of the size of a pinhead. It is a remarkable source of minerals, a good source of vitamins, and has a relatively high protein content, approximately 10 percent. With an amino acid composition, according to Schaefer, similar to that of egg protein, its biological value is among the best of the cereal proteins, although nutritive value is improved by the addition of lysine. Here is an instance where a cereal grain rather rare on a world basis serves to improve considerably the protein as well as general nutritional value of a regional diet which is relatively low in animal protein. Of a total of 65 grams of protein eaten per capita per day in Ethiopia in 1958, 41 grams were furnished by teff, and 6 grams by meat.

## Legumes

There is an interesting speculation by Linton on the relationship between crops, agriculture, and ancient culture in America which might well serve to introduce the subject of legumes. Linton takes the position that the kind of food available and the skill of the population in obtaining sufficient quantities of balanced foods were great factors in determining the kind of culture which developed in ancient America.

Complex technology and elaborate political organizations can develop or survive only in the presence of a fairly dense population. This density in any region is linked with the local food supply. In ancient Eurasia and Africa a balanced ration was provided by a combination of starch crops and dairy products. This combination made possible large and settled populations, for milking provided good protein and fats which might not have been obtained by killing the herd. In Asia where the dairying pattern never penetrated, the need for protein was met in some regions by local protein crops such as the soybean and in others by rearing pigs and chickens, supplemented by fishing and local small game. Where the people were within reach of the sea, sufficient proteins and fats could be obtained by fishing alone, as was the situation in most of Oceania. In those areas where there was no native game and where there was no access to the sea, the people were in desperate straits even when there was abundant land for agriculture. This held for America, where there were comparatively few domestic animals who made only a slight contribution to the aboriginal food supply. Proteins and fats had to be obtained by hunting and fishing, by gathering wild plants, and by raising special crops. Actually, all the higher American cultures were based on a combination of starch and protein crops. There was a multiplicity of starch crops but the number of protein crops was decidedly limited: there were only two of any importance, the peanut and the bean, the latter in numerous varieties.

In the Southwest there is evidence of a comparatively brief period of rapid cultural advance with a strong suggestion that this was correlated with the great increase in population. The period of advance seems to have been preceded by a much longer period during which development was slow, and was followed by another long period of comparative cultural stabilization. It seems probable that this period of advance coincided with the appearance of the bean and the consequent raising of the population ceiling.

In the Southeast of America the time interval separating the production of corn and bean was short. The sudden advance of Southeastern culture may therefore have been the result of introduction of a maize-bean complex into a region where agricultural techniques were already known, but where crops were inadequate. Such introduction would provide a balanced diet in a single stroke and make possible a rapid population increase. The sudden flowering of the Mayan civilization also suggests some stimulating factor and this may have been the addition of beans to a pre-existing agricultural complex. Morley confirms that the second most important food crop of the Maya, after maize, was beans *(buul)*. Beans still contribute a large part of the protein intake of the Maya now, as they must have in ancient times.

The *Leguminosae* ranks with *Gramineae* (cereals and grasses) as the two groups of plants of greatest importance to world agriculture. There are at least 12,000 recognized species of the family *Leguminosae;* the great majority of seed-yielding legume plants are derived from one of the key subfamilies, the *Papilionatae.* Considerable confusion exists about the names of various plants; the groups beans and peas have been used so broadly that they are often interchanged. There are many local names: for example, *Phaseolus vulgaris* is called variously the kidney bean, French bean, the haricot bean, the navy bean, the pinto bean, and the snap bean. In India there are some generic terms for beans: "gram," for example, refers to the dried seed in the husk, and "pulse" refers to the decorticated and split seed. Often the word pulse has been used synonymously with legume or bean and so has the word gram. It is for this reason that most authorities on the subject prefer the botanical rather than the colloquial names of the plants. (See also Deschamps, Whyte et al., Hand.)

Legume seeds have the highest protein content of all plants. Dried beans contain at least 20 percent protein and there are some species which have over 30 percent; the soybean is a particular example of the latter. Their inclusion in the diet has a profound influence on the protein value. Platt has calculated the protein value of some tropical diets containing legumes: the range of net dietary protein value of the meals containing the legumes is from 3, where manihot is the staple, to 7.4 for sorghum as compared to a range of 2.8 to 5.7 without the addition of the legumes. (See report of FAO/CCTA Technical Meeting on Legumes.) There is no question that these have been a major source of protein in areas where animal protein is scarce. In some parts of Africa, for example, consumption may be as high as 400 to 600 grams of dry beans per person per day; a consumption of 240 grams person per day has been recorded for India, and it is estimated that beans of *Phaseolus vulgaris* variety provide from 20 to 30 percent of the protein in the rural diet in Central America.

Some of the ways in which legumes are utilized in diets are given in Table 15-1. The reader will obviously know

## TABLE 15–1

### *Examples of Food Preparations Containing Legumes*

| | |
|---|---|
| *Guiso* (Peru) | These are stews of many ingredients. Some contain assorted legumes and the staple, rice or corn. [1] |
| Bean stew (Israel and Middle East) | Typical ingredients are 200 g assorted dried beans, 50 g oil, 250 g mixed vegetables (potatoes, celery, parsley, carrots), 50 g onions, 15 g tomato puree, spices, and 500 g boiling water. This is popular among Jews in Near and Middle East. It contains 5% crude protein. [7] |
| Soup (Indonesia) | Rice is eaten mixed with a soup or stew containing leaves, pulses, and green fruits. A typical dish consists of steamed vegetables covered with a groundnut (peanut) sauce called "gado-gado" or "petjel." [12] |
| Rice and pulse (India) | Rice and pulse *(Phaseolus aureus)* in the proportion of 2:1 are mixed and cooked together until soft. Salt and simple spices are usually added during cooking. [8] |
| Stew (Haiti) | The main dish is a vegetable stew containing mixtures of legumes, maize, plantain, bread fruit, rice, and, if possible, an extremely small piece of fish or meat. This is flavored with such spices as garlic, cloves, cinnamon, and aniseed. A popular mixture of legumes on the market is *pois à la manièra* or *pois mélange,* consisting of red and black species of *Phaseolus vulgaris* and lima beans *(Phaseolus lunatus).* [6] |
| *Gallo pinto* (Costa Rica) | Rice and black beans are fried in animal or vegetable fat and seasoned with onion and pepper. Sometimes tomato is added. Eaten |

for breakfast. [Ministry of Public Education, Costa Rica.]

*Idly* and *Appam* (India)

Black gram *(Phaseolus mungo)* is cooked with rice into a steam-cooked cake, *idly,* or a pancake, *appam.* These are principally breakfast items. [9]

Assorted legumes (Peru)

Beans are soaked overnight and then cooked with onions, garlic, fat, and salt. Frequently they are prepared in the morning and eaten in the afternoon. [1]

Assorted grams or pulses (India)

Whole gram or pulse is soaked in water overnight and then cooked with spices. [8]

Peanuts (China)

Peanuts *(Arachis hypogaea)* boiled with salt are popular for breakfast. Contain 25% protein. [5]

*Phaseolus vulgaris* (Central America)

The three major elements of the population each treat this bean in a characteristic manner: Indians boil beans with flavoring herbs such as chenopodium; Spanish add lard and onion during boiling and usually mash, strain, and fry the beans afterward; Caribs fry the beans whole. [3]

*Techina* salad (Middle East)

Composed of the following proportions: 160 g crushed roasted sesame seeds, 100 ml water, 40 g lemon juice, 30 g parsley, 1 tablespoon of oil, and salt and garlic. Contains 10.4% protein. [7]

*Humus* salad (Middle East)

Composed of cooked chickpeas *(Cicer arietinum),* oil, and *techina* salad in the proportions: 50 g *techina* salad, 50 g chickpeas, and spices. Contains 8.6% protein. [7]

*Falafel* (Middle East)

Small balls made from chickpeas and bread and deep-fat fried. Eaten with *pittah* (flat bread), olives, pickles, and strong seasoning. Their composition is 50 g chickpeas and 2 slices of white bread. Contains 8.5% protein. [7]

*Falafel* (Middle East)

Parboiled wheat is mixed with ground broad beans *(Vicia faba)* and chickpeas and fried. [10]

Pulse snacks (India)

Pulse flour is mixed with water into a thin paste; salt, spices, and cut onions are added, and small amounts of the mixture are deep-fat fried. [8]

*Chaing tou chia* (China)  Cowpea *(Vigna unguiculata)* with pods are stir-fried, either alone or with shrimp or meat. Contain 3.1% protein. [5]

*Pien tou (H'sien)* (China)  Flat, fresh beans similar to string beans *(Dolichos lablab)* are stir-fried and eaten alone or with meat. Contain 8% protein. [5]

*Ts'ai tou* (China)  Dried kidney beans *(Phaseolus vulgaris)* are stir-fried alone or with meat. Contain 23% protein. [5]

*Ts'an tou (Kau)* (China)  When fresh, the pods of *Vicia faba* are removed and the beans stir-fried alone or with meat. Immature pods are pureed and eaten as a delicacy. Mature beans are generally fried in deep fat until crisp, then salted and eaten between meals or at breakfast with rice congee. The mature beans contain 25% protein. [5]

*Dahl* (India)  The dry legumes (yellow, *Cajanus indicus;* red, *Lens esculanta;* black, *Phaseolus mungo;* green, *P. radiatus*) are cracked to loosen skins. This process is repeated until a dry powder is produced which can be boiled into a soft food as a thick, cooked soup free of hard grains. This is consumed either with cooked rice or with unleavened bread made from wheat or millets. [2, 8]

Chickpea (Lebanon)  Chickpeas are boiled and ground into a fine paste and mixed with wheat flour and soured milk. Has been successful in infant feeding. [2]

Chickpea flour (India)  Toasted *Cicer arietinum* and toasted wheat or barley are mixed and made into a flour. The mixed flour is made into a dough with water and eaten with salt and chillies. [8]

Unleavened bread, *Chapattie* (India)  Flour made from *Cicer arietinum* pulse is added to whole wheat flour at a level of 10–15%. The mixture is made into a dough; unleavened bread is made by baking in heated pans on an open circular fire. The dough is rolled into small circular pieces, which are fried in vegetable oil or butter fat. [8]

Unleavened bread (India)  The flour from *Lathyrus sativus* is mixed with wheat flour in equal proportions and made into a thick unleavened bread. [8]

*Fen t'iao* (China)

Mung bean *(Phaseolus mungo)* flour dough is pressed through circular orifices directly into boiling water. The most important step is that of kneading the proteinaceous material. The diameter of the strings as they come from the sieve is about ½ inch, but this is reduced to 1/16 inch by stretching. These are cooked, cut into 2-meter lengths, and hung on bamboo supports for drying. The dried strings are put into soups with Chinese cabbage, meat, and eggs or are stir-fried with meat. [5, 11]

*Makhlouteh* (Middle East)

A mixture of roasted chickpea, peanuts, squash, and watermelon seeds is a popular snack. [10]

Horse beans (China)

Horse beans *(Vicia faba)* are ground to a paste and fermented. [5]

*Phaseolus mungo* (India)

One part of bean is mixed with two parts of rice, covered with water, and soaked overnight. The mixture is ground and allowed to ferment for a day with organisms of the atmosphere or the grain. The fermented product is made into pancakes and other steamed or fried preparations. [8]

African locust bean condiment (Africa)

The hard, tough-skinned seeds *(Parkia biglobosa)* are covered with water and boiled until all the water is gone. This is repeated three times. Then the seed is covered with cold water, is decorticated by rubbing between hands or with sand, and sun-dried. The dried grain is boiled for ½ hour then placed in a basket lined with leaves and is covered with leaves. Fermentation lasts for 48 hours, after which the grain is crushed and mixed with the ash of sheanut wood. The paste is held thus for 12 hours. Small pieces of paste are placed in a dry dish and kept in the sun for one day to yield black balls or sticks with a strong odor. This product is similar to the *nuocmam* of Vietnam. It is eaten as a seasoning or as a supplement to cereals. The yellow pulp in the pods is liked by children; it is made into a drink or sauces. [4]

Germinated legumes (India)

Beans are soaked in water for 12–24 hours and then tied in a wet cloth. They are

|  | germinated for 24–48 hours and are eaten raw or cooked after first removing the husk. [2] |
| Mung bean sprouts, *Tu tou ya* (China) | Beans *(Phaseolus aureus)* are germinated for 70 hours, at which time sprouts are 2–4 cm. long. These contain 5.6% protein and are put in soup or in stir-fried vegetable dishes. The average composition of the mung bean is 12% water, 22% protein, 58% carbohydrate, 0.8% fat, 3.1% fiber, and 3.3% ash. It is an important part of the Chinese diet; it is eaten as flour, sprouts, milk, protein curds, starchy vermicelli, or a whole bean cooked in cereals, particularly rice. [5] |

1. C. C. Chiriboga, I. M. Franklin, Y. B. De Rueda, A. Castellanos, A. De Fuentes, A. Roca, and R. B. Bradfield, "La Alimentacion y el Estado de Nutricion en el Peru," *Anales Fac. Med. Univ. Nac. Mayor San Marcos Lima,* vol. 43, no. 1 (March 1960).

2. R. F. A. Dean, "Use of Processed Plant Proteins as Human Food," in A. M. Altschul (ed.), *Processed Plant Protein Foodstuffs* (New York: Academic, 1958).

3. M. Flores, "Food Patterns in Central America and Panama," in *Proceedings of the Third International Congress of Dietetics* (Bradford, England: Wm. Byles & Sons, 1961).

4. "Report of the FAO/CCTA Technical Meeting on Legumes in Agriculture and Human Nutrition in Africa" (Rome, Italy: Food and Agriculture Organization of the United Nations, 1959).

5. R. S. Harris, F. K. C. Wang, Y. H. Wu, C. S. Tsao, and L. Y. S. Loe, "The Composition of Chinese Foods," *J. Am. Dietet. Assoc.,* vol. 25 (1949), p. 28.

6. D. B. Jelliffe and E. F. P. Jelliffe, "The Nutritional Status of Haitian Children," *Acta Trop.,* vol. 18, no. 1 (1961), p. 1.

7. S. Joseph, A. Goldberg, and K. Guggenheim, "Composition of Mixed Israeli Dishes," *J. Am. Dietet. Assoc.,* vol. 40 (1962), p. 125.

8. V. N. Patwardhan, "Pulses and Beans in Human Nutrition," *Am. J. Clin. Nutr.,* vol. 11 (1962), p. 12.

9. K. S. Rao, M. C. Swaminathan, S. Swarup, and V. N. Patwardhan, "Protein Malnutrition in South India," *Bull. World Health Organ.,* vol 20 (1959), p. 603.

10. E. I. Sabry, "Protein Foods in Middle Eastern Diets," in *Progress in Meeting Protein Needs of Infants and Preschool Children,* Publication 843 (Washington, D. C.: National Academy of Sciences–National Research Council, 1961).

11. A. K. Smith, "Oriental Methods of Using Soybeans as Food," AIC-234 (Peoria, Ill.: U. S. Dept. of Agriculture, Northern Regional Research Laboratory, June 1949).

12. G. J. A. Terra, "Food Patterns in Indonesia," in *Proceedings of the Third International Congress of Dietetics* (Bradford, England: Wm. Byles & Sons, 1961).

other examples from personal observation and from reading, but the ones listed will suffice to provide an idea of the diversity of uses and the universality of inclusion of this family of seeds in the diet. This is aptly put by Dean: "Nevertheless, although other sources of protein will be mentioned in this chapter, it will be obvious that the legumes will present one of the most important sources of protein for the future and their utilization must dominate any discussion of man's use of plant proteins."

It will be noted that most of the uses to which legumes are put require little or no processing; simple operations such as soaking, cooking, and removing of the shells generally suffice. Such a simple pattern of utilization obviously has advantages, since it requires no complicated technology and can be done in the home. It has, of course, the drawback that it does not permit full benefit from the seeds, particularly from those varieties containing toxic factors which must be removed prior to utilization. It is for this reason, as we shall point out later, that legumes, already a very important source of protein, represent a potential for supplying still more protein for man with advances in information and in processing technology.

## The Soybean

Although the soybean is a legume, it deserves special mention because of its prominent role in the dietary of the Orient. The soybean, *Glycine max,* has a higher protein content than most common legumes—up to 40 percent—and also contains appreciable amounts of lipid, 18 percent or so. The soybean grows in temperate climates and hence has not achieved the widespread distribution of the other legumes. Soybeans are major crops in the Orient and in the United States. Soybean oil is a major vegetable oil; it is an ingredient of shortenings and margarines. Soybean meal and flour, the residues after the removal of oil, are a major protein supplement for feeding livestock, particularly monogastric livestock. In the Orient, however, the soybean has for centuries been a major source of supplementary protein for humans. At present, approximately 40 percent of the world production is consumed as human food, most of it in the Orient.

Examples of soybean food products made in the Orient are given in Table 15-2; Japanese menus which include soybean products are given in Table 15-3.

## TABLE 15–2

*Examples from the Orient of Protein Products from Soybeans*

| | |
|---|---|
| *Kinako* (Japan) | Roasted soybeans are ground into a flour and sprinkled on rice or rice cake. Contains 38% protein, 19% lipid, 29% carbohydrate, 4.7% ash, and 5% water. [5] |
| *Huang tou yu* (China) | Soybeans are germinated six days. Sprouts are 6–7 cm long. Contains 10% protein and 57% water. [1] |
| Boiled soybeans (Korea) | Soybeans are boiled in sweetened soybean sauce. The composition is as follows: cooked and roasted soybeans 70%, soybean sauce 25%, and sugar 5%. [8] |
| Fermented soybeans, *Tou chi* (China) | Whole soybeans are boiled or steamed, then allowed to ferment. They are salted, hot peppers and spices are added, and they are sealed in a jar. Contains 14% protein, 16% ash, and 53% water. [1] |
| Fermented soybeans, *Natto* (Japan) | Whole soybeans are cooked and fermented with *Bacillus natto (B. subtilis)*. Contains 19% protein, 9% lipid, 10% carbohydrate, 3% ash, and 60% water. [5] |
| Fermented soybeans, *Hamanatto* (Japan) | Whole soybeans are cooked and fermented for several months with *Aspergillus oryzae*. Contains 26% protein, 12% lipid, 9% carbohydrate, 13% ash, and 38% water. [5] |
| *Miso* (Japan) | Polished rice is washed, soaked, steamed and inoculated with *Aspergillus oryzae* mold. The rice is kept moist enough for mold growth but not so moist so that bacteria can grow. After 50 hours the *koji* or mold rice is mashed with steamed soybeans, salt, and an inoculum of *miso;* the mash is packed into a container and fermented at 28°C for one week. The temperature is then raised to 35°C and the fermentation continued for several months. The product is ripened for two weeks at room temperature, is removed, |

and ground to a paste. Salt acts as a preservative to prevent dangerous bacterial fermentation. Other cereals sometimes are incorporated into the formula. *Miso* is put into soups and is added as a flavoring agent. Contains 10-17% protein, 2-7% lipid, 14-30% carbohydrate, 5-12% salt, and 50% water. [2, 3, 5]

Soy paste (China)
Soybean mash (Korea)

The counterpart of *Miso.*
Barley is cooked, cooled, and treated for a day at 90°F with an enzyme made from *Aspergillus oryzae.* This is milled together with cooked soybeans and salt, and fermented in concrete tanks for about 3 months. The pastelike product is eaten directly or is incorporated into other cooked foods. [8]

Pepper mash (Korea)

This is similar to soybean mash, but contains in addition 10% of powdered red pepper. [8]

*Tempeh* (Indonesia)

A highly digestible product prepared by inoculating washed and cooked soybeans with a certain fungus. The inoculated beans are spread in thin layers between banana leaves and kept for one or two days. A grayish-white cake is formed of beans held together by the abundant mass of fungus mycelium. The following is a more detailed description as given by Hesseltine: Soybeans are washed and soaked. The seed coats are removed and the cotyledons are boiled with excess water for ½ hour, after which they are cooled, drained and inoculated with spores of *tempeh* mold, *Rhizopus* species, and tightly packed in containers. After 24 hours, the entire contents are one solid mass. In most practice, the inoculum is with mold from a previous fermentation. *Tempeh* may be eaten fresh or preserved by slicing and sun drying. Sliced *tempeh* is dipped into salt water and deep-fat fried. *Tempeh* cubes are put into soups. [3, 7]

Soy sauce, *Shoyu* (Japan)

Soy sauce is a fermentation product of soybeans to which wheat or rice are added. Wheat is molded with special strains of *Aspergillus oryzae;* the fermentation of the wheat-soybean mixture is carried out with strains of a yeast, *Hausenula,* and a lactic bacterium, *Lactobacillus delbrueckii*. The final product is a brown-colored liquid with a pronounced flavor. Contains 5–9% protein, 2–5% carbohydrate, 18% salt, and 60–70% water. [3]

Soy sauce (China)

Washed soybeans are soaked for 24 hours and then strained. The beans are then mixed with an equal weight of wheat flour, wheat bran or other cereal grain. The mixture is inoculated with the culture and placed in shallow trays; the mold is allowed to grow to the spore stage (about 72 hours). In the next stage, the mixture and spores are put in earthware jars with a quantity of salt solution so that the final concentration is 18% in salt. Fermentation goes on for 3 months to a year. The sauce is sterilized at 65°C for 30 minutes. [4]

Soybean milk,
  *Tonyu* (Japan)

Soybeans are washed, soaked in water, ground into a mash, and pressed. The liquid "milk" is often supplemented with oil, vitamins and minerals. It is boiled for about 30 minutes. This milk is used extensively in Japan and China. Contains 3.6% protein, 3% carbohydrate, 2% lipid, 0.5% ash, and 91% water. [4, 5]

Soybean curd,
  *Tou fu* (China)

Soybeans are soaked overnight in water, are ground, water is added, and the ground material is strained in cheesecloth. The liquid is simmered over a low flame for 2 hours, is cooled, and is treated with lime. The coagulate is separated and pressed into a cake. The curd is put into soups, stir-fried with meat, vegetables or mushrooms, or is eaten alone. It is salted, smoked, eaten in a dry form, or fermented into a "cheese." Contains 9% protein, 1% ash, and 88% water. [1]

*Tofu* (Japan)

Soybean milk is coagulated with calcium sulfate into a curd. The curd deep fried in vegetable oil is called *aburage*. A fermented product is *nyufu*. Contains 7% protein, 4% lipid, 2% carbohydrate, 0.6% ash, and 86% water. [2, 5]

*Tofu* (Korea)

A calcium or magnesium precipitated gel made from liquid expressed from cooked soybeans. It is used almost daily in soups. It is also fried in deep fat and put into a

| | |
|---|---|
| | composite food called seasoned vegetable and bean curd which contains: small fish (12%), soy sauce (23%), bean curd (25%), seaweed (16%), dry radish (14%), and red pepper, sugar and vegetable oil. [8] |
| Frozen *tofu*, *Kori-tofu* (Japan) | The curd is frozen for about 3 weeks, dried in a hot air oven and treated with ammonia to increase the water absorbing and swelling properties. Contains 53% protein, 26% lipid, 7% carbohydrate, 1.5% ash, and 10% water. [2, 5] |
| Soybean curd sheet, *Ts'ian chang tou fu* (China) | Made by compressing soybean curd between layers of cheesecloth into very thin sheets. Contains 32% protein, 1.8% ash, and 45% water. [1] |
| Soybean cheese, *C'hou tou fu lu* (China) | Soybean curd is putrefied and sealed in a jar with wine and spices. After one month, it can be eaten with sesame oil without cooking. Contains 14% protein, 12.5% ash, and 80% water. [1] |
| Soybean curd, fermented (China) | This is prepared like the cheese but the putrefaction is not as advanced and the flavor is milder. Contains 12% protein, 21% ash, and 64% water. [1] |

1. R. S. Harris, F. K. C. Wang, Y. H. Wu, C. S. Tsao, and L. Y. S. Loe, "The Composition of Chinese Foods," *J. Am. Dietet. Assoc.*, vol. 25 (1949), p. 28.

2. S. Hayashi, "Problems Involved in Increasing Use of Soybean Products in Japan," in *Proceedings of Conference on Soybean Products for Protein in Human Foods* (Peoria, Ill.: U. S. Dept. of Agriculture, Northern Utilization Research and Development Division, September 1961), p. 178.

3. C. W. Hesseltine, "Research at Northern Regional Research Laboratory on Fermented Foods," *ibid.*, p. 67.

4. A. K. Smith, "Oriental Methods of Using Soybeans as Food," Northern Regional Research Laboratory Report No. 234 (Peoria, Ill.; U. S. Dept. of Agriculture,. June 1949).

5. A. K. Smith, "Use of United States Soybeans in Japan," Bull. ARS 71-12 (Peoria, Ill.: U. S. Dept. of Agriculture, Northern Utilization Research and Development Division, April 1958).

6. "Standard Tables of Soybean Food Composition," Food Research Institute (Tokyo: Ministry of Agriculture and Forestry, 1961).

7. K. H. Steinkraus, D. B. Hand, J. P. Van Buren, and L. R. Hackler, "Pilot Plant Studies on Tempeh," in *Proceedings of Conference on Soybean Products in Human Foods* (Peoria, Ill.: U. S. Dept. of Agriculture, Northern Utilization Research and Development Division, September 1961), p. 75.

8. R. R. Williams, G. F. Combs, W. J. McGanity, and Z. I. Kertesz, "A Nutrition Survey of the Armed Forces of the Republic of Korea," *J. Nutr.*, vol. 68 (1959), supp. 1.

In some areas of China, diets based on soybeans are described as being completely adequate. Guy and Yeh (1938) pointed out that in Peking there are two distinct types of diet, one eaten by the rich and the other by the poor. Although they are fundamentally different, both, at their best, are excellent. The diet of the poor may be described as whole cereal-legume and that of the rich, milled cereal-meat; both contain fresh vegetables. The whole cereal-legume diet uses mixed flours of maize and soybean (9:1) and of millet *(Setaria italica)* and soybean (6:4); fresh vegetables, sesame oil, and salt turnip. It is entirely vegetarian and is monotonously the same from day to day; only the vegetable varies with the season. The great bulk of the rural population of North China thrives on it. Meat is only eaten three or four times a year at festivals; it cannot be considered a nutritionally significant component. This type of diet is usually eaten in two meals: the cereal is prepared as steamed bread; the vegetable is cooked for a short time in water to which oil is added. The vegetable and the cooking water are all eaten at once.

This diet is also described as excellent for weaning. As soon as teeth begin to erupt, bits of raw turnip are given to be nibbled and whole cereal bread is given, at first, softened by soaking in the vegetable soup and later dry, as the child is able to chew. Tastes of soup are given at an early age and increased according to the desires of the child.

The trouble with such a diet comes when it is not followed because of poverty, ignorance, or fads. Omission of fresh vegetables and reduction or elimination of the soybean will undermine this diet and render it inadequate.

No doubt there may have been changes in this Peking diet since its description in 1938, and there is no denying its monotony. Moreover, deficiencies not noted at that time might have been encountered with more refined medical techniques. But there is no question that large populations exist in apparent good health on all-vegetable diets in which the soybean is a major component.

When we examine the various forms of soybean which appear in the human dietary in the Orient, we find parallels to the general methods of introducing legumes in the diet, but there is a major difference. Throughout the centuries, more sophisticated forms of soybean products have been developed. Most of these can be produced at the household

## TABLE 15-3

*Examples of Food Menus Containing Soybean Products*

| | |
|---|---|
| Breakfast | Cooked rice, *miso* soup (*miso*, green beans with pods, eggs), white bait (fish half dried) with mashed radish. |
| Lunch | Cooked rice, minced beef cooked with potatoes (with carrots and vegetable oil), *miso* soup (*miso, tofu,* and leeks). |
| Dinner | Cooked rice, fish (yellow tail) broiled with soysauce (with mashed radish), seasoned rape seedlings (with sesame oil, red pepper, soysauce, sesame), vegetable soup (*tofu,* marsh parsley). |

*Source:* T. Watanabe, National Food Research Institute, Tokyo, personal communication, 1959.

level, but several types are produced more efficiently by organized efforts and by more advanced technology. The various forms run the gamut from soy flour and soy sprouts to boiled soybeans, fermented soybeans, molded soybeans, joint fermentations with other cereals, sauces, "milks," curds, and "cheeses." It is not alone the desire to make available a wide range of products which is responsible for this variety of treatments. Another fundamental principal is also involved. Soybeans contain inhibitors which interfere with growth. Some of these have been identified as trypsin inhibitors and hemagglutenins; and there are other yet unidentified materials in the soybean which are deleterious. Some but not all of these are heat-labile and hence destroyed by toasting or cooking, and some are water-soluble and might be removed by soaking and extraction. There are insoluble carbohydrates in the soybean which add bulkiness to this source of food. And the protein content, even though it is high, much higher than most other plant protein sources, is not as high as in some meat products. The various forms of processing which have been developed solve some of the above-mentioned problems.

This is a lesson in successful food technology, even though the means of arriving at the solutions may have been empirical. A potential food resource has, in fact, been rendered effective by proper processing. In so doing the Orientals have shown consumate skill in adapting a plant source of protein in an economy where there is a scarcity of animal protein. The wonder is that others have not shown equal skill and imagination, and that the soybean is not as well utilized in other areas where there is scarcity of animal protein.

The lesson of the soybean is one to which we will return as we deal with the general problem of increasing protein supply where there is little, if any, chance of increasing supplies of animal protein.

## SELECTED BIBLIOGRAPHY *

Bressani, R., L. G. Elias, and D. A. Navarrete. "The Essential Amino Acid Content of Samples of Black Beans, Red Beans, Rice Beans and Cowpeas of Guatemala," *J. Food Sci.*, vol. 26 (1961), p. 1.

Deschamps, I. "Peas and Beans," in A. M. Altschul (ed.), *Processed Plant Protein Foodstuffs.* New York: Academic, 1958.

Guy, R. A., and K. S. Yeh. "Peking Diets," *Chinese Med. J.*, vol. 54 (1938), p 201.

Hand, D. B. "Nomenclature Guide to Plant Products Cited," in *Progress in Meeting Protein Needs of Infants and Preschool Children.* Publication 843. Washington, D. C.: National Academy of Sciences—National Research Council, 1961.

Jelliffe, D. B., B. E. R. Symonds, and E. F. P. Jelliffe. "The Pattern of Malnutrition in Early Childhood in Southern Trinidad," *J. Pediat.*, vol. 57 (1960), p. 922.

Linton, R. L. "Crops, Soils and Culture in America," in C. L. Hay, R. L. Linton, S. K. Lothrop, H. L. Shapiro, and G. C. Vaillant (eds.), *The Maya and Their Neighbors.* New York: Appleton-Century, 1940.

Millis, J. "The Feeding of Chinese, Indian, and Malay Infants in Singapore," *Quart. Rev. Pediat.*, vol. 14 (1959), p. 42.

Morley, S. G. *The Ancient Maya.* Stanford, Calif.: Stanford U.P., 1947, p. 156.

Schaefer, A. E. "Food Patterns in North Africa — Ethiopia," in *Tradition, Science, and Practice in Dietetics:Proceedings of the Third International Congress of Dietetics.* Bradford, England: Wm. Byles & Sons, 1961.

## 227     *Partial Solutions to the Protein Problem*

Snapper, I. *Chinese Lessons to Western Medicine.* New York: Interscience, 1941.

*Soybean Products for Protein in Human Foods.* Proceedings of Conference, Northern Regional Research Laboratory, Sept. 13–15, 1961. Peoria, Ill.: U. S. Department of Agriculture, 1961.

"Teff—A Source of Protein," *Nutr. Rev.,* vol. 20 (1962), p. 310.

Whyte, R. O., G. Nilsson–Leissner, and H. C. Trumble. *Legumes in Agriculture.* FAO Agricultural Studies No. 21. Rome, Italy: Food and Agriculture Organization of the United Nations, 1953.

 ° See also references in tables 15-1 and 15-2.

# CHAPTER 16

# *The Animal Protein Deficit*

THE READER MIGHT well be persuaded at this point that there exists evidence of protein deficiency for specific groups and in definite localities. This is a qualitative conception well documented by clinical reports and epidemological surveys. But can this be done in more quantitative terms—in numbers of people, percentages of populations, tons of food? How much is the deficit in terms of our present supply?

First we must assume a goal. And the most reasonable, certainly the first to come to mind, is that the deficient areas will want to approach in performance and practice the now successful areas, the developed areas. Even if there might be some *a priori* reservations to this goal, it must be still considered first and evaluated; it would not occur to anyone from a so-called developed country to do otherwise. As a consequence our solution commits us to increasing and improving the protein supply by enlarging the animal component of the diet. This is the classical approach; this is what happened whenever the wealth of a nation increased (see Table 13-1). We shall later examine alternative goals.

## Malnutrition and Undernutrition

We have repeatedly called attention to the difficulties and dangers of isolating the protein aspects from the entire food

228

problem. Inquiries into the quantitative aspects of protein supply can be divorced partially from the total picture by considering the distinction between "undernutrition," a deficiency in total available calories, and "malnutrition," a deficiency in quality of the food. Most often the latter is attributable to reduced protein quality, but there are instances of vitamin and mineral deficiency which would be classified as malnutrition. Since we are assuming as a goal an increase in the animal component, we can agree to consider low percentages of animal protein in the diet as a criterion of malnutrition.

There is no question that there is undernourishment and malnourishment; the problem is to be able to define these deficiencies in quantitative terms, both in percentages of population and in the amount of additional food and food types needed. Such a calculation, however sophisticated the mathematics, is no better than some of the basic data and assumptions (see Farnsworth). Among the types of information important to the quantitative conclusion are the needs of the people for calories and food quality, particularly protein quality, what people are actually eating—the food supply, and what goals must be achieved to provide adequate amounts and quality of food. Since all three of these matters are subject to debate, there will be a variety of conclusions. But here we are interested only in the magnitude of the problem; the present information will serve to illustrate this magnitude. Even if later improvements in our understanding of the basis for the calculation will occur, it is unlikely that the order of magnitude will be changed that much. One of the most thoroughgoing analyses of this question is by Sukhatme; we shall deal primarily with his treatment.

## Availability of Nutrients

The availability of nutrients for selected countries and areas is listed in Table 16-1. One set of data is from Suk-

# TABLE 16–1

## Availability of Nutrients for Present Population (1958–1961)

### (per capita, per day)

| Country or Area | Calories | | Animal Protein (grams) | | Total Protein (grams) | |
|---|---|---|---|---|---|---|
| | A[1] | B[2] | A | B | A | B |
| Canada | 3,080 | | 62 | | 94 | |
| United States | 3,220 | | 66 | | 97 | |
| North America | | 3,120 | | 66 | | 93 |
| Latin America | 2,640 | 2,470 | 23 | 25 | 66 | 67 |
| Europe | | 3,040 | | 36 | | 88 |
| Mediterranean Europe | 2,660 | | 25 | | 75 | |
| Other Western Europe | 2,920 | | 41 | | 79 | |
| Soviet Union | 2,985 | | 26 | | 92 | |
| Other Eastern Europe | 2,925 | | 28 | | 78 | |
| Far East | 2,100 | 2,070 | 8 | 8 | 56 | 56 |
| Mainland China | 2,200 | | 6 | | 65 | |
| Oceania | 3,210 | 3,250 | 67 | 62 | 103 | 94 |
| Africa | 2,455 | 2,360 | 11 | 11 | 64 | 61 |
| Near East (Western Asia) | 2,365 | 2,470 | 15 | 14 | 75 | 76 |
| Group I[3] | | 2,150 | | 9 | | 58 |
| Group II[3] | | 3,060 | | 44 | | 90 |
| World | | 2,420 | | 20 | | 68 |

[1] Source: *The World Food Deficit*, U. S. Department of Agriculture, 1961.

[2] Source: P. V. Sukhatme, "The World's Hunger and Future Needs in Food Supplies," *J. Roy. Statist. Soc.*, vol. 124, part 4 (1961), p. 463.

[3] Group I comprises the low-calorie areas and includes the Far East, Near East, Africa, and Latin America, excluding the River Plate countries, Argentina, Uruguay, and Paraguay; Group II are the remainder of the countries.

hatme, the other from a preliminary approximation of the world food deficit prepared by the U. S. Department of Agriculture. Notice that in general there is agreement both on the available calories as well as protein supply.

## Present Food Deficit

Sukhatme based his calculations of the deficit in calories and animal protein on a range of objectives for such areas as the Far East and Africa. In both those areas the discrepancy between the availability and the need is so great that it would be difficult to achieve anything close to balance in the short range; therefore, there is a range of targets. For the Far East the low or immediate target is for 2,300 Calories per capita per day, 2,300 for the intermediate target and 2,400 for the eventual, long-term objective; for the Near East the target is 2,470 Calories; for Africa the immediate target is 2,400 Calories and the ultimate one 2,450 Calories; and for Latin America the target is 2,400 Calories.

Steps were also programmed for the increase in animal proteins. The low or immediate target is an increase of three grams of animal proteins per capita per day; this goal might be achieved over approximately a ten-year period. The medium or intermediate target is one which seeks to raise the level by seven to eight grams per day and might be achieved in twenty years, while the high or long-term target is one which aims at raising the animal protein content by twelve grams per capita per day, and might be achieved by the turn of the century. Even the high target which for the Far East means an increase of 12 grams per person would only provide an overall level of 20 grams of animal protein per day against a level of 44 grams now prevalent in the so-called developed countries. It is on the basis of these targets that the deficits shown in Table 16-2 were calculated. Sukhatme estimates that about one-fifth of

# TABLE 16–2

## Deficit of Calories and Animal Protein for Present Population (1958–1961)
### (per capita, per day)

| AREA | CALORIES | | | ANIMAL PROTEIN (GRAMS) | | |
|---|---|---|---|---|---|---|
| | Short-term | Intermediate | Long-term | Short-term | Intermediate | Long-term |
| Latin America, excluding River Plate countries | | 40 | | | 2 | |
| Far East | 230 | 230 | 330 | 2 | 7 | 12 |
| Near East | | 0 | | | 6 | |
| Africa | 60 | | 100 | 4 | | 9 |

Source: P. V. Sukhatme. The deficit is based on targets for calories and animal proteins as follows: Far East, low, medium and high targets of 2,300, 2,300 and 2,400 Calories per capita per day and 10, 15, and 20 grams of animal protein per capita per day, respectively; for the Near East and Latin America 2,470 and 2,400 Calories respectively and 20 grams of animal protein; for Africa, low and high targets of 2,400 and 2,450 Calories, and 15 and 20 grams of animal protein, respectively.

the population in the Far East and possibly more is under-nourished; for the world, the proportion would seem to be between 10 and 15 percent. This means that in 1960 between 300 and 500 million people did not receive sufficient calories to support normal activities. A much greater percentage suffered from malnutrition.

Let us now consider what the par capita deficit means in terms of the present supply of proteins. Such an estimate in terms of the present population is given in Table 16-3; usually, the intermediate target was the basis for calculation. The total world production of animal protein is estimated as 20 million metric tons per year; the total animal protein deficit is 4.8 metric tons, or 23 percent of the existing supply. If we consider the individual deficient areas, the range is from a low of 9 percent for the Latin American countries to a high of 87.5 percent for the Far East. For all of the Group I countries, which in Sukhatme's classification are those with a deficit of calorie and protein supplies, the amount of animal protein required to meet the deficit for the medium target is 66 percent. It is an interesting commentary that as the viewpoint is broadened, the problem becomes proportionately less. However, even on a worldwide basis, the 23 percent deficit is a formidable sum; it amounted in 1960 to five million tons of animal protein per year.

## Projected Food Deficit

These calculations are based on the present population. If we consider the projections of population growth for the remainder of the century, we reach estimates of increased food requirements as summarized in Table 16-4. In the year 2000, the supplies in the Far East will have to be increased to 292 percent to achieve a low target. This is a requirement for all food supplies based on an index which takes into account the relative cost of the various food items.

## TABLE 16-3

### Deficit of Animal Protein in Terms of Present Supply (1958)[1]

| AREA | POPULATION MILLIONS | AVAILABLE SUPPLY | | DEFICIT (MEDIUM TARGET) | | |
|---|---|---|---|---|---|---|
| | | Per Capita per Day (grams) | Total Millions of Tons per Year | Per Capita per Day (grams) | Total Millions of Tons per Year | Percent of Present Supply |
| Latin America excluding River Plate countries | 170 | 23 | 1.43 | 2 | 0.13 | 8.8 |
| Near East (Western Asia) | 125 | 15 | 0.68 | 6 | 0.25 | 40 |
| Far East | 1,498 | 8 | 4.38 | 7 | 3.83 | 87 |
| Africa | 208 | 11 | 0.84 | 9 | 0.69 | 82 |
| Group I countries | 2,001 | 10 | 7.33 | 6.6 | 4.83 | 66 |
| World | 2,859 | 20 | 20.00 | 4.6 | 4.83 | 23 |

[1] Calculated from information in P. V. Sukhatme (see footnote Table 16-1), and from data in tables 16-1 and 16-2.

Sukhatme concludes that should the population grow according to the United Nations' medium forecast, the world's total food supplies would have to be doubled by 1980 and

TABLE 16–4

*Implications of Population Growth on Food Requirements*

| AREA | POPULATION MILLIONS | | | | TOTAL FOOD SUPPLIES REQUIRED (AVAILABLE = 100) | | |
|------|------|------|------|------|------|------|------|
| | 1958 | 1970 | 1980 | 2000 | 1970 | 1980 | 2000 |
| Far East | 1,498 | 1,863 | 2,317 | 3,639 | | | |
| Low target | | | | | 148 | 186 | 292 |
| Medium target | | | | | 175 | 219 | 343 |
| High target | | | | | 207 | 259 | 406 |
| Near East | 125 | 165 | 203 | 327 | 154 | 190 | 307 |
| Africa | 208 | 232 | 283 | 421 | | | |
| Low target | | | | | 128 | 155 | 230 |
| High target | | | | | 143 | 174 | 259 |
| Latin America | 170 | 235 | 314 | 548 | 145 | 194 | 338 |
| Excluding River Plate countries | | | | | | | |
| Group I | 2,001 | 2,495 | 3,117 | 4,935 | | | |
| Medium target | | | | | | 207 | 329 |
| High target | | | | | | 234 | 371 |
| World | 2,859 | 3,480 | 4,220 | 6,267 | | | |
| Medium target | | | | | | 169 | 251 |
| High target | | | | | | 181 | 268 |

*Source:* Based on United Nations' medium projections and data in P. V. Sukhatme, "The World's Hunger and Future Needs in Food Supplies," *J. Roy. Statist. Soc.*, vol. 124, part 4 (1961), p. 463.

trebled by 2000 in order to provide a reasonably adequate level of nutrition to the peoples of the world. In terms of animal protein it would mean that by the year 2000 the world annual production of animal protein would have to be of the order of 60 to 100 million tons. This is a threefold to fivefold increase over the present supply.

Wright (in Russell and Wright, *Hunger*), on the basis of Sukhatme's statistics, states that for every future increase of 100 million in population, the world will need to provide a total of about 13 million tons of additional cereals and 14 million tons of animal products. By 1980 in order to bring the world up to a reasonable diet and to take into account additional population, the world cereal production will have to be increased by not less than 33 percent and the world's production of milk, meat, eggs, and fish by not less than 100 percent. By the year 2000, if there is a world population of six thousand million, the needed increase will have to be over 100 percent for cereals and over 200 percent for animal products; and to achieve a fully adequate level, the animal product increase will have to be 300 percent or more.

## Progress in Increasing the Food Supply

Before going on to consider the possibilities for increasing food supply, particularly animal protein, to meet the present and anticipated needs, it may be well to view what has happened in recent years. If we set population and food supplies at the pre-World War II level as 100, world population has increased to the level of 135 by 1950–60 and food production to a value of 150. On a world scale, food is ahead slightly, but this is deceptive since the greatest increases have been in regions which already enjoy adequate food supplies. In Africa, the Far East and in Latin America, population and food supplies have increased at about the same rate; there is no improvement in an already deficient diet.

Another view on the same subject is given by deVries as summarized in Table 16-5. Even on a world basis there was a decline in per capita milk production in the 25-year period prior to 1960; the modest increases in total amount of cereals and meats available per capita do not begin to compensate for the existing deficit. Where the need is greatest, the improvements, if any, have been the least.

TABLE 16-5

*Production per Capita of Selected Foods:*
*1959–60 as Percent of 1934–38*

| COUNTRY OR AREA | CHANGE IN PRODUCTION | | |
| --- | --- | --- | --- |
| | All Cereals | Meat | Milk |
| Western Europe | 131 | 150 | 107 |
| North and Central America | 133 | 117 | 84 |
| South America | 74 | 79 | 97 |
| Asia, excluding Mainland China | 99 | 129 | 90 |
| Africa | 97 | 98 | 84 |
| Oceania | 121 | 124 | 93 |
| Soviet Union | 109 | 210 | 139 |
| Mainland China | 126 | 94 | – |
| World | 110 | 114 | 94 |

Source: E. deVries, *Proceedings of the World Food Forum*, May 15, 1962 (Washington, D. C.: U. S. Department of Agriculture, 1963), p. 85. See also *Report of the Technical Meeting on Nutrition in Food Policy and Planning in Asia and the Far East*, Bangkok, Thailand, June 6-13, 1960 (Rome, Italy: Food and Agriculture Organization of the United Nations, 1961).

Trends in intake of animal proteins reflect the same pattern. Over the six-year period from 1949 to 1955 there was a decrease in the Far East from 7.7 to 6.9 grams per capita per day, in Latin America from 29.2 to 28.3, and in Oceania from 65.2 to 61.0 (this latter change still leaves an abundance of animal protein); the Near East showed a slight increase from 12.2 to 13.1, greater increases were observed in Europe (36.2 to 41.1) and in North America (61.7 to 65.7).

It is clear from an analysis both of the needs and projection of needs and of the performance in recent years that a continuation of the present trend of growth in food production and a continuation unchecked of population growth can only intensify the problems of under- and malnutrition to the point where political stability and world peace are completely dominated by this one consideration. And as one delves more into the details, the problems, staggering enough in their statistics, become even more terrifying as the figures become embellished with the deterrents of social customs, political problems, and economic stresses.

May and Jarcho concluded their study of Asia with the comment that the diet structure is fragile; this fragility is the result of overpopulation because few die of starvation before the reproductive stage. In other parts of the world (Europe and the urban areas of the United States) overpopulation has no fatal consequences because of economic resources supplied by industry. There is a tendency to believe that the same panacea could protect the countries of Asia. It is overlooked that the industrial power of the West developed on the basis of unexploited resources, accumulated capital, a scientific culture, and a market ready to absorb their products. The nations of Asia have few known unexploited resources, little capital, a magnificent spiritual culture that does not prepare the masses for science and industrial development, and a saturated market. May and Jarcho see no reason to believe that an abatement in the population explosion is in sight, and conclude that the prospect of a drastic change in the food geography of Asia does not seem very bright at present.

But we are engaged here in examining the possibilities of increasing the food supply. The very complexity of the problem, the local variations and intensifications of critical social, economic, and political elements obscure any generalizations which might be made. Therefore, if we are to continue with this analysis we must try to abstract from this complex only matters pertinent to scientific and technological capability, and leave for the moment other considerations, however overriding they may be. There are a number of obvious ways for increasing world food supplies, and we will mention some of them. Often a general increase will suffice to increase the animal component as well, but there are also specific approaches to increasing animal food and these, too, will be reviewed.

SELECTED BIBLIOGRAPHY

deVries, E. "Food Production Trends in Selected Countries," in *Proceedings World Food Forum, May 15, 1962,* Washington, D. C.: U. S. Dept. of Agriculture, 1963, p. 79.

"FAO Index Numbers of Food Production by Countries," *Monthly Bulletin of Agricultural Economics and Statistics,* vol. 11, no. 4 (1962), p. 14.

Farnsworth, H. C. "Defects, Uses, and Abuses of National Food Supply and Consumption Data," *Food Res. Inst. Studies,* vol. 2, no. 3 1961, p. 179.

"Food Supplies and Population Growth," proceedings of a conference of The Royal Statistical Society, *J. Roy. Statis. Soc.,* vol. 125, part 3 (1962), p. 373.

May, J. M., and J. S. Jarcho. *The Ecology of Malnutrition in the Far and Near East.* New York: Hafner, 1961.

Russell, E. J., and N. C. Wright (eds.). *Hunger: Can It Be Averted?* London: British Association for the Advancement of Science, 1961.

Sukhatme, P. V. "The World's Hunger and Future Needs in Food Supplies." *J. Roy. Statist. Soc.,* vol. 124, part 4 (1961), p. 463.

*The World Food Deficit, a First Approximation,* Washington, D. C.: U. S. Dept. of Agriculture, 1961.

# CHAPTER 17

# *Possibilities for Increasing Food Supplies*

### Land Resources

Perhaps the first approach toward increasing food supplies is through greater use of land resources. It is generally agreed that approximately 10 percent of the land surface of the earth is cultivated and that perhaps 30 to 40 percent is the maximum potentially cultivable area. But the additional areas include vast equatorial forests as well as huge stretches of tropical savanna and grassland. According to Stamp (in Russell and Wright, *Hunger*), in 1960 there were available on a worldwide basis 12.5 acres per capita of which actually 1.1 acres were cultivated and four acres were potentially cultivable. Some estimates by Stamp and by Pawley of possibilities for increasing the available acreage are given in Table 17-1. Stamp calls attention to the difficulty in collecting these figures which are, at best, estimates, particularly the column listing potentially cultivable lands. There exists the potential for an increase in the area cultivated in the United States and Canada, for example, and a possible increase of 25 percent in India. But in Great

## TABLE 17–1
### Availability and Cultivation of Land

ACRES PER CAPITA [1]

| | Total | Potentially Cultivable | Actually Cultivated |
|---|---|---|---|
| World | 12.5 | 4.0 | 1.1 |
| United States | 12.5 | 6.0 | 3.0 |
| Canada | 140.0 | 21.5 | 3.5 |
| Great Britain | 1.1 | 0.6 | 0.55 |
| India | 2.5 | 1.0 | 0.75 |
| Japan | 1.1 | 0.2 | 0.17 |

HECTARES PER CAPITA [2,3]

| | Total | Potentially Cultivable | Actually Cultivated | Inadequate Soil | Too Arid | Too Mountainous | Too Cold |
|---|---|---|---|---|---|---|---|
| World | 5.05 | 1.07 | 0.45 | 0.50 | 1.01 | 1.01 | 1.01 |

[1] L. D. Stamp in E. J. Russell and N. C. Wright, *Hunger: Can It Be Averted?* (London: British Association for the Advancement of Science, 1961), p. 34.

[2] W. H. Pawley, *Possibilities of Increasing World Food Production*, Basic Study No. 10 (Rome, Italy: Food and Agriculture Organization of the United Nations, 1963), p. 30.

[3] 1 hectare = 10,000 square meters = 2.471 acres.

Britain and Japan, practically all of the possibly cultivable land is already exploited.

Pawley too underlines the difficulty of arriving at world-wide estimates; his analysis deals with specific areas. Cereals, the major world crop, are now planted on 30 percent more land than before World War I and on 18 percent more than before World War II. Between 1953 and 1957, about 36 million hectares of new land were opened to cultivation in the Soviet Union.

There could be an agricultural revolution in the handling of equatorial lands comparable to the opening up of the grass and forest lands in the temperate areas. But this would require the coordinated efforts of governments with their full resources of technology and capital.

The savannas of South America, Australia and Africa are underused and offer large possibilities for extension of agriculture by flood control and irrigation. Livestock production in Australia could be put on a more stable basis through pasture improvement and water control—perhaps the cattle population could be tripled. A substantial portion of the tropical grasslands of Brazil could be converted from poor grazing to cultivation of cereals, improved pastures, and better breeds of cattle. In Africa there is the added problem that some of the savannas have been destroyed and rendered useless by fire. Here is an instance of destruction and underutilization of resources existing side by side.

Contrary to the little-used savannas of Africa, South America, and Australia are the densely settled monsoon and savanna lands of Asia. Despite current intensive development, the opportunities for increasing production through better conservation and control of water are enormous. Of the 1,356 million acre-feet of water available annually in India, only 450 million acre-feet can be utilized. In 1951, 76 million were utilized, representing 17 percent of the usable flow. At the end of the second five-year plan, 27 percent was utilized; this portion is expected to increase to 36 percent at the end of the third five-year plan.

In India, millions of hectares have been left idle because of malaria or deep-rooted grasses which cannot be eradicated except with modern equipment. Burma has an area classed as potentially cultivable approximately equal to the area now being worked. Over one-half million hectares in Ceylon, equal to the present agricultural land, await development.

The rivers that arise in mountainous areas and find their way across land that receives too little precipitation can make a substantial additional contribution to the world's food supply. In some of the older irrigation areas, inadequate attention to drainage has led to waterlogging and salinity; in Pakistan, two million hectares of cultivated land in the Indus plain are damaged this way. These lands can be reclaimed but at enormous expense.

Ten million hectares of desert land in the United States are supplied by irrigation; water is available for still another 8.5 million hectares. Six and a half million hectares were irrigated in the Soviet Union in 1950 and 12.4 million hectares in 1960. Tauber estimates that out of 1,440 million hectares of arid land 700 million could be made available through irrigation.

Even in the temperate zones there is room for increase in cultivated land, particularly in the Southern Hemisphere. The discovery that vast lands in Australia are deficient in molybdenum provided opportunities for improving these lands by treatment with trace elements and nitrogen. Sixty million hectares are awaiting improvement.

It is a matter of proper land management, but it is not all that simple. The best possibilities for extending agricultural production come from increasing the cultivated land surface in temperate zones. Much less is known about the handling of lands in tropical zones: the proper management procedures, the proper seeds and animals, and insect control devices. Moreover, irrigation, aside from being expensive, brings with it other problems. Water-borne diseases can negate advantages which accrue from increased production. There are warnings about the rampant misuse of our land resources and disruption of the delicate ecological balance by destruction of forests and other means of conserving a balance of our plant and animal population (Bouillene). Indiscriminate clearing of land and destruction of flora and fauna have reduced the number of existing animal and plant varieties and have further reduced the chances of finding new varieties to serve society. It is not only a question of increasing the amount of land available, but of making the best use of available and potential land resources.

Actually, the history of civilization provides many examples of the contrary, of man's destroying cultivable land by improper handling, by overgrazing, and by destruction of forests. Remains of what were once flourishing civilizations and concentrated populations are now buried in deserts and in areas no longer available for agricultural exploitation. It must be realized that the easy-to-cultivate lands with the highest yields are now in production (Masefield). The new lands will require extensive irrigation and the kind of preparation and cultivation which depends on tractors and other mechanical equipment. The increment of foodstuff will require a greater proportionate increment in cost. While we may expect to be able to put more land in production, we must expect that our costs per unit of food will increase.

## Improvements in Yield of Agriculture

Perhaps a cheaper and better investment is to upgrade good agricultural land. There is a potential for increasing food supplies, total and animal, by more efficient operation: compare efficiency of food production in various locations and analyze the reason for such differences. Yields of selected foodstuffs for the regions of the world are compared in Table 17-2. There is a tenfold range in efficiency of utilization of animals, fivefold in efficiency of rice pro-

TABLE 17-2

*Yields of Selected Foodstuffs Per Land or Animal Unit[1,2] (1958)*

| Region | Wheat 100 Kg/Hectare | Rice (Paddy) 100 Kg/Hectare | Milk and Meat per Head of Cattle |
|---|---|---|---|
| Western Europe | 17 | 48 | 1.65 |
| North America | 13 | 29 | 1.32 |
| Soviet Union | | | 1.25 |
| Australia-New Zealand | | | 1.00 |
| Latin America | 11 | 16 | 0.41 |
| Near East | 10 | 26 | 0.38 |
| Africa | 6 | 10 | 0.23 |
| Far East | 9 | 22 | 0.16 |
| World | 12 | | 0.61 |

Source: N. C. Wright in E. J. Russell and N. C. Wright, *op. cit.*, p. 13; Pawley, *op. cit.*, p. 166; see also E. deVries, "Food Production Trends in Selected Countries," in *Proceedings of the World Food Forum, May 15, 1962* (Washington, D. C.: U. S. Dept. of Agriculture, 1963), p. 86.

[1] In terms of milk equivalent, 1 unit of meat is equal to 10 units of milk.

[2] Eggs per hen per year: highest, 160; lowest, 40.

duction, and an almost threefold variation in the yield of wheat. These represent averages; within each of the regions the range between individual good and poor producers is manyfold higher than the ratio of the averages. How can we account for these differences? Are they built-in to the available land and, therefore, unalterable? Or, are these differences in practice?

Some of the variations in Table 17-2 could reflect fertilizer practice. The careful conservation of all waste products for compost production or direct application to the soil has been a feature of Chinese agriculture for centuries and probably spread from there to Japan and Korea (Pawley). Japan applies fertilizer at the rate of about 100 pounds per acre and this, together with natural manure, brings about average yields of 3,500 pounds of rice per acre. India applies one pound of fertilizer per acre and manages less than one quarter the yield. Tauber, assuming 120 kilograms of nutritive substance as the average consumption of total nitrogen, phosphorus, and potassium fertilizer, has arrived at estimates of the percentage of arable land fertilized. In Western Europe this amounts to 52 percent and in North America and Oceania, 23 percent. Compare this to 4 percent for Asia, 3 percent for Latin America, and 1 percent for Africa. In 1959–60, Latin America, the Near East, the Far East (excluding Mainland China), and Africa consumed only approximately 15 percent of the world's annual fertilizer supply.

Over the past 50 years there has been a 25 percent increase in yield because of more fertilizer. The amount of fertilizer applied in the United States was doubled in the period 1945–60. Good fertilizer practice is reflected even in differences among the good producers. In 1957, the yield of wheat in Denmark was four times the world average, twice that of the United States average, six times the yield in India, and eight times the yield in Africa.

Whenever there has been an improvement in agricultural practice by more irrigation, addition of fertilizer, or utilization of better seeds and stock, there has been a definite improvement in yield of food supplies. Shaw reports that from 1945 to 1960 there has been an increase in the United States of 13 percent more pork per sow, 34 percent more milk per cow, and 30 percent more eggs per hen. Yields per acre in India have increased from 1948–49 to 1954–55: rice has gone up from an average of 698 pounds per acre to 720; maize from 251 to 707; wheat, 566 to 713; gram from 496 to 547; jowar, 305 to 469; and ragi, 613 to 693. Consumption of ammonium sulfate increased from about 275,000 tons in 1950 to 610,000 tons in 1955, and the amount of improved seeds went up from 56,000 tons in 1950 to 74,000 tons in 1955 (Guha). It is estimated that per-acre yields of grain in India could be increased by 30 percent in ten years: 5 percent by improved varieties, 20 percent by manuring and fertilizing and 5 percent by pest protection. Japan has 80 percent of rice area planted with high yielding varieties; few countries have more than 10–15 percent; most have less.

Cuthbertson points out that the addition of boron and

manganese to soil has increased peanut crops in Gambia fourfold at little additional expense. Hybrid maize in Italy increased crop yield by a third to twofold; world production (exclusive of United States) could increase from 114 to 250 million tons annually by shifting to the hybrid variety. In the United Kingdom in the last 20 years the yield of pastures on the more progressive farms increased by over 50 percent by better management and by more economical use of fertilizer, grass, and silage. On this basis Cuthbertson estimated that the world supply of milk and beef could be increased by nearly 100 percent.

Concomitant with increased yields through good practice is the protection of these increases by eliminating or minimizing losses to insects, rodents, parasites, weeds, and other sources of damage. It has been estimated that the United States loses $13 billion per year in foodstuffs from damage by various sources and this is equivalent to the production from 120 million acres. Two hours of every working day in gardens, fields, and orchards is spent in feeding these pests. Rats, alone, eat enough food each year to feed the combined population of New York and Philadelphia. In the Soviet Union, control of pests could increase the value of agricultural output by 45 billion rubles. In India, the annual loss of crops as a result of pests and diseases is estimated at 600 rupee crores (six billion rupees). In England, crop losses in 1947 were equivalent to the production of 33,000 farms; in France, the losses were estimated at 18 percent. Potato blight disease precipitated the great famine in Ireland in the 1840s. The famine in North Africa in 1866, which caused the death of 5 percent of the population, was caused by the destruction of the entire food supply by locusts. But in Tanganyika, in modern times, 96 percent of the locust population was destroyed by spraying with insecticides. Equally important is the control of pests which interfere with man's ability to work and cultivate his land. In 1900, over 7,000 square miles of agricultural land were not cultivated because of insect-borne malaria (Dajoz).

## More Efficient Animal Production

Greater production of animal protein benefits from general improvement in the overall agricultural process. Beyond this, there are specific improvements which come from improved breeds of animals and better feeding practice. The yield of milk per cow in 1958 was 4,330 kilograms in Israel, 4,150 in the Netherlands, 402 in Turkey, and 220 in India; the better performance is a direct result of improved practice (Pawley).

Combs showed that in the period from 1952 to 1960 the time required to produce three-pound broilers has been reduced from ten to seven or eight weeks; the amount of feed required per unit of live weight has been decreased from 2.81 to 1.96 under practical conditions; and has been reduced further to a value as low as 1.04 pounds of feed per pound of broiler in experimental rations. He estimated that the percentage of metabolizable energy retained in the carcass has increased from approximately 21 percent in 1952 to 32 percent on some of the most efficient rations.

No less important in increasing animal production is the prevention of disease. Newcastle disease in the Far East has commonly resulted in mortality of 70 to 100 percent among the flocks of poultry. In Singapore, a systematic vaccination campaign resulted in an increase in poultry number from 500,000 to 3½ million in four years, and an 800 percent increase in egg production (*Man and Hunger*). Cuthbertson pointed out that the yield of dairy herds in the United Kingdom which varies from below 600 to over 1,000 gallons per year could be increased and the present milk supply maintained with 30 percent less cows if inferior stock were graded up and tuberculosis were eliminated. In Tunisia, 50 percent of the goats and 20 percent of the sheep are lost annually because of brucellosis. In some areas one-third of the population suffers from this disease (undulant fever).

Reduction by more than 50 percent of this disease among cattle in the United States has saved the livestock industry 50 million dollars annually (Pawley).

## Fish Protein

Although 75 percent of the earth's surface is covered by water, only 10 percent of the animal protein and 1 percent of total food supplies come from aquatic sources. Even so, world production of fish of over 41 million tons annually is greater than the annual production of beef and veal, 28 million tons in 1960. The catch can be increased by more efficient fishing and particularly by mechanization. In Ceylon the average catch per boat per day was 13.3 pounds; after mechanization this increased to 139 pounds. In the period 1945 to 1958, India doubled its fish catch to a value of one million metric tons; Peru increased from 30,000 to one million metric tons; and Japan which already had a high proportion of fish protein in the diet went up from $3\frac{1}{2}$ to $5\frac{1}{2}$ million tons in the 20-year period 1938–58. Animal protein intake in the Congo was estimated at 4.4 grams daily in 1949 and 7.7 grams in 1957. Part of this rise came from more efficient cattle production, but some of it is a reflection of the increased production from sea and inland fisheries from 41,000 tons in 1950 to 120,000 tons in 1957.

In 1961 the global fish catch was 41,200,000 metric tons compared to 38 million in 1960. Japan's catch was 6.7 million tons followed in turn by Peru with 5.24 million tons, Mainland China with approximately 5 million tons, Soviet Union with 3.25 millions, and the United States with 2.9 million tons. It is estimated that the water resources can support an annual harvest of 250 million tons provided that proper methods of handling and processing fish are developed. In some countries a considerable proportion of the fish is processed for later consumption: 80 percent of the Canadian catch, 70 percent in the United States, 90 percent in Norway, and 70 percent in Japan. But in India one-half and in Pakistan three-fourths of the fish supplies are consumed fresh (Pawley). Five million tons of fish are now processed for animal foods. Several national and international agencies are interested in production of fish flours for human consumption. The objective is to process the fish at low cost and produce products which retain high quality protein as well as satisfactory flavor and stability (Olden, Morrison et al., Allen).

## Improved Technology

Perhaps one of the best examples of the influence of science and technology on the availability of food from present agricultural production is the story of skim milk powder distributed by UNICEF. Surplus milk in the United States was converted into skim milk powder and made available to the United Nations Agencies for distribution in 1953 at a nominal price. Some was also made available by the Canadian Government. UNICEF paid the cost of ocean freight on this powder at the rate of 2½ cents a pound. By 1957 UNICEF was paying 2½ million dollars annually to ship 100 million pounds of milk a year, and in 1959, five million children and mothers were receiving daily rations of skim milk in 62 countries. This program had many repercussions: First of all, it saved many lives of children and mothers. Secondly, it demonstrated that in many areas the critical foodstuff deficiency was protein. Thirdly, it demonstrated that it is possible to transport and distribute large amounts of protein safely without spoilage. Had the protein been in the form of liquid milk, this would have been out of the question both in terms of expense and perishability of the product.

We have mentioned just a few of the mechanisms by which food production could be increased, food supplies maintained, and better distribution obtained. No wonder it is so often said that with the present techniques and agricultural practices a much larger world population could be fed.

## Some Reasons for Failure to Increase Food Supplies

Professor Blackett (in Russell and Wright, *Hunger,* p. 65) summed this up as follows: "In general, I am convinced that the existing level of scientific technology is in the main amply sufficient to allow the solution of the world's food problem over the next few decades by the wide application of known methods. Scientific and technological advances will come, and should be welcomed as windfall profits, but should not be planned for. We, as scientists and technologists, have already given ourselves the tools by means of which hunger could be banished from the world—it is now up to us as citizens of the world to make sure they are used, so as to finish the job."

Cuthbertson stated that if present knowledge were fully exploited, a world population of six billion could probably be supported.

Stamp (in *Hunger,* p. 35) said: "On a world level it seems clear that even without further advances in knowledge which are taking place continuously, the full application of known techniques will enable the world to support three to four times its present population. But the world is far from being a unit, and contrasts between one country and another are very marked."

Certainly the accumulated knowledge of food production techniques is reflected in continued increased efficiency of production. Many of the data already presented testify to the proficiency of industrialized society to feed adequately its population. Another such presentation is in Table 17-3. Clearly, the average yields and production per capita of the industrialized West are steadily increasing. It is one of the

## TABLE 17-3

Average Production of Selected Cereals for the Prewar
Period (1935–39) and 1959 per Unit Area and
per Capita

| Area or Country | Yield Quintals per Hectare[1] | | Production (Kilograms per Capita) | |
|---|---|---|---|---|
| | 1935-39 | 1959 | 1935-39 | 1959 |
| Industrialized West | | | | |
| Western Europe | 17.9 | 25.3 | | |
| Japan | 31.8 | 39.4 | | |
| Australia and New Zealand | 8.8 | 13.4 | | |
| Canada | 9.0 | 13.1 | | |
| United States | 12.5 | 22.6 | | |
| Average | 13.7 | 22.0 | 417.2 | 528.6 |
| Sino-Soviet Countries | | | | |
| Soviet Union | 8.5 | 8.6 | | |
| Eastern Europe | 14.0 | 16.4 | | |
| Mainland China and other Communist countries in Asia | 17.9 | 17.7 | | |
| Average | 12.4 | 12.9 | 308.2 | 280.8 |
| Less-developed Areas | | | | |
| Other Europe | 10.4 | 12.7 | | |
| Latin America | 11.0 | 12.2 | | |
| Africa | 8.0 | 8.3 | | |
| West Asia and Far East | 11.8 | 11.5 | | |
| Other Oceania | 20.0 | 18.1 | | |
| Average | 11.1 | 11.4 | 196.2 | 168.9 |

Source: Food and People, Subcommittee on Foreign Economic Policy of the Joint Economic Committee, Congress of the United States (Washington, D. C.: U. S. Department of Agriculture, 1961).
[1] 1 hectare = 2.471 acres; 1 quintal = 100 kilograms = 220.46 pounds.

properties of a fully industrialized society that within the foreseeable future the increase in food production will exceed the greater demand arising from a larger population. Cochrane estimates that unrestricted food production in the developed countries coupled with a low and continuously lowering income elasticity of food could lead to surpluses of 43 billion dollars worth of food in 1980 and 126 billions in 2000 compared to a one billion dollar surplus in 1960.

Yet as huge as the surpluses would seem to be now, their distribution would only temporarily alleviate hunger. It was estimated that in 1962 the annual world deficit in wheat was 44 million tons; this is 120 percent of the annual wheat production in the United States (World Food Deficit). Surpluses of wheat in North America, which have been accumulating for several years, are of the same order of magnitude as the annual wheat deficit.

But the benefits of the present agriculture and food science are almost completely restricted to the developed countries. The less developed areas show little gain in yields of cereals over a twenty-year period (Table 17-3) and a reduction in production per capita. Techniques so successful in other areas are not carrying over at all, or rapidly enough.

Surely there are many reasons for failure of the less-developed countries to take advantage of existing knowledge and apply it to their special situations. The various elements we have mentioned are highly interactive. Better use of land, better use of fertilizer, availability and use of better varieties depends finally on the interpretation of all of these good practices by the farmer himself and this implies better training for farmers. Since the majority of the world population is engaged in farming, this is a huge educational problem; it is bound to be cumbersome and proceed slowly. Israel is cited by Cuthbertson as on outstanding exception; the level of agricultural practice has been raised through gigantic training efforts of the government and the people. As a result, thousands of trained farmers return annually to their settlements and farms equipped with the latest knowledge and information on the best agricultural practice.

And the reasons for lack of food in a world which has the technical capability of producing it will vary from region to region within a country, even as they vary from country to country. No doubt, bad political practice of land tenancy contributes in many areas; so does the practice of cutting up estates through inheritance. It may simply be the practice of considering cattle as currency or special treatment of cattle for religious reasons which interferes with their efficient utilization as sources of food. May, quoted in Chap. 16, summarized this complex of factors for one area of the world. And for every local situation there are good local reasons, not necessarily related to science and technology, which mitigate against a greater rate of improvement in food procurement. It would not be difficult to conclude that it is not science or technology which is limiting, but local customs, politics, prejudices, inadequacies, illiteracies. One gets the impression that if it were possible somehow to wipe out all of these difficulties and come to grips with the problem only as one of food production, then there would no longer be any deficiencies nor no longer any differences between the developing and the developed countries.

But there are reasons to believe, or to suspect, that it is not quite so simple a diagnosis. Underlying the local traditional-cultural-religious factors, there is one basic requirement which mitigates against solution of the problem of malnutrition in the same manner as it is now solved in the developed countries: this is the problem of cost. Theoretically, it should be possible to increase the world production of foodstuffs, and particularly animal foodstuffs, to take care of present and anticipated populations—but at a price. Tractors are required for opening new lands to production, and tractors require money and an industrial economy; May states that tractor production in China is not likely to reach the required needs for several years to come.

Four tons of coal are required for production of one ton of nitrogen. According to Lord Fleck (in Russell and Wright, *Hunger*), this is equivalent to $1\frac{1}{2}$ tons of oil, 60,000 cubic feet of natural gas, or 17,000 kilowatthours of electricity. Even though the electrical generating power in India is increasing, there are many claimants for this power, and only a proportion can be set aside for fertilizer production.

India's goal for March 1966 was an annual production capacity of 800,000 tons of nitrogen in fertilizer products; the best estimate is that it will reach 500,000 tons; the requirements for 1970 are put at two million tons annually.

Water is required for irrigation, but water either from wells or by new watershed control requires large outlays of capital. The theoretical minimum energy requirement for converting sea water to fresh water is estimated at 2.9 kilowatthours per 1,000 gallons. Present processes require many times this amount.

Insecticides and fungicides can control damage to plants and animals, but they are expensive, and require an industrial output to supply the wealth for their purchase or for their manufacture.

It is interesting to contemplate the cost of achieving improvement in health as against increasing food supplies. Even if the cost of research for both of these developments is borne completely by the developed countries, as has been done, the application of the information in practice requires a different approach. In health and medicine, it is a small number of well-trained people using a small amount of material (albeit expensive) who can eradicate a disease or control it. But large quantities of bulk material are required to improve the food situation, and this cannot be provided by gifts, as a permanent solution. Improvements in food production require the cooperative efforts not only of many trained people from the developed countries, but of the majority of the people in the recipient countries. It is for this reason, we believe, more than any other, that improvements in health have gone so much faster than improvements in food. It is for this reason that one may question whether it is possible rapidly enough to achieve eradication of malnutrition and undernutrition by the same techniques as are practiced by the developed countries.

Japan is an example of a nation which in a short period of several decades has managed to revolutionize its food supply and its food picture. In this instance customs of long standing were modified. But more important, a serious effort was made to build an industrial economy which could support food imports and a more sophisticated food science and technology. Even so, although the nutritional level of the Japanese is superior to many of their neighbors, their diet contains a considerably lesser proportion of animal protein than prevails in the Western countries. It is an example, therefore, of a concentrated effort to change ideas of food, to increase the industrial and economic output, and to raise the sophistication of food science. This effort has succeeded, but has not approached the Western standards.

A modest diet supplying 2100 Calories and 10–12 grams of animal protein per person per day at 1953 retail prices cost the average factory worker in India, Italy, Denmark, and the United States 2.1, 1.1, 0.3, and 0.2 hours, respectively (FAO, 1957). In Western societies a truck driver earns enough money in five to ten minutes to buy a liter of milk; two hours' effort at the same level is required in India to earn the same amount of milk (UNICEF). These are ways of portraying the relationship between industrial efficiency and output, and cost of food as hours of labor.

## Adjustment to Lower Agricultural Potential

Lord Russell graded the various parts of the world on the basis of availability of cultivated land per head of population. Those countries which possess more than 2½ acres per head are able to exist on a full animal protein diet, and even produce a surplus for export. Such include North and parts of South America, Australia, New Zealand, and parts of Soviet Europe. Those countries which possess one to 2½ acres per head, such as Western and Central Europe, are almost wholly, or certainly nearly, self-sufficient on a mixed dietary, i.e., on a mixed animal and vegetable dietary. Countries which have less than one acre per head can survive on a mixed dietary—one containing a substantial amount of animal protein—but they must import food. This group includes the United Kingdom, Belgium, Holland, and Switzerland. Others are close to self-sufficiency on a physiologically adequate, although monotonous, vegetarian dietary.

Even for those countries which have been affording at least a mixed animal-vegetable diet, their increasing population decreases the availability of land per person. The cost of food is increasing. Russell questions whether the prevailing pattern of food in the United Kingdom can continue to be maintained at the present expenditure of hardly 20 percent of the total personal income. The question, then, is: What percentage of the total income is society willing to spend for food, and what other elements of the standard of living is it willing to exchange for the more expensive food?

It is clear that there is not one road to adequacy, that a diet based on a full animal protein economy, however delicious and delectable, and however easy to compound in a nutritious way, is not the only way of achieving sufficiency. Perhaps this is the ultimate, what all societies will want to achieve, but it is not the only approach to sufficiency, and is certainly the most expensive. In intermediate stages of development it might be desirable to consider means for increasing the vegetable protein component without impinging on the sensibilities of the human and his desire for a pleasing and interesting dietary.

### SELECTED BIBLIOGRAPHY

Allen, L. E. "Fish Flour Production in Chile," *Fishing News International*, January 1963.
Bouillene, R. "Man, the Destroying Biotype," *Science*, vol. 135, (1962), p. 706.
Clark, Colin. "Future Sources of Food Supply; Economic Problems," *J. Roy. Statist. Soc.*, vol. 125, part 3, series A, (1962), p. 418.
Cochrane, W. W. "The World Food Budget: A Forward Look to 2000 and Beyond," in *Proceedings World Food Forum*, May 15, 1962. Washington, D. C.: U. S. Dept. of Agriculture (1963), p. 86.
Coleman, R. "World Fertilizer Requirements," *Chem. Eng. News*, December 2, 1963, p. 84.

Combs, G. F. "Quality and Quantity of Final Product, Poultry," *Federation Proc.*, vol. 20, no. 1, part III, supp. 7 (1961), p. 306.

Cuthbertson, D. P. "Food and the Future," *J. Franklin Inst.* vol. 261 (1956), p 121.

Dajoz, R. "Insect Pest Control," *Impact Sci. Soc.*, vol. 11 (1961), p. 257.

DeMaeyer, E. M. "Nutrition in the Congo," *Nutr. Rev.*, vol. 20 (1962), p. 225.

DeVries, E. "Food Production Trends in Selected Countries," in *Proceedings World Food Forum*, May 15, 1962, p. 79.

"FAO Index Numbers of Food Production by Countries," *Monthly Bulletin of Agricultural Economics and Statistics*, vol. 11, no. 4 (1962), p. 14.

*Fertilizers, An Annual Review of World Production, Consumption, and Trade.* Rome: Food and Agriculture Organization of the United Nations, 1960.

Finn, D. B. *Fish, The Great Potential Food Supply.* World Food Problems No. 3. Rome, Italy: Food and Agriculture Organization of the United Nations, 1960.

Guha, S. *India's Food Problem.* New Delhi: Indian National Congress, 1957.

McElroy, W. D. "The Promise of the Sea," *Johns Hopkins Magazine*, vol. 12, no. 8 (May-June 1961), p. 21.

"India's Fertilizer Output May Not Meet Goal," *Chem. Eng. News*, July 1, 1963, p. 48.

*Man and Hunger.* World Food Problems, No. 2. Rome: Food and Agriculture Organization of the United Nations, 1957.

Masefield, G. B. "Population Increase: A Possible Effect on Crop Yields." *World Crops*, vol. 15 (1963), p. 135.

Mrak, E. M. "Foods and Chemicals," *Borden's Review of Nutrition Research*, vol. 23, no. 2 (April-June 1962), p. 21.

May, J. M. and J. S. Jarcho, *The Ecology of Malnutrition in the Far and Near East.* New York: Hafner, 1961.

Morrison, A. B., Z. I. Sabry, and E. J. Middleton. "Factors Influencing the Nutritional Value of Fish Flour," *J. Nutr.*, vol. 77 (1962), p. 97.

Olden, J. H. "Fish Flour for Human Consumption," *Comm. Fisheries Rev.*, vol. 22, no. 1 (1960), p. 12.

Ovington, J. D. (ed.). *The Better Use of the World's Fauna for Food.* London: The Institute of Biology, 1963.

Pawley, W. H. *Possibilities of Increasing World Food Production.* Basic Study No. 10. Rome, Italy: Food and Agriculture Organization of the United Nations, 1963.

Pirie, N. W. "Future Sources of Food Supply: Scientific Problems," *J. Roy. Statist. Soc.*, vol. 125, part 3, series A (1962), p. 399.

*Population and Food Supply.* Basic Study No. 7. New York: United Nations, Office of Public Information, 1962.

Russell, E. J. *World Population and World Food Supplies.* London: Allen and Unwin, 1954.

Russell, E. J., and N. C. Wright (eds.). *Hunger: Can It Be Averted?* London: British Association for the Advancement of Science, 1961.

Sen, B. R. *The Basic Freedom—Freedom from Hunger*. Rome, Italy: Food and Agriculture Organization of the United Nations, 1960.

Shaw, B. T. "Prospective World Production and Distribution of Food," *Federation Proc.*, vol. 20, no. 1, part III, supp. 7 (1961), p. 373.

Sinha, R. P. *Food in India*. Bombay: Oxford U. P., 1961.

Stamp, L. D. *Asia, A Regional and Economic Geography*. 11th ed. London: Methuen, 1962.

Sweeney, G. C., Jr. "World Fertilizer Production," *Chem. Eng. News*, December 2, 1963, p. 89.

Tauber, A. "Social and Economic Aspects of World Food Production," *Impact Sci. Soc.*, vol. 12, no. 1 (1962), p. 39.

UNICEF. *Compendium*, Vol. 7. 2d ed. New York: United Nations Children's Fund, 1961.

*World Food Deficit, A First Approximation*. Foreign Agricultural Service. Washington, D. C.: U. S. Dept. of Agriculture, March 1961.

# CHAPTER 18

# Vegetable Protein Concentrates

## Attitudes toward Vegetable Proteins

If there is to be less of animal proteins then the deficiency must be made up with vegetable proteins. A good part of the world is already on a diet based on vegetable proteins. A poor man's diet in China consisting entirely of vegetable sources of protein was described in an earlier chapter as adequate, but monotonous. Although it is generally conceded that vegetable protein diets are cheaper than those involving large proportions of animal protein, any suggestions for increasing the importance of vegetables as a source of protein are not popular as an ultimate goal and are generally opposed by those who are concerned with improving the world food situation.

Wright (in *Hunger*, p. 11) presents the brief against worldwide adoption of vegetarian diets. He admits that the production of animal products is a wasteful process—at least 6/7 of the available calories in the plant are lost thereby; and even though the weight of the world's animal population is about twice the whole human race, domesticated animals eat at least five to ten times the amount of food consumed by man. However, Wright contends that domesticated animals do not in general compete with man for the same plant nutrients. They are great consumers of grass and grass products, and in Africa and the Far East graze on natural herbage. Moreover, these livestock are consumers of inedible by-products such as milling offals and straw, *the inedible cake and meal of oilseeds,* pulp and leaves of economic plants—all these are not used or useful to the human being. His telling argument, however, is that by passage through the animal the proteins of plants are not only improved in quality but are concentrated and converted into a more readily available form than in the plant. Whereas the protein content of grass ranges from 10 to 20 percent, that of milk, cheese, eggs, and meat ranges from 30 to 50 percent. And in this process of concentration and conversion, trace elements such as minerals and vitamins are also concentrated. Wright concludes with the following:

> In view of the universal tendency for populations to increase the proportion of animal products in their diet as they progress from poverty to plenty (itself surely an unconscious indication of the nutritional need for such products), it would appear inconceivable to expect the countries of North America and Europe to reverse a trend which has developed over a century or more — to revert, for example, in Britain to the dietary pattern of the 1850's.

Bigwood stated that to achieve the proper balance of the overall diet of a population by meeting the larger proportion of its calorie requirement with food of animal origin is an expensive proposition both physiologically and economically, because domestic animals convert only 10 to 20 percent of the calories of the foodstuffs which they consume. Covering the human requirements with staples of vegetable origin alone, however, cannot be done without prejudice to the proper balance of protective nutrients which require fresh vegetables and fruits, themselves expensive. He contends that a diet adequately balanced in all nutrients is more easily obtained from foods of both vegetable and animal origin, than from purely vegetarian diets alone.

Sinha, in discussing prospects for self-sufficiency in India, rejects all-vegetarian diets or vegetarian diets with milk as being too costly. He considers the cheapest diet in terms of land requirement as one in which animal protein is provided by fish and eggs. Such a diet would require 0.43 hectares of land, would provide 2820 Calories and 92 grams of protein per person per day, and would be generally adequate in supply of minerals and vitamins. Sinha, too, speaks of the residues of oilseed cakes as inedible and suitable only for feeding to cattle. We mention this point and have italicized the equivalent statement by Wright because we wish to return to it.

## Relative Cost of Animal and Plant Proteins

It might be well to summarize some of what is known about the relative cost of protein from animal and vegetable sources. Some examples are given in terms of protein, and in others the comparison is with animal as against vegetable products.

Yield of protein per acre is one measure of relative cost; some comparable figures are given in Table 18-1. It should be remembered that yield of protein is not the entire story; other nutrients furnished by each crop must also be put in the balance. For these comparative purposes, we shall assume that the other nutrients will be forthcoming from other sources and that the most expensive and critical item is protein. Animals provide the smallest yield of protein, grasses and leaves the largest. Figures for the latter are as yet academic since methods for obtaining isolated protein suitable for human consumption from leaves and grasses are still being developed. (See, however, Pirie.)

MacGillivray and Bosley calculated that soybeans produce 7.1 times more available amino acids per acre than milk and 8.2 times more than eggs. In terms of the average pounds of amino acid per acre, the soybean produces close

# TABLE 18-1

## Production of Protein from Various Animal and Plant Crops

| Farm Product | Source of Protein | Edible Protein, Pounds per Acre per Year | Supply for Moderately Active Man,[3] Days per Acre |
| --- | --- | --- | --- |
| Forage and grain fed to steers | Beef | 43[1] | 77 |
|  | Beef | 54[2] |  |
|  | Hogs |  | 129 |
|  | Eggs |  | 188 |
| Forage and silage fed to cows | Milk | 77[1] | 236 |
|  | Milk | 90[2] |  |
|  | Wheat | 269[2] | 527 |
|  | Legumes | 370[2] |  |
|  | Soybeans | 450[1] | 1,116 |
|  | Dry edible beans |  |  |
| Alfalfa | As extracted protein | 500[1] |  |
| Grass | As extracted protein | 500[2] |  |
| Irrigated alfalfa | As extracted protein | 1,500[1] |  |

Sources: 1. H. Brown, J. Bonner, and J. Weir, The Next Hundred Years (New York: Viking, 1957), p. 71.
2. S. Kuppuswamy, M. Srinivasan and V. Subrahmanyan, Proteins in Foods (New Delhi: Indian Council of Medical Research, 1958).
3. R. P. Christensen, Efficient Use of Food Resources in the United States, Tech. Bull. No. 963 (Washington, D. C.: U. S. Department of Agriculture, October 1948).

to 17 pounds per acre, compared to about two for milk and less than one for beef.

The lower yield of protein from animals is evident from their efficiency as converters of calories and proteins; the range of protein conversion is 10–32 percent of the protein equivalents fed and 7 to 19 percent of the calories fed. There are, of course, improvements in conversion efficiency—witness Combs in Chap. 17. But there is an upper limit built into animals, determined by the need to support their own life processes and to synthesize nonedible proteins such as skin, wool, and feathers.

Stamp (in *Hunger*) compares the efficiency of vegetable and animal sources of food in terms of a unit of one million Calories of farm output per year which would provide a reasonable standard of food for one person. A meat- and milk-based diet may require as much as 3½ acres to produce one Standard Nutrition Unit; this would provide close to 2500 Calories per day for one person. A wheat bread-based diet requires only a quarter of an acre, while six to seven Standard Nutrition Units of a rice-and-beans diet in Japan are produced per acre. Therefore, depending upon the type of diet, the capacity of the land to support a population ranges from 20 to 1.

Tauber defines animal and plant calories as follows: an animal must consume seven plant calories in order to produce one calorie's worth of human food. On this basis he compared the cost in terms of plant calories of diets in two countries: one which provides only 10 percent of animal calories, whereas the other contains 35 percent. In the first country which provides 2,025 Calories per person per day, of which 10 percent are animal calories, this amounts to a total of 3,240 plant Calories per person per day. In the country which provides 3,140 Calories, of which 35 percent are animal calories, this is equivalent to a total of 9,734 plant Calories per person per day. This means that the diet of a person in the second country contains three times more agricultural products than that of someone in the first country.

Bonner proposed an estimate of the total number of people supportable on the earth. The most generous estimate was 50 billion, but in order to do this, all animal protoplasm would be replaced by human protoplasm. One could not afford the luxury of maintaining pigs or cows, or horses, or dogs—all edible material would have to go down the throats of hungry people. If, instead, one had a less intensive food economy, equivalent perhaps to the one of Japan, this would support 16 billion people, but this would require that the present level of Japanese agricultural activity be spread over the whole world and that there be an increase of about 50 percent in the total food production. This program would still require that all the population agree to a primarily vegetarian diet. A population of eight to ten billion people could be supported under a food production program characterized by the efficiency of Japan spread over all of Asia and by the efficiency of Western Europe spread over all the rest of the world, and by expanding the agricultural acreage by 50 percent. Nowhere in his estimate does he conceive of a situation in which the entire world would be supported on the basis of the present Western European efficiency and food habits.

Perhaps one of the most interesting comparisons between diets based on vegetable and animal proteins is in terms of water, itself a commodity of ever-increasing scarcity. Bradley compares the cost of a diet of 2½ pounds of bread a day as against one which contains one pound of animal fat and protein as beef and two pounds of vegetable food as bread per day. The all-vegetable regimen would require 300 gallons of water per person per day; the mixed animal and vegetable diet requires 2,500 gallons. For food alone, the cost of maintaining one human being is somewhere between 300 and 2,500 gallons of water per day. The cost of water per pound of meat is about 25 times that of the cost for a pound of vegetables.

No matter how it is analyzed, there is no question that the cost of animal products is materially greater than the cost of vegetable products. Despite this realization and general admission, we find an almost universal lack of enthusiasm for considering seriously programs for increasing the contribution of vegetables to the daily protein intake. It is obvious, therefore, that cost alone is not the answer; that food not only must be inexpensive but must be in the form suitable for utilization by the human; that the protein must be in high enough concentration and of good quality; that there must be the adequate amount of trace elements; above and beyond that, the food must be attractive and must include the possibility for sufficient variation to counteract monotony.

## Some Disabilities of Plant Proteins

Animal proteins have the virtue of fitting in perfectly in a diet based primarily on cereals. They occur in high concentration, from 20 to 90 percent of the dry matter, hence they may easily complement cereals to produce diets adequate in protein content; they are of high quality—it is well-nigh impossible to formulate a cereal-based diet that would be inadequate in protein quality if a substantial amount of the protein is from animal sources. (There are some exceptions; gelatin, for example.) They contain many vitamins and minerals. The animal is a filter—toxic constituents in his plant foods are eliminated and not found in the animal's flesh itself. Animal protein products provide the condiments for good taste and flavor, and exist in many forms, which mitigate against monotony.

Conversely, naturally occurring vegetable sources of protein have disadvantages where the animal sources list advantages. They are usually not high enough in protein concentration and often not adequate in quality. They are deficient in certain vitamins, and in some instances put a strain on the requirement for minerals. Many plant products contain factors which interfere with growth. In general, these differ for each seed or source of plant protein: cottonseed has its gossypol; soybean has a number of growth inhibitors, some known, others unknown; castor bean contains ricin and allergens; other seeds contain glycosides which release cyanide and other inhibitors.

Certain species of legumes have long been known to contain interfering materials. It is said that Pythagoras was being pursued by the people of Croton until he came to a field of beans whereupon he halted, saying that he would rather be taken than set foot in the field. And so he was slain. Pythagoras forbade his disciples to eat beans or even to walk among beans. Arie suggests that Pythagoras suffered from "favism," a hemolytic anemia which occurs in certain people after ingestion of or contact with pollen or products of the broad bean, *Vicia faba*. This syndrome exists with rare exception only in the Mediterranean basin and is particularly prevalent in isolated communities of long standing—in Sardinia and Calabria, and among the Jews from Iraq.

Lathyrism is another disease associated with the consumption of legumes. A graphic description of this syndrome in India in the 1830s is provided by General Sleeman. In 1829 and again in 1831 the wheat crop failed in Sangor and the inhabitants subsisted mainly on *Lathyrus sativus* which grew wild in the blighted wheat fields. By 1833 the younger part of the population of this area began to be deprived of the use of their limbs below the waist by paralytic strokes. None attacked recovered the use of their limbs.

Selye has distinguished at least two distinct syndromes in lathyrism: one which he named "osteolathyrism" because it involves skeletal changes and the other "neurolathyrism" because of nervous derangement associated with this type. It has been established that ingestion of nitriles such as $\beta$-amino propionitrile or $\beta$-(N-$\gamma$-L-glutamyl)-amino propionitrile cause the former type and that $\alpha$, $\gamma$-diaminobutyric acid is a neurotoxin. Thus naturally occurring compounds related to amino acids and found in seeds of *Lathyrus* species can cause diseases in experimental animals similar to those found clinically. Evidence is accumulating that nitriles interfere with normal collagen synthesis.

And there are other toxic factors in seeds—hemagglutinins among them. Liener isolated such heat-labile fractions from seeds of *Phaseolus vulgaris*. Some of the toxic factors are destroyed by heat and others are removed by soaking in water. But unless something is done, many of these plant products are not suitable in their natural state as food for humans, and often also to animals. More than ever, we can appreciate the "filtering capacity" of animals.

There is the paucity of forms and flavors. All-vegetarian diets are rated as monotonous; they are not as pleasing as animal dishes, and they do not have the status of animal-based diets.

If one takes into account all of these considerations, then perhaps there is some justification for lack of enthusiasm for vegetarian diets, based on present practices. Perhaps it is too naïve even to have thought that one could substitute vegetable sources of protein as they exist, with only minor modifications, for animal sources.

## Possibilities for Processed Plant Proteins

It is obvious that when we speak of a possible greater role for vegetable proteins, we must refer to *processed* plant proteins. We must have in mind modifications which will transform natural plant materials into entirely new forms approaching, if not equaling or surpassing, animal proteins in suitability. Just as the animal can convert inferior plant sources into highly suitable protein, so must we conceive of man-designed processes for doing the same job. In this context, the listing of all the undesirable attributes and the careful identification of toxic components becomes an asset;

## TABLE 18–2

### World Production of Some Plant Protein Sources[1]

| Commodity | Annual Production,[2] Thousands of Metric Tons | Year[3] | Average Protein Content,[4,5] Percent | Average Available Protein Annually, Thousands of Metric Tons |
|---|---|---|---|---|
| | | *Cereals* | | |
| Wheat | 235,900 | 1960–1961 | 14.3 | 33,700 |
| Rice (paddy) | 239,500 | | 7.5 | 18,000 |
| Corn (maize) | 211,300 | | 10.4 | 22,000 |
| Barley | 87,900 | | 13.1 | 11,500 |
| Small grains, (millet, sorghum, others) | 71,000 | 1960–1961 | 12.0 | 8,600 |
| Oats | 54,580 | | 13.1 | 7,100 |
| Rye | 36,310 | | 13.4 | 4,900 |
| | | | Cereals total | 105,800 |
| | | *Legumes* | | |
| Dry beans | 9,100 | 1960–61 | | |
| Chickpeas | 7,600 | | 26 | 7,410 |
| Dry peas | 6,600 | | | |
| Dry broad beans | 4,500 | | | |
| Lentils | 770 | | | |
| | | *Oilseeds* | | |
| | | 1960 | | |
| Soybeans | 31,300 | | 38 | 11,900 |
| Cottonseed | 20,400 | | 20 | 4,000 |
| Peanuts (groundnuts), shelled | 10,364 | | 25 | 2,652 |
| Sunflower seed | 6,840 | | 15 | 990 |
| Sesame | 1,400 | | 25 | 350 |
| | | | Oilseeds total | 19,892 |

[1] There is a variation in protein content of the commodities depending on variety and growing conditions. The figures that are listed, therefore, are significant only as a basis for calculating an order of magnitude of protein supplies; the original references should be consulted for more details on composition.

[2] *Monthly Bulletin of Agricultural Economics and Statistics* (Rome, Italy: Food and Agriculture Organization, United Nations).

[3] Unless otherwise noted, the production figures are for the season 1961–62.

[4] Nitrogen $\times$ 6.25.

*Sources:* A. M. Altschul (ed.), *Processed Plant Protein Foodstuffs* (New York: Academic, 1958); R. S. Harris and H. von Loesecke (eds.), *Nutritional Evaluation of Food Processing* (New York: Wiley, 1960); D. Harvey, *Tables of the Amino Acids in Foods and Feedingstuffs* (Farnham Royal, Slough, Buckinghamshire: Commonwealth Agricultural Bureau, 1956); S. Kuppuswamy, M. Srinivasan, and V. Subrahmanyan, *Proteins in Foods* (New Delhi: Indian Council of Medical Research, 1958); *Composition of Cereal Grains and Forages*, Publication 585 (Washington, D. C.: National Academy of Sciences-National Research Council, 1958); J. C. Abbott, personal communication, 1964.

it provides the information for the blueprint of processing. The problem before us is to determine whether this is a quixotic notion or one which on the basis of past experience and altogether reasonable projections has attainable practical reality.

Table 18-2 lists the various amounts of proteins available from cereal grains, from oilseeds, and from legumes. This does not exhaust the amount of protein available from vegetable sources, but lists the major sources. The main supply of proteins, of course, comes from the cereal grains; the major ones supply over 100 million metric tons of protein annually. Twenty million tons of protein are supplied from animal sources (see Chap. 16); this is approximately equal to the total amount of protein available from oilseeds. To the supply of vegetable protein we may add another seven million tons or so available from legumes. The main point in this table is that if the proteins of the oilseeds could be utilized in the same manner as the proteins of animal products, an amount of protein at least equal to the present animal protein supply would be made available for human consumption without further increase in agricultural production.

Let us now consider perhaps the major disability of vegetable sources of protein: their lesser protein concentration. Although some seeds approach animal products in protein concentration, soybeans approaching the closest, none of the rest, as harvested, contain sufficient protein concentration to allow them to be substituted directly for animal sources. As was pointed out in Chap. 2, however, oilseeds have the virtue that concentration of the proteins is achieved simply by removal of oil. Further concentration comes from removal of carbohydrate and fiber. In Table 18-3 are listed the oil and protein content of some representative oilseeds and of oilseed protein concentrates. Protein concentrations of 50 percent and higher are relatively easily achieved by removal of oil and fiber; protein concentrations approaching 100 percent are achieved either by complete removal of carbohydrate or by isolation of the protein from the other constituents of the seed. The first difficulty, that of concentration, is fairly easily overcome by standard processing operations carried out on oilseeds. Even in ancient times the orientals recognized this possibility when they prepared products from soybeans which contained at least 50 percent protein.

Once they become available through processing, plant protein concentrates could be added to primarily cereal diets to raise the protein content to an adequate level. We have learned (see Chaps. 7–10) that inadequacy in quality, e.g., ingestion of proteins of lower biological value, can be compensated up to a point by eating more of the poorer protein. Dean states that the question of the quality of protein is secondary in importance to the amount of total proteins. In his experience no disease of man is known that can be attributed to an amino acid deficiency, but there seems to be little doubt that in many parts of the world young children, and possibly adults, suffer from protein deficiency. Nevertheless it is important to achieve the best protein quality possible even if only for the sake of economy in total amount of protein required.

A glance at the amino acid compositions of a number of protein sources given in Table 18-4 shows that, in fact,

## TABLE 18-3

### Oil and Protein Content of Some Oilseeds and Oilseed Protein Concentrates[1]

| Material | Oil, Percent | Protein, Percent (N×6.25) | Hulls, Percent | Fiber, Percent |
|---|---|---|---|---|
| Soybean | 20 | 38–43 | 8 | 2–3 |
| Protein concentrate (lipid and hulls removed) | 1 | 50–54 | | 3 |
| Protein concentrate (lipid, hulls, and carbohydrate removed) | 1 | 72–74 | | |
| Protein (isolated from low fat protein concentrate) | 1 | 93 | | 0.7 |
| Tofu (curd from whole soybeans) | 29 | 50 | | 0.7 |
| Cottonseed | 18 | 18–20 | 37 | 1–2 |
| Protein concentrate (lipid reduced and hulls removed) | 2–6 | 55–58 | | |
| Peanut (groundnut) | 46–52 | 25–30 | | 3 |
| Protein concentrate (lipid reduced) | 0.5–10 | 50–66 | | 2–3 |
| Protein (isolated from low fat protein concentrate) | 1 | 95 | | 2–3 |
| Protein (isolated from whole kernels, "lipoprotein") | 33 | 65 | | |
| Protein (isolated from whole kernels) | 9 | 85 | | |
| Sesame | 50 | 25 | | 4 |
| Protein concentrate (lipid reduced) | 7 | 46 | | 5.3 |

Source: A. M. Altschul, "Seed Proteins and World Food Problems," Economic Botany, vol. 16, no. 1 (1962), p. 2. See also Table 2-1.
[1] Dry basis.

## TABLE 18-4

### Essential Amino Acid Composition of Some Food Proteins

| Amino Acid | FAO Pattern | ANIMAL | | | CEREAL | | | | OILSEEDS AND OTHERS | | | | |
|---|---|---|---|---|---|---|---|---|---|---|---|---|---|
| | | Whole Egg | Cow's Milk | Beef Muscle | Wheat | Rice | Corn | Millet* | Soy-bean | Cotton-seed | Pea-nuts | Broad bean, Vicia faba | Barley leaves |
| | | | | | *Mg Amino Acid per G Nitrogen* | | | | | | | | |
| Isoleucine | 278 | 386 | 341 | 323 | 253 | 290 | 225 | 338 | 319 | 200 | 224 | 333 | 793 |
| Leucine | 305 | 564 | 620 | 488 | 409 | 501 | 717 | 594 | 483 | 362 | 407 | 438 | 381 |
| Lysine | 270 | 383 | 475 | 537 | 174 | 239 | 169 | 197 | 429 | 269 | 218 | 476 | |
| Methionine and cystine | 275 | 344 | 214 | 253 | 265 | 316 | 200 | 354 | 197 | 161 | 173 | 112 | 137 |
| Phenylalanine and tyrosine | 360 | 574 | 599 | 428 | 457 | 629 | 496 | 525 | 557 | 556 | 571 | 567 | 387 |
| Threonine | 180 | 309 | 280 | 278 | 192 | 235 | 225 | 241 | 269 | 213 | 171 | 284 | 212 |
| Tryptophan | 90 | 71 | 81 | 63 | 67 | 78 | 33 | 88 | 80 | 75 | 64 | 69 | 81 |
| Valine | 270 | 437 | 409 | 321 | 272 | 398 | 263 | 416 | 336 | 314 | 274 | 373 | 406 |
| *References* (p. 274) | | [1, 2] | [2, 3] | [1] | [2, 4] | [2, 4, 6] | [2, 5, 6] | [2] | [7] | [8, 4] | [2, 1, 9] | [2] | [10] |

° Ragi, *Eleusine coracana.*

*References:* Often there is not good agreement between several amino acid analyses of a commodity. One set of values for each commodity is listed; the reference for each is the first one listed at bottom of the column. Additional references are provided.

[1] J. B. Allison, "Biological Evaluation of Proteins," *Physiol. Rev.,* vol. 35 (1955), p. 664. See also *Trans. N. Y. Acad. of Sci.,* Ser. II, vol. 25, no. 3 (1963), p. 293.

[2] *Amino Acid Content of Foods,* Provisional (Rome, Italy: Food and Agriculture Organization of the United Nations, July 1963).

[3] A. E. Bender, "Determination of the Nutritive Value of Proteins by Chemical Analysis," in *Progress in Meeting Protein Needs of Infants and Children,* Publication 843 (Washington, D. C.: National Academy of Sciences–National Research Council, 1961), p. 407. The value of tyrosine is from D. Harvey, *Tables of the Amino Acids in Foods and Feedingstuffs* (Farnham Royal, Slough, Buckinghamshire, England: Commonwealth Agricultural Bureaux, 1956).

[4] E. E. Howe, "Summary of Progress on the Use of Purified Amino Acids in Foods," in *Progress in Meeting Protein Needs of Infants and Children, op. cit.,* p. 495.

[5] R. Bressani and N. S. Scrimshaw, "The Development of INCAP Vegetable Mixtures," *ibid.,* p. 35.

[6] Calculated from D. F. Miller, *Composition of Cereal Grains and Forages,* Publication 585 (Washington, D. C.: National Academy of Sciences-National Research Council, 1958).

[7] J. J. Rackis, R. L. Anderson, H. A. Sasame, A. K. Smith, and C. H. Van Etten, "Amino Acids in Soybean Hulls and Oil Meal Fractions," *J. Agr. Food Chem.,* vol. 9 (1961), p. 409.

[8] E. J. Bigwood, "Acides amines du lait de vache, de la viande de boeuf, des aliments pour bétail et du rumen," *Compt. Rend. Rech.,* no. 30 (May 1963), p 34. Institut pour l'Encouragement de la Recherche Scientifique dans l'Industrie et l'Agriculture, Brussels.

[9] M. N. Satyanarayana, M. V. L. Rao, M. Srinivasan, A. Sreenivasan, and V. Subrahmanyan, "Amino Acid Composition of Groundnut Protein Isolates," *Food Sci.* (Mysore), vol. 11, no. 5 (1962), p. 133.

[10] N. W. Pirie, "The Present Position and Future Needs of Research on Leaf Protein," in *Progress in Meeting Protein Needs of Infants and Children, op. cit.,* p. 509.

vegetable protein concentrates do complement the cereal proteins. Deficiencies of lysine in cereal proteins are compensated by soybean and pulse protein. Other amino acid deficiences are reduced if not eliminated in mixtures of vegetable proteins. Animals and humans, even young humans, have been fed completely vegetarian diets consisting of mixtures of cereal proteins and protein concentrates with no evidence of protein deficiencies, provided, of course, that vitamins and mineral deficiencies were compensated by adequate supplementation. Malnourished children have been cured on such diets. The nutriment is further improved by mixing several protein concentrates, e.g., soybean and cottonseed, or by supplementing with amino acids or with small quantities of animal protein. The evidence is impressive that sufficient protein content and adequacy of protein quality are achieved with mixtures of vegetable proteins.

We should comment on the concept of inedibility and, in particular, on the frequent reference to the residues after removal of oil from oilseeds as *inedible oilseed residues.* Inedibility is not an absolute condition. It is subject to change in the hands of human ingenuity. Sources of protein might be inedible either because of the presence of toxic minor components or because the protein and other major components are not digestible. But the toxic components can be removed or destroyed, and often indigestible proteins and carbohydrate materials can be rendered digestible by proper chemical or heat treatment. It is simply a matter of understanding, technology, and cost. There was a time when soybean meal could not be fed to monogastric animals. Yet now the residue after removal of oils from soybeans is the major source of proteins for poultry in the United States. The residue after removal of oil from cottonseed was at one time considered inedible even for cattle. Now hundreds of thousands of tons of cottonseed meal are fed to poultry in the United States, let alone vaster amounts to cattle. One might be tempted to consider castor bean pomace as inedible, but even this might not be a secure concept because some day someone will learn how to remove or destroy the toxicity of ricin in the castor bean and how to measure the safety of the treated product. The classification of the twenty or more million tons of protein from soybean, cottonseed, peanuts, and the like as inedible may have been valid in the nineteenth century; but to maintain this position in the present day is not consistent with the practical realities.

Finally, the issue is not mostly animal protein versus all-vegetable protein. No one who has tasted or striven for animal products would voluntarily banish animals. We are discussing a spectrum of alternatives between these extremes, demanded by economic circumstances and circumscribed by constellations of human and social values. The issue is whether a reduction in the proportion of animal protein in a diet signifies, *pari passu,* a lowering of the standard of living in terms of nutrition, or interest, or aesthetics, or any other important human value. At this writing, it means just that. But perhaps it need not be so. Perhaps through processing it should be possible to create vegetable forms of protein which will satisfy equally as well all human needs. Then status in foods need not be limited to the animal and to the most expensive; cost and original source would not be the determining factors, rather the ability through modern technology to satisfy the human desire for good and interesting foods.

## SELECTED BIBLIOGRAPHY

Altschul, A. M. "Seed Proteins and World Food Problems," *Econ. Botany*, vol. 16 (1962), p. 2.

Arie, T. H. D. "Pythagoras and Beans," *Oxford Med. School Gaz.*, vol. 11 (1959), p. 75.

Bell, E. A. "α, γ-Diaminobutyric Acid in Seeds of Twelve Species of *Lathyrus* and Identification of a New Natural Amino Acid, L-Homoarginine in Seeds of Other Species Toxic to Man and Domestic Animals," *Nature*, vol. 193 (1962), p. 1078.

Bigwood, E. J. "Problems of Animal Nutrition in Underdeveloped Areas," *Federation Proc.*, vol. 20, part 3, supp. no. 7 (1961), p. 261.

Bird, G. W. G. "Haemagglutinins in Seeds," *Brit. Med. Bull.*, vol. 15 (1959), p. 165.

Bonner, J. "The World's Increasing Population," *Federation Proc.*, vol. 20, no. 1, part III, supp. no. 7 (1961), p. 369.

Bradley, C. C. "Human Water Needs and Water Use in America," *Science*, vol. 138 (1962), p. 489.

Dean, R. F. A. "Use of Processed Plant Proteins as Human Food," in A. M. Altschul (ed.), *Processed Plant Protein Foodstuffs*. New York: Academic, 1958.

Gardner, A. F. "Experimental Lathyrism — Review of the Literature," *Am. J. Clin. Nutr.*, vol. 7 (1959), p. 213.

Liener, I. E. "Toxic Factors in Edible Legumes and Their Elimination," *Am. J. Clin. Nutr.*, vol. 11 (1962), p. 281.

MacGillivray, J. H., and J. B. Bosley. "Amino Acid Production per Acre by Plants and Animals," *Econ. Botany*. vol. 16 (1962), p. 25.

Patwardhan, V. N. *Nutrition in India*. Bombay: Indian Journal of Medical Science, 1952.

Pirie, H. W. "The Present Protein Position and Future Needs of Research on Leaf Protein," in *Meeting Protein Needs of Infants and Children*, National Research Council Publication No. 843. Washington, D. C.: National Academy of Sciences-National Research Council, 1961.

Russell, E. J. *World Population and World Food Supplies*. London: Allen and Unwin, 1954.

Selye, H. "Lathyrism," *Rev. Can. Biol.,* vol. 16 (1957), p. 3.

Sinha, R. P. *Food in India.* London: Oxford U.P., 1961.

Sleeman, W. H. *Rambles and Recollections of an Indian Official.* Vol. 1. London: Hatchard, 1844.

Smith, D. J., and R. C. Shuster. "Biochemistry of Lathyrism. I: Collagen Biosynthesis in Normal and Lathyritic Chick Embryos," *Arch. Biochem. Biophys.,* vol. 98 (1962), p. 498.

Stamp, L. D. "Land Use and Food Production," in E. J. Russell and N. C. Wright (eds.), *Hunger: Can It Be Averted?* London: British Association for the Advancement of Science, 1961.

Tauber, A. "Social and Economic Aspects of World Food Production," *Impact Sci. So.,* vol. 12, no. 1 (1962), p. 39.

Wright, N. C. "The Current Food Supply Situation and Present Trends," in E. J. Russell and N. C. Wright (eds.), *Hunger: Can It Be Averted?* London: British Association for the Advancement of Science, 1961.

# CHAPTER 19

# Soybeans, Cottonseed, and Peanuts

## Soybeans

The foremost example of the possibilities and realities of vegetable protein concentrates is the soybean. This legume has a high protein concentration, among the highest of economic plants. Even without further modification, its content of close to 40 percent protein is sufficient to classify it as a natural vegetable protein concentrate. Protein may be concentrated further, first by removal of oil, second by removal of carbohydrate, and third by isolation, to yield products with protein concentrations ranging from 50 to close to 100 percent. (See Fig. 19-1.)

Raw soybeans cannot be fed to man and animals because they contain growth inhibitors of the type mentioned in previous chapters; but these are thermolabile: heating or toasting will overcome the growth-inhibiting effects. Heating also may destroy amino acids or reduce their availability. Hence it is necessary to achieve just the right amount of heat—enough to destroy the inhibitors but not enough to reduce protein value. A good compromise can be accomplished this way with soybeans; products so treated have a high biological value. Soybeans have more than

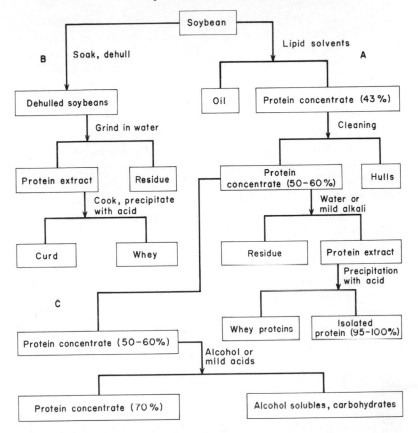

FIG. 19-1. Protein concentrates from soybeans.

enough lysine and therefore may be considered a source of supplementary lysine in mixtures with cereals. Mixtures of soybean and corn are adequate in lysine content, but are limiting in methionine. This limitation can be overcome by supplementing with methionine or by feeding more of the mixture.

There is a history of utilization of soybean protein concentrates by man, dating back at least to 2838 B.C. in China. In the form of partially isolated products, fermented, or sprouted derivatives, it has been a substantial source of protein in the Chinese diet for close to 5,000 years; in this manner was the problem of growth inhibitors handled—by fractionation or by fermentation. This might be considered the first stage of utilization of soybeans: the ancient technology. In modern times there has developed a second technology built around factory-processed soybean products. The majority of the soybeans are processed into protein concentrates with lipid removed, containing from 43 to over 50 percent protein—all heat-treated to destroy growth inhibitors. The great bulk of such protein concentrates are now produced for animal rations; there are also full-fat flours designed primarily for human food. But only a small proportion of soybean protein products is directed toward human consumption in the United States.

In recent years attempts to increase the proportion of processed soybean products incorporated in human foods have met with success. A program spearheaded by the American soybean industry has the objective of finding more ways for incorporating soybean products into a variety of national dietaries. Full cooperation has been obtained from the local authorities and institutions. For example, there is a project in Israel to develop diets containing soybean flour under the direction of the government group responsible for nutrition education. Various recipes are being tested for human appeal as well as nutritive value; and this effort is not limited to Israeli foods. Similarly, close American-Japanese cooperation has been achieved in finding more outlets for soybeans by both ancient and modern technologies.

Those responsible for the program do not feel that they have by any means reached the limit of incorporation of soybean products into human foods. Certainly, the products of the ancient technology can spread among populations having food habits closely related to those in China and Japan and other countries where soybean is already an established protein source. No one can foretell how far this development might extend into India and Southeastern Asia.

The more recent soybean products, full-fat and low-fat concentrates, are being reconstituted into protein drinks for children and are incorporated in local foods, in breads, in gruels, in pasta, and other products. The problem is to gain acceptance for a new foodstuff or a modified product enriched with soybean products; and this problem occurs even on the most primitive levels, because people are essentially conservative about new foods. Some of this resistance can be overcome by education and by introducing the new food at levels where it does not appreciably affect the color, taste, and appearance of the product. This is true of drinks, of gruels, and of salads; but there is a limit to the amount which can be added to more sophisticated foods such as pasta, breads, or tortillas. People who eat large quantities of these products daily have well-developed tastes and preferences and are sensitive to even minor changes in appearance and taste.

In addition to these cultural factors, there are nutritive factors which are of concern. Processed soybean products are variable in nutritive quality depending on the conditions of processing, for reasons which we have previously discussed. When the product is only a small proportion of a diet, otherwise adequate, this is no serious matter. But if it becomes a large proportion of the protein intake, then the quality of the protein is critical. Further widespread utilization of soybean concentrates will require achievement of a high degree of reproducibility in the quality of the product, more uniform than now exists. More and more of this is being done, but further uniformity at a high nutritive level depends in part on information not yet available. There is needed further knowledge about the inhibitors and their removal. Simple and rapid measurements are needed to test the quality chemically. These would become part of specifications of products to be fed to humans, safely and with good nutritive performance. These could ensure uniformity of quality. Most scientists agree, however, that the problem of developing methods of measuring protein quality in soybean products is by no means settled satisfactorily.

Even with the limitations, cultural and nutritional, soybeans remain a bright spot in the potential for increasing protein supplies and are available today for millions who do not use them only for lack of proper information, who lack confidence in their usefulness based wholly on ignorance of the successes in human and animal nutrition with soybean protein concentrates.

Is it possible to delineate the absolute limit of incorporation of soybean products in food, not in terms of total amount, but in terms of kinds of uses? We have brought out one limitation: the point at which soybean products change the taste and appearance of familiar and popular foods. But such limitations of the present-day soybean protein concentrates need not be limitations of the soybeans themselves. One must consider the possibility that other types of soybean products would overcome some of the difficulties of acceptance in terms of flavor, color, and odor. An oil-free soybean protein concentrate can be extracted further by alcohol or mild acid to remove the soluble carbohydrates, yielding a product with 70 percent protein which is free of many of the flavors in the original material. This product still has to be heat-treated to destroy the inhibitors, but it should be possible to incorporate it more easily and at higher levels into many food products for which there now exists a real taste limitation.

There is a more fundamental difficulty. The soybean products of the modern technology are at best additives to a diet. They are flours which can be added to other ingredients to modify foodstuffs or food forms in the direction of increased nutritive value. But they themselves cannot, in their present form, be a major component of a meal. In this respect some of the products of the ancient technology may have the advantage. Bean sprouts, some of the fermented products of whole soybeans, or perhaps some of the derivatives of curds have shape and form; they perhaps can be a major item on the plate. We are dealing here with a difficult concept—with the concept of monotony, of interest, and with the reasons why people naturally prefer animal products when they can get them. It is true that animal products have a high nutritive value; but other reasons for being preferred are in the field of aesthetics, in taste and form and flavor, and in the ability to create from the animal products portions around which the entire meal can be designed. This is a fundamental limitation of soybean products and of all protein concentrates of vegetable origin which seek to serve as major sources of protein and hence to become major items on the table. It is probably for this reason that diets based on vegetable sources of protein are considered monotonous and those containing animal products of higher status and interest.

As we related earlier, the prevailing opinion is that this is an inviolate relationship—that animal protein products will always be superior and more desirable, of higher status, and the envy of those who cannot afford them. While it is not considered unlikely that nations in time, as the population increases, will have to resort to decreasing the proportion of animal products in the diet, this move is generally considered tantamount to lowering the standard of living, of substitution of foods of lower status for the more desirable foods.

To insist on the permanent inferiority of vegetable proteins is to deny the progress in the understanding of flavors, taste, appearance, texture, feel, sound on chewing—all factors which together make for food acceptance or rejection. So many different flavors are available to modify the taste of a product. So much more is known about conditions which arouse a desire to eat more, which create interest and about those which promote satiety. There are so many ways of overcoming monotony and these have been applied successfully to many food products. The protein problem is not the only one to contend with monotony. Every day in the marketplace products compete for the housewife's fancy, not on the basis of nutrition or cost, but on appearance, taste, attractiveness—antidotes to monotony. New food forms are required for space feeding; monotony must be eliminated there as elsewhere.

Isolated seed proteins such as those from the soybean, peanut, or cottonseed, and no doubt other seeds, can be extruded in fiber-forming equipment into long threads or fibers. (See Fig. 19-2.) This is not a general property of

FIG. 19-2. Photograph of fibers of edible soybean protein.°
°Courtesy of Ralston-Purina Co.

proteins, nor is it a unique property of seed proteins. Insulin, for example, can be drawn out into fibrils. Nevertheless, this is an important property which makes it possible to create the basis for structure. Patents are extent and products have been made on a pilot-plant scale with the structural properties of meat products. One can now imitate the flavor, appearance, and structure (and chewiness) of ham, chicken, and other meat materials starting with isolated soybean protein; and no doubt new forms can be created. Here then is a new dimension in vegetable protein concentrates and their incorporation in human diets; and this is a dimension which differs from the ancient semi-isolation process which is prevalent in the Far East. Here is the beginning of a third era of plant protein technology: the exploitation of modern technology for the creation of new forms. While this achievement is yet at a primitive level, one can even now appreciate the enormous possibilities of this approach. There are several companies in the United States manufacturing isolated and concentrated soybean protein. There are plants in various parts of the world experimenting with isolation and modification of soybean protein. This is not a vision nor a dream, but a development under serious consideration.

One of the serious present disadvantages of these isolated and highly concentrated proteins is their cost. Even soybean protein concentrates of 50 percent protein are considered expensive by many peoples who ordinarily spend their money on cheaper foodstuffs, far inferior and actually insufficient as a source of protein. This unwillingness to pay for nutrition must be overcome by education; people must learn that they need a certain amount of protein, that the slight increase in cost which comes from including a good vegetable protein concentrate must be afforded as an absolute minimum. But the higher concentrates and isolates cost much more on protein basis (Table 19-1). More of these

## TABLE 19-1

### Cost of Protein in Some Soybean Protein Fractions[1]

| Fraction | Protein Content % | Cost, pennies/lb. | Cost of protein, pennies/lb. |
|---|---|---|---|
| Whole soybean | 38 | 4.4 | 11.6 |
| Protein concentrate [2] | 44 | 3.9 | 8.9 |
| Protein concentrate | 50 | 4.2–5.7 | 8.3–11.4 |
| Protein concentrate | 70 | 19–25 | 27-35 |
| Isolated protein, industrial | 98 | 21 | 21.5 |
| Isolated protein, edible | 96.5 | 35–38 | 36.3–39.3 |

[1] Prices quoted in February, 1963, U. S. A. In this calculation no credit is given to the other constituents of the soybean or the protein concentrates. Crude oil, for example, was selling at the same time for about 9⅝ cents per pound.

[2] In some usage, products containing up to 50% protein are called "meals" or "flours," those with 70% protein are named "concentrates," and those above 95% protein are designated "isolates." In this table, all products in which the protein content is increased, short of isolates, are designated as concentrates.

might go into sophisticated foods, were they not so expensive. This added cost comes about for a number of reasons: the additional operations, cost of plants, solvent recovery and losses, and cost of adding and removing water. Part of this cost could be reduced if there were no intermediate step of producing the dry protein isolate; if, instead, it was directly incorporated into a food product.

Another reason for the higher cost lies in the loss of economic value of the materials which are removed in the process of concentrating and isolating the protein. These are carbohydrates, fibrous material, nonprotein nitrogen, and some acid-soluble protein which at present are wastes or have low-cost outlets, much lower than their value in the original 50 percent concentrate. This loss must be overcome by higher prices for the isolated or concentrated product. There are problems in nutrition as well. Any manipulations required to produce a protein isolate (schemes A or B, Fig. 19-1) will also fractionate the soybean proteins. Although 50 to 75 percent of the total protein is recovered as the isolate, this has a nutritional value lower than the original concentrate (Hackler et al.). These differences are, of course, not serious and can be remedied by supplementation or proper mixing of proteins. Such considerations do not hold for concentration by removing soluble carbohydrates (scheme C, Fig. 19-1). There is no evidence of substantial fractionation of the proteins or of change in nutritive value.

Cost and nutritional quality are the two principal factors which stand in the way of utilizing the intrinsic value of the soybean proteins for more widespread and sophisticated utilization; but these, obviously, need not be permanent obstacles. As more information develops on the constituents of the seed, it should be possible to find more economic outlets for all of the fractions. And it might be possible to modify the isolation scheme and mix various original constituents in new proportions so that the new isolate will actually have a higher nutritional value than the original soybean, rather than a lower value as now prevails. The limiting factor finally is technology—the ability to produce products economically and the know-how to achieve versatile and complex new food products.

## Cottonseed

Even if all the soybeans were made available for human consumption, this would not exhaust the need for still more protein from other vegetable sources. There are land areas where soybeans thus far have not been grown and where other sources of vegetable protein concentrates might merit serious consideration. Cottonseed is second to soybean in total amount produced annually. Moreover, it is grown in tropical regions and therefore is available in Africa, Central and South America, as well as the United States and India and other parts of Asia. Cottonseed does not have the history and tradition of being a food protein as does the soybean. Cottonseed truly at one time was considered an inedible material, the residue after oil extraction being spread as fertilizer; this is still done in many parts of the world. In the United States for many years it was a food supplement for cattle, but was not considered at all as a supplement for monogastric animals such as poultry and swine. The primary deterrent was gossypol, a pigment, whose presence in the lipid-free protein concentrate interfered with the growth of monogastric animals. After intensive research to determine the conditions of processing and the chemical properties of protein concentrates suitable and safe for monogastric animals, it was found that screw pressing and a combination of screw pressing and solvent extraction produced protein concentrates with reduced gossypol content, yet maintained protein value. Here again a compromise was made: the detoxification of gossypol was at the expense of binding lysine and other amino acids.

Examination of the amino acid composition of cottonseed protein would suggest that it has ample lysine and that other amino acids, principally the sulfur amino acids, would be limiting. But the maximum lysine content is rarely attained in present practice; in the cottonseed, lysine is particularly sensitive to heat destruction during processing, or to being rendered unavailable to digestion even if it is not destroyed. Thus lysine becomes, in fact, the limiting amino acid in cottonseed-cereal mixtures; measurements of available lysine correlate well with the nutritive value of cottonseed protein concentrates. Preservation of the existing lysine content by careful control over processing becomes one of the means of improving the nutritive potential of cottonseed protein.

Today several hundred thousand tons of cottonseed protein concentrates are fed annually to poultry—a development not considered possible nor dreamed about fifteen years ago.

For several decades cottonseed protein concentrate in small quantities was manufactured in the United States for human consumption, particularly as a bakery additive. When it was demonstrated that this concentrate could be utilized safely and efficiently for monogastric animals, the question arose whether it could be utilized in the same manner as a major source of protein for humans, particularly for children suffering from protein deficiency. Among those who investigated this matter were Dr. Nevin S. Scrimshaw and his associates at the Institute of Nutrition for Central America and Panama (INCAP). One of the mixtures which they developed and fed to children contained 38 percent cottonseed protein concentrate (made by screw pressing), containing over 50 percent protein, and the remainder corn flour with the addition of small amounts of vitamins and trace materials. This mixture was entirely suitable; when fed in a gruel to children, it cured them of protein deficiency disease. A remarkable before-and-after picture demonstrating this accomplishment is in Fig. 19-3, which shows the same child upon admission to the hospital and 8 weeks later after having been fed a corn-cottonseed protein concentrate diet. The overwhelming evidence is that cottonseed protein concentrates produced under carefully controlled conditions can be fed safely in mixtures with cereals to children.

Of course, it would be better were there no concessions in the processing of cottonseed, if it were possible to remove completely all interfering materials without compromising amino acid availability. There are two general approaches which may eventually solve this problem. Wild cottons have been found without pigment glands, the repository of gossypol; this character is being bred into commercial cottons. It may turn out that all cottons can be bred without pigment gland character and, therefore, to be completely free of gossypol. This development has advantages beyond the protein concentrate question since it also improves the color of the oil and enhances its quality. There are many who feel enthusiastic about the possibilities of this development. Since cottonseed contributes only about 15 percent to the economic value of the cotton crop, every step in the breeding process must be checked for its

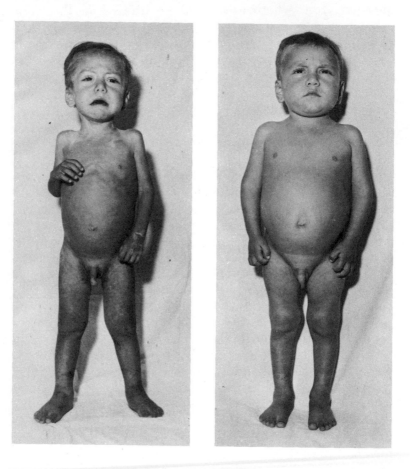

FIG. 19-3. Cure of protein deficiency with all-vegetable mixture. The child on the left is shown as he was admitted to the hospital suffering from kwashiorkor; the same child eight weeks later is shown at the right. He was fed Incaparina, a protein mixture containing 29 percent corn flour, 29 percent sorghum, 38 percent cottonseed protein concentrate, 3 percent torula yeast, calcium carbonate, and 4,500 units of vitamin A.

*Photographs courtesy of Instituto de Nutricion de Centro America y Panama, Guatemala, C.A.

effect on yield and quality of cotton lint, the major economic product of the cotton plant.

The other approach is by extraction with solvents which will remove the gossypol and other interfering materials without damaging the amino acid availability. Some processes under investigation seem to hold promise of accomplishing this. The great difficulty is that gossypol must be removed from the protein concentrate without reducing or impairing the yield or quality of the oil, which provides more income than the protein. But economics have changed; protein in cottonseed is now almost as valuable as the oil. The time may come when it will be profitable to process cottonseed directly as protein for humans, with oil a secondary consideration.

There are now ways of producing cottonseed protein concentrates suitable for human consumption. The prospects of improving these concentrates are good, and the chances that it can be done economically, equally as good. Therefore, once the gossypol question is solved, chances are that the product will not require further elaborate treatment for any other reasons.

There are many areas in the world and there are many types of foods where a cottonseed protein concentrate, properly made and controlled, can assist in increasing the protein content of a people's diet. It will be cheap; it will be indigenous to many of the countries which need protein. We do not know and cannot predict how far this application will extend, but would expect that it could be important and significant. But beyond that, we have the problem of status and form which would seem to be limiting for soybean and will be limiting for cottonseed as well. Here again, further information on the composition of the seed, greater skill in separating the components of the cottonseed, of concentrating the proteins, and producing therefrom other forms could make of cottonseed a major source of protein for humans.

## *Peanuts*

Peanuts, or groundnuts as they are known over most of the world, do not have the long history of known usefulness to the human race as do the other two oilseeds. They are indigenous to Brazil, were discovered there by the early explorers of America, and were spread from there to the rest of the world. Even so, in the relatively short time that they are part of the recorded civilization they have established a position as a human food. Peanuts are almost entirely a human food in the United States, either as such, or in confections, or as peanut butter; actually peanuts are hardly an oilseed in the United States since so small a proportion of the crop is processed for oil and protein concentrate. But in the rest of the world peanuts are primarily processed for their separate constituents. Peanut oil is important in the manufacture of margarine and cooking oils, and peanut protein concentrate has been fed extensively to animals. As an oilseed, peanuts have the advantage of not containing any known toxic factors. Peanuts grow in the tropics and, hence, are available in Central and South America, in Africa, and many parts of Asia where there is a protein deficiency. It is no wonder then that it is tempting to consider how far peanut protein concentrate can be incorporated directly into human foods. That peanuts themselves and peanut products have already found wide acceptance in human food is the more reason to consider such possibilities seriously.

Agencies of the United Nations have been aware of this possibility and so have scientists in countries where there coexist protein deficiency and availability of peanuts. At an International Conference held in 1960 on "Progress in Meeting Protein Needs of Infants and Preschool Children" numerous reports were given of the incorporation of peanut protein concentrates in mixtures for children. Some of the findings are summarized in Table 19-2. It was demonstrated that products containing large proportions of pea-

## TABLE 19–2

*Examples of Protein Foods Containing Peanut*
*(Groundnut) Products*

| | |
|---|---|
| Biscuit (Uganda) | Composition: 41% peanuts, 26% corn meal, 12% sucrose, 6% cottonseed oil, and 15% dried skim milk. Baked into a biscuit containing 20% protein, it can be mixed with water into a gruel or with more water into a drink. It gave the same weight gain as a milk biscuit. (R. F. A. Dean) |
| Flour (Senegal) | A mixture of 60% millet, 30% peanut flour, and 10% fish flour. Was satisfactory for infants. (Jean Senecal) |
| Flour (Congo) | Biscuits made from fish flour, millet, and peanut flour (50% protein). These were eaten as such and readily accepted by children. The biscuits have a good nutritive value and can be recommended for prevention of malnutrition in children aged 2 to 6 years. (E. M. DeMaeyer and H. L. Vanderborght) |
| Flour (India) | Composition: 25% roasted Bengal gram, 74% peanut flour (low-fat), and 1% lucerne powder or 25% roasted Bengal gram, 49% peanut flour, 25% low-fat sesame, and 1% lucerne powder. These mixtures were eaten with bread and Jaggery. Such vegetable protein diets were nearly as effective in controlling clinical manifestations of malnutrition as those based on skim milk, but were somewhat inferior to milk in serum albumin regeneration. (C. Gopalan) |
| High protein food (India) | A blend (1:1) of peanut protein isolate and skim milk powder. This has been incorporated into a high-protein food suitable for treatment of protein malnutrition. (V. Subrahmanyan et al.). |

Source: *Meeting Protein Needs of Infants and Preschool Children*, Proceedings of an International Conference Held in Washington, Aug. 21-24, 1960, Publication 843 (Washington, D. C.: National Academy of Sciences-National Research Council, 1961).

nut protein concentrate can be fed to children without ill results. In some instances all-vegetable protein mixtures containing peanut concentrate were satisfactory, but, in general, peanut protein concentrate was most advantageously employed to reduce the requirement for animal peanut protein is less rich in lysine than soybean or cotton-protein such as milk or fish flour. This comes about because seed, is deficient in methionine as is soybean, and also seems to be limiting in threonine. Supplementation of peanut protein with these three amino acids converts it into the equivalent of milk protein. The incorporation of unsupplemented peanut protein into cereal diets improves them, but more adequate protein mixtures are obtained if thereto is added animal protein such as milk or fish meal. This is not too serious a handicap since the ability to reduce the requirement for animal protein in many areas to the minimum needed to balance the proteins of peanut would increase the actual protein supply of completely adequate foods.

Although investigations on incorporation of peanut protein concentrate in human diet have barely begun, fundamental studies on the peanut protein, their isolation, composition, and physical properties are of much longer standing. The individual peanut proteins have been studied and isolated, methods are available for separating these various proteins and identifying them. Peanut protein isolates have been spun into textile fibers. Isolated peanut protein is being produced commercially either as 100 percent protein or as a mixed protein-lipid combination, and is being produced on a pilot-plant scale in several research institutions. Many of the patents mentioned earlier in the discussion on soybean also include peanuts. Indeed several of the patents cite peanut protein as their prime examples. It is possible to prepare peanut protein free of color and flavor. The scientific and practical knowledge already accumulated on peanuts makes it hopeful to think seriously of more complex products capable of assuming a more important role in a dietary. When these more complex products are formed, it should be possible, if necessary, to supplement with the missing amino acids so that all-vegetable protein products may be formulated with peanut protein without requiring any animal protein supplementation. Thus the limitation of peanut concentrate in the form of flour need not be the limitation of peanut protein.

The same economic problems which have arisen in the consideration of protein isolates from soybeans hold for protein isolates from peanuts as well. This is a deterrent to more sophisticated application of peanut products. When the cost of peanut protein can be reduced further and its quality enhanced, one might expect that peanut protein will make a significant contribution to human diet. Since it is found particularly in those areas where there now is protein deficiency, its introduction as a major human food source may come faster than some of the others.

## General Considerations

Although each of the seed protein concentrates has characteristic properties, we might summarize the status of the entire field and deal generally with the entire problem. There is no question that there is a large reservoir of raw material from which protein concentrates may be made; no doubt, the number of sources will increase. These seeds are now being regularly processed for removal of oil; with the exception of the soybean, oil is the most valuable component of the seed. Hence prevailing methods of processing have been oriented around the maximum yield and the quality of oil, with the quality of the protein a secondary consideration. In recent years with the development of enormous protein concentrate markets for more sensitive monogastric animals, more thought has been given to quality of the proteins. Empirical methods of processing have been developed for reaching a compromise between oil quality and yield, and protein quality. No doubt, there is considerable room for improvement in the nature of the compromise. More information is needed on the interfering factors, and more adequate methods of measuring amino acid availability and the residual quantities of toxic substances are needed to be able to engage in adequate quality control and to accelerate experimentation. The amino acid composition, granted that it is totally available and all toxic factors are removed, is generally not as well balanced as for animal proteins. This deficiency can be corrected first by blending with other proteins, by supplementation with other amino acids, perhaps by rearranging the various protein components within seeds to improve the aminogram, or perhaps even by modification of the proteins themselves to remove some of the nonessential amino acids to increase thereby the proportion of the essential ones.

Certainly no one can conclude that we are not in need of further research. On the contrary, we have barely emerged from the empirical periods of handling this vast vegetable protein resource. Further progress will demand a better knowledge of the seed constituents and of their protein composition and structure. The job of converting seed protein concentrates into forms useful directly for man is no more complicated, provided that adequate information is available, than other problems solved by society.

We must, therefore, conclude that insofar as vegetable protein concentrates from oilseeds are concerned, the objection to making them a more substantial part of human protein supply is often based on the lack of information about accomplishments in the fields of technology and nutrition. This situation is improving all along as scientific information on these proteins increases and the technology of converting them into more nutritious and a greater variety of forms develops.

A more optimistic view of the outlook for plant protein concentrates and isolates is provided by Anson (in Altschul, 1958) as follows:

> Given Nature's supply of cheap plant protein of high protein nutritional value, the technologist and the factory can do many of the manufacturing jobs that have been done, at high cost, only by animals. The technical possibilities of bypassing the animals have been realized so recently, however, that no one can tell to what extent and in what myriad of forms they will

be put into practice or how long it will take for the vast new industry to be established. My own opinion is that, just as the conversion of oilseeds to oilseed meals through processing created a revolution in animal feeding, so the further processing of oilseed meals into isolated protein and into complex foods containing isolated protein will create a second revolution. The million of tons of oilseeds throughout the world, the basic complex raw materials which neither man nor beast can synthesize cheaply, are readily available as the starting point for the new technology.

## SELECTED BIBLIOGRAPHY

1. GENERAL

Altschul, A. M. "Present Status of Proteins from Oilseeds," in *Progress in Meeting Protein Needs of Infants and Pre-school Children.* Publication 843. Washington, D. C.: National Academy of Sciences-National Research Council, 1961.

Altschul, A. M. (ed.). *Processed Plant Protein Foodstuffs.* New York: Academic, 1958. Note particularly the following chapters: M. L. Anson, "Potential Uses of Isolated Oilseed Protein in Foodstuffs," p. 227; I. E. Liener, "Effect of Heat on Plant Proteins," p. 79; A. K. Smith, "Vegetable Protein Isolates," p. 249.

Anson, M. L. "Oilseed Proteins in Foods," *Arch. Biochem. Biophys.,* supp. 1 (1962), p. 68.

Ascarelli, J., and B. Gestetner. "Chemical and Biological Evaluation of Some Protein Feeds for Poultry," *J. Sci. Food Agr.,* vol. 13 (1962), p. 401.

Boyne, A. W., K. J. Carpenter, and A. A. Woodham. "Progress Report on an Assessment of Laboratory Procedures Suggested as Indicators of Protein Quality in Feedingstuffs," *J. Sci. Food Agr.,* vol. 12 (1961), p. 832.

2. SOYBEANS

Circle, S. J., and D. W. Johnson. "Edible Isolated Soybean Protein," in A. M. Altschul (ed.), *Processed Plant Portein Foodstuffs,* p. 399.

Cravens, W. W., and E. Sipos. "Soybean Oil Meal," in A. M. Altschul (ed.), *Processed Plant Protein Foodstuffs.* New York: Academic, 1958, p. 353.

"Factors Affecting Growth Depression by Raw Soybeans," *Nutr. Rev.,* vol. 21 (1963), p. 19.

Hackler, L. R., D. B. Hand, K. H. Steinkraus, and J. P. Van Buren. "A Comparison of the Nutritional Value of Protein from Several Soybean Fractions," *J. Nutr.,* vol. 80 (1963), p. 205.

Payne, D. S., and L. S. Stuart. "Soybean Protein in Human Nutrition," in M. L. Anson and J. T. Edsall (eds.), *Advances in Protein Chemistry.* Vol. 1. New York: Academic, 1944, p. 187.

Rackis, J. J., R. L. Anderson, H. A. Sasame, A. K. Smith, and C. H. Van Etten. "Amino Acids in Soybean Hulls and Oil Meal Fractions," *J. Agr. Food Chem.*, vol. 9 (1961), p. 409.

*Soybean Products for Protein in Human Foods,* Proceedings of Conference held in Peoria, Illinois, Sept. 13-15, 1961. Peoria, Ill.: U. S. Department of Agriculture, Agricultural Research Service, 1961.

Smith, A. K. "Theories on Improving the Nutritive Value of Soybean Meal," in *Soybean Products for Protein in Human Foods.*

## 3. COTTONSEED

Altschul, A. M., C. M. Lyman, and F. H. Thurber. "Cottonseed Meal," in A. M. Altschul (ed.)., *Processed Plant Protein Foodstuffs,* p. 469.

Bressani, R., L. G. Elías, A. Aguirre, and N. S. Scrimshaw. "All-Vegetable Protein Mixtures for Human Feeding. III. The Development of INCAP Vegetable Mixture Nine," *J. Nutr.,* vol. 74 (1961), p. 201.

Bressani, R., and N. S. Scrimshaw, "The Use of Cottonseed Flour in Vegetable-Protein Mixtures for Human Feeding," in *Proceedings of a Conference on Cottonseed Protein for Animal and Man,* Nov. 14-16, 1960. New Orleans, La.: U. S. Dept. of Agriculture, 1961, p. 6.

Mann, G. E., F. L. Carter, V. L. Frampton, A. B. Watts, and C. Johnson. "Evaluation of Cottonseed Meals Prepared by Extraction with Acetone-Hexane-Water Mixtures," *J. Amer. Oil Chem. Soc.,* vol. 39 (1962), p. 86.

Rubins, R. K., K. L. Baringer, and D. B. Skau. *Improved Cottonseed Meals for Feeding Poultry and Swine, 1944-1955, An Annotated Bibliography.* ARS 72-10. New Orleans, La.: U. S. Department of Agriculture, 1957.

Scrimshaw, N. S., et al. "The Development of INCAP Vegetable Mixtures," in *Progress in Meeting Protein Needs of Infants and Preschool Children,* p. 35.

Swan, T. H., and A. M. Altschul (eds.). *Proceedings of a Conference on Cottonseed Protein for Animal and Man.* New Orleans, La.: U. S. Dept. of Agriculture, 1961.

## 4. PEANUTS

Arthur, J. C., Jr. "Peanut Protein: Isolation, Composition, and Properties," *Advan. Protein Chem.,* vol. 8 (1953), p. 393.

McOsker, D. E. "The Limiting Amino Acid Sequence in Raw and Roasted Peanuts," *J. Nutr.,* vol. 76 (1962), p. 453.

Milner, M. "Peanuts as a Protein Resource in International Feeding Programs," *Food Tech.,* vol. 16, no. 7 (1962), p. 46.

Rosen, G. D. "Groundnuts (peanuts) and Groundnut Meal," in A. M. Altschul (ed.), *Processed Plant Protein Foodstuffs,* p. 419.

# CHAPTER 20

# A Matter of
# Sophistication

## Simple versus Complex Solutions

There are many who contend that the only effective solutions to problems of malnutrition are simple ones, solutions which may easily be adopted by the average community and average housewife. Traditional foods would be fortified with better sources of protein, preferably local sources. Primitive methods of upgrading proteins by fermentation or simple processing would be improved and extended, but left at the point where they can be applied at the village and home level. There is considerable merit to this approach because it is the only one that has the possibility of immediate success and application; so many deficiencies in people's diets are not deficiencies through lack, but from ignorance in utilizing indigenous foods. Such an approach also avoids conflict with local cultural and social practices, not only those which dominate food patterns, but economic patterns and the social organization. While this approach would not increase materially the types of foods, neither would it complicate procedures for their handling, packaging, or distribution.

Indeed it is even possible that certain societies would succumb to the imbalance in food supply caused by improved medical practice, lower death rate, and higher birth rate, rather than change their mode of living. And there is reluctance by others to force a change in the lives of the people as the price for improving their food supply. Hence simple solutions have the advantage of buying time until better solutions can be developed, or at least of delaying failure.

But the simple approach is at best only a temporary expedient and does not succeed in coming to grips with the basic problem: that of developing a system of organization and a technology which will allow maximum production of food at the lowest cost, be it cost in land or water, or energy, or manpower, or other resources. Insistence on simplicity lays upon the housewife and other members of the household the burden of increasingly complex requirements in food processing. It involves training of large numbers of people and does not allow for obvious benefits from advances in food processing. It assumes a static situation, a withdrawal from general progress, even as sons of these same people are going to technical schools and colleges. As has been true for every facet of civilization, progress comes through sophistication in effort, organization, and technology. This requires training, organized operations on a level higher than the family or even the village, capital expenditures for plants and equipment, and other concomitant social and economic changes. No other field of endeavor has succeeded with simple solutions. Many who would advocate simple solutions in solving food problems unhesitantly accept the complex products of technology for travel or communication, or for most other aspects of living.

Introduction of complexities in a society where individual income is extremely low, where labor is plentiful, and advanced technology scarce or nonexisting involves a major revolution in the life of the people, is expensive, and certainly must take time to develop. Every aspect of the change involves radical departures from the norm. It is difficult to change social structures and economic ways. It is difficult to train people, and it is difficult to change food habits. Perhaps this latter might be considered by some as the most difficult of all.

Most sociologists are impressed with the difficulty in changing food habits even for the wealthier in any given group. Harper, who studied food consumption in a village in India, points out that knowledge of nutrition does not necessarily change eating habits, that values other than nutrition very often take precedence. He observes that the human animal is quite capable of starving or of at least remaining undernourished in the midst of adequacy; nor does he doubt that some South Indian Brahmins would prefer to starve than to eat meat. The factors which favor rejection or acceptance of a food or those which define some nutritious substances as edible while others equally nutritious are rejected, are not necessarily taste, odor, color, or texture, let alone nutrition. Other determinants such as emotion, values, prestige factors, and the relationship of food to social structure are equally or even more pressing.

In general, animals have the ability to choose a nutritionally correct diet; when presented with two alternative diets one of which is more nutritious, they choose the better one. Or when they are suffering from a particular deficiency, for example phosphorus deficiency, they seem to be able to distinguish between foods containing lesser or greater quantities of this element (Lepkovsky, Yudkin). This ability to choose a nutritionally correct diet is retained to a much greater degree in animals than in man. Thus, while in animals, and perhaps very young humans, physiological factors are decisive in control of food intake, in most humans a group of factors best defined as psychological confuse the issue and often overcome the choice based on physiological needs.

It has often been stated that adult man has no food instincts in the same sense as animals do toward specific foods. His omnivorous ways must have enabled him to adjust to the new areas and climates and have accelerated his conquering of the earth and its inhabitants. But, as pointed out by Clark, this same omnivorous ability permitted man to make serious nutritional mistakes when living in societies away from sources of food as in urban centers, aboard ships, and in prison camps. Moreover, man can involve food in so many of his superstitions and taboos. Perhaps the only food "instincts" man has are the acquired emotional compulsions to select food on the basis of family habits and upbringing, not necessarily of rational origin.

It is quite clear from the foregoing that arguments in favor of changing food habits based upon improvement in nutrition are not necessarily telling to humans and are no more likely to succeed because of a rational basis. This behavior is not confined to those who suffer from malnutrition; all of humanity exhibits this characteristic. Tastes and physiological habits are now being maintained which are still not far different from those practiced in the Stone Age. Man has not adapted in the evolutionary sense to all the demands and temptations implicit in a completely changed environment; man has not completely adapted to the civilized and industrialized life. There are some who contend that conditions such as coronary thrombosis, dental caries, obesity, and premature senility are related to nutritional habits and might possibly be prevented. But arguments about changes in food habits for purely rational reasons to prolong life and increase happiness are no more likely to succeed than the simpler argument of eliminating malnutrition.

This does not mean that food habits are static or immutable. There have been changes in food habits over the centuries and some of them have been to the credit side. Wheat, which was introduced in some oriental countries when rice was rationed in wartime has remained a component of diets of those who can afford it. Many foodstuffs such as corn, potatoes, and peanuts which originally were limited to one part of the world have spread to other areas once they were discovered. In Western societies there has been a revolution in the development of convenience foods which now occupy a substantial proportion of all processed foods. The point that must be clearly understood, however, is that food habits do not necessarily change for rational reasons. For each society in each period, the profitable arguments will depend on what is considered important. Probably one of the more effective ways of making a change in food habits is through example of practice by the upper classes. Indeed it has been said that cooks hired by the wealthier classes were among the most effective agents for changing food habits and for introducing new customs.

At this stage of the argument, one can easily find himself lecturing from a pinnacle. It is difficult to avoid a superior feeling about one's diet if it is more adequate nutritionally. Sympathy for the undernourished is not unmixed with condescension, and patience in dealing with changes is that of a patron. It is hard to approach another's culture without a bias for one's own. Yet this ethnocentricity makes it almost impossible to help others adjust their food habits (Cassel). The following quotation from Lee illustrates how deep is the involvement of culture even in the way food is presented.

From the very first, for the human being ingestion is culturally structured. Is the infant put to the breast, or given the bottle? Will his first suckling be that of colostrum, or of milk, or of some other fluid? Will he be held in a fetal position as he suckles, cradled in naked contact with a mother who curves herself around him, experiencing simultaneously comfort, social warmth, solace, emotional communication and nutrition? Or will he experience his first feeding held in meticulous sanitation against the starched bosom of someone to whom he is merely a case with a name, of someone who regards this situation as one of sheer nutrition? . . . The first experience with solid food will differ according to culture. If he is a Tikopia (Polynesia) he will get premasticated food, warmed with the mother's body-warmth, partly digested through her salivary juices; his mother will put it directly to his mouth with her lips. In our society he will get food with a hard metal spoon, introduced into a mouth which has never experienced anything so solid or hard, into which not even teeth have yet erupted.

Obviously this is not a problem solely of improving nutrition; it involves the question of whether a particular culture can be reshaped to allow for better food supply with the least possible disruption of other values, perhaps considered more important than nutrition. It requires substitution of empathy for people for sympathy for the underprivileged. It requires of the would-be advisors that they achieve a Schweizerian plane of understanding and feeling for other people.

Surely it would be foolhardy to consider lightly propositions to change dietary habits. Yet it would border on indolence to neglect the opportunities through modification of food patterns. It is in this spirit that we approach the matter of sophistication. Much of what has been presented in previous chapters illustrates various aspects of a sophisticated approach. We should like to consider further three areas: photosynthesis, processing, and synthesis.

## Photosynthesis

It was a great event in the evolution of biological forms when photosynthesis became a reality. Now the energy of the sun became a means for producing complex organic materials out of the simple components of the atmosphere. These became the building blocks and sources of energy for the majority of living things, which were heterotrophs. Plants, the photoautotrophs, provided food supply; no longer was it necessary to depend upon abiogenically synthesized "nutrient broths."

For millions of years before man, and even for the majority of the time that man was on the earth, the various forms of life developed without his intervention. Then there was a second great revolution involving photosynthesis: that was man's recognition that he could plan his food production by agriculture. Ames attributes the beginning of the Neolithic revolution to man's discovery of the economic significance of the angiosperm seed. Instead of foraging and consuming the food as he found it, he could lay some seeds aside and ensure larger and ever-increasing stores for the future. Then it was possible for population centers to develop. It is estimated that during the food gathering stage, the population of settlements ranged from 25 to 100. But the population of Jericho in the sixth millenium was close to a thousand; Ur in Iraq in the second millenium had perhaps 25,000 people; and Nineveh, made famous by Jonah, had a population that was perhaps measured in the hundred thousands (Pettersson). Hence, in about eight thousand years, human life and custom became complex as a consequence of agriculture.

With the advent of agriculture came selection and unconscious improvement of the economic plants. There was preservation of the favorite types; many of such species were actually converted into a dependency for survival on the human race. As stated by Helbaek, "From the archaeologically derived evidence itself, it is clear that any domesticated plant is an artifact, a product of human manipulation. Hence, rather than corresponding particularly to clear-cut genetic principles, the history of domesticated plants seems to show various of the perversities of the manipulator, man himself."

The history of photosynthesis, therefore, is one of evolutionary developments of biological forms and of genera and species of plants upon which were superimposed in the last eight thousand years manipulations of man himself.

The opportunities for manipulation have not ended. Bonner speculates on the possibilities for increasing crop yield through fundamental changes in the photosynthetic mechanisms. Efficiencies of 2 to 2½ percent conversion of the incident light energy into crops have been achieved in some countries such as Japan and Denmark. But generally, the photosynthetic efficiency is lower than 2 to 2½ percent because of deficiencies in mineral nutrition, or in water, because of pests, or because of unsuitable temperatures. With the present plants, the upper limit of crop yield corresponds to a conservation in plant material of 2 to 5 percent of the energy of the incident light. The question is whether it is possible to continue to manipulate plants so as to increase their efficiency, for example, by increasing conductivity of carbon dioxide in leaves or by modifying the properties of the fundamental unit of photosynthesis, the chloroplast, so that, as Bonner puts it, its efficiency would modulate depending on the light intensity.

But low yield in photosynthesis is not always the limiting factor; the yield in fact is much lower because so many products of photosynthesis are not utilized directly for human foods.

Consider green leaves. A number are eaten as human foods, but not particularly as a source of protein. Some leaves from young foliage contain up to 5 percent nitrogen in the dry matter. Not all of this is protein, but concentrates containing from 40 to 60 percent protein may be produced from fresh leaves by maceration, expression of the juice, and coagulation of the protein (Byers, Morrison, and Pirie). When dried at low temperatures, products made from mixed grasses, kale, barley and rye leaves, and tares were equivalent to soybean protein concentrate for growing chicks and rats (Duckworth and Woodham) and to fish protein for the nutrition of pigs. Leaf proteins contain 5 to 7 percent lysine, 1.3 to 2.7 percent methionine, and 1 to 2 percent tryptophan; it should be expected that leaf protein concentrates would be excellent sources of protein. The failure to realize this potential in many of the preparations may be attributed to an unusually low digestibility of the proteins owing to improper processing or to inadequate removal of inhibitors in the raw material.

Other problems remain to be solved, once the conditions of proper processing to preserve nutritive value are established. A nutritious product must be converted into a material that humans will be willing to put in their food. And all this must be done at minimum cost so that the intrinsic low cost compared to animal protein is realized.

More advantage must be taken of photosynthesis in the sea. It has been estimated that 12 billion tons of organic matter are produced annually in all the seas (Nielsen). Only a small fraction is in locations permitting man's harvest; most of the organic matter is best collected by fish. But most commercial fish are carnivorous and feed on other carnivores. Fish have about the same efficiency of conversion of plant to animal protein as do land animals; the long chain of intermediates between plankton and commercial fish reduces the ultimate efficiency of conversion to about 1 percent. It may be possible in some instances to encourage herbivorous marine forms as, for example, some types of salmon; certainly carp and other herbivorous fish could be emphasized in fish ponds (Pirie, 1962; Dean).

It is known that a high photosynthetic yield may be achieved by growing simple plants such as algae in ponds or in illuminated vessels. Some of these, such as *Chlorella*, can contain as high as 58 percent protein and significant quantities of vitamins as well (Black). These can, of course, be grown either on synthetic or prepared nutrient media. They can also be incorporated into coordinated systems for waste purification, which would bring about concomitantly nutrient recovery and food production. There exist, on an experimental basis, systems combining algae and bacteria in shallow ponds exposed to sunlight which are efficient both in disposing of sewage and in producing protein at a rate of up to 10 to 100 times greater than accomplished by conventional agriculture in an area of the same size. There are many problems to be solved. Although algae are rich in nutrients, their proteins do not have the amino acids in the proper proportion and are not directly suitable for incorporation into human foods in large concentrations. There is, of course, the question of remaining pathogens and also the question of aesthetics. The pressure is to continue this kind of effort because of the need for more efficient sewage disposal and because of the increasing cost of water. There is the added interest in this type of approach because a similar system of combinations of algae and bacteria can create in space vehicles a biosphere which will be self-balancing and self-generating in terms of waste elimination and regeneration of oxygen. Here, again, the ability to convert the algae into food would be a big factor in determining the extent and length of time of space exploration (Casey and Lubitz).

The great reserves of petroleum, themselves ancient products of photosynthesis, may contribute additional protein supply. Microorganisms will grow on petroleum; concentrates containing 44 percent protein have been produced in this manner; these also contain vitamins, and the petroleum is dewaxed in the process (Champagnat et al.).

In recent years it has been possible to propagate plant tissue from single cells. Carrot tissue and grape stems, among others, have been grown in good yield on simple nutrient media containing carbohydrate and a source of nitrogen. Some of the products contain up to 30 percent protein. In this instance photosynthesis is utilized for the production of carbohydrate materials, always easier to produce in larger yield, and the protein material is then biosynthesized from carbohydrates and simple nitrogenous compounds.

Actually, although the new possibilities are attractive, we must not neglect the fact that many of our old friends still present untold opportunities. An increase in a few percent in the protein content of rice would revolutionize the protein position in many parts of the world. As we pointed out in the preceding chapter, removal of gossypol in cottonseed by breeding would change completely the human feeding complexion of this major source of protein. It is not known whether the many inhibitors and nonprotein amino acids in leguminous seeds are immutable to modification by breeding. Nor is it known whether ricin is an intrinsic part of the castor bean. Although in his history man has looked at at least 3,000 species of plants for food and has cultivated at least 150 of these, the tendency has been to concentrate on the more efficient ones so that today the majority of the world's people are actually fed from 12 to 15 species of plants. One wonders what uncovered possibilities lie in some of the other plants which have had at one time or another merely a cursory evaluation (Mangelsdorf).

## Processing

Sophisticated processing differs from ordinary processing in the degree of empiricism, in its tools, and in its objectives. Empirical methods may have been adequate when there was more food or when we did not know any better. Modern processing requires maximum information on the structure, composition, and chemical properties of the raw material and the products. A wealth of information is already available but most often this was not amassed from the point of view of food science, rather because the food source served as a model for biochemical research. When one is studying, for example, muscle chemistry for the purpose of understanding the mechanism of muscle action, he is also providing information of value to meat processors. When the chloroplasts of spinach are studied, information is also supplied on the composition and characteristics of the spinach leaf. And when genotype and phenotype are traced in corn seed, more becomes known about that seed, in general.

There is a problem of communication. The food scientist must range far and wide in his interests and cross disciplines to gather information. It could easily be that some particular medical-oriented research might provide information of immense value to food science. The more advanced departments and institutes of food science reflect this broad view, and here and there are noticed similar tendencies in some food processing institutions.

Unfortunately many of the economic sources of food have not been investigated as extensively as other living matter, only for the reason that other biological models were more convenient or suitable for solving the problems of the individual investigator, or perhaps only because of caprice. As biochemistry continues to broaden and the need develops for greater diversity of subject matter for investigation, more information will become available on economic seeds, including the cereals and some of the oilseeds. This might be one of the great contributions of agriculture-oriented research: to accelerate the introduction of economic plants as models for biochemical studies.

Take, for example, the wealth of new information on subcellular organization. Constituents of cells occur in discrete packages. This is true for the nuclei and the "biological machinery" such as mitochondria, chloroplasts, and ribosomes. But it is also true of reserves: the large carbohydrate reserves are in starch grains, protein exists as internal secretions in subcellular bodies, and, in some instances, has been found together with lipid and phosphorous (phytic acid). With the exception of starch grains most of these bodies are fragile and not easily isolated after cell rupture. But protein bodies and protein-lipid and protein-phytic acid "packages" have been isolated. Food ingredients, therefore, are already packaged in the cells of the food sources. Ordinarily in processing the cells are ground, their structure is destroyed, and all components are mixed and interacted to be separated later, as needed, in refining operations. Unquestionably many desirable ends are served by this intermixing: new flavors and colors are produced, pleasing textures are developed, and some ingredients are improved by the action of one component on the other as in the aging of meat. But there are instances where the opposite holds, where the avoidance of mixing could prevent undesirable side reactions, and where refining could be made simpler by eliminating mixing in the first place. One might, in a crude way, compare the processing of seeds, where the entire kernel is ground and then the components —oil, protein, and carbohydrate—are separated to a similar approach to animal processing. No one would consider grinding the entire carcass followed by separation of components as a satisfactory substitute for the present method of dissection. It may some day be practical to practice dissection of food materials on a subcellular level; indeed, air-classification of flours is a step in that direction.

Knowledge of subcellular organization could aid materially in the study of minor components, beneficial or harmful. On a tissue basis these are minor components, but there may exist subcellular locations where they are major components. Then it would become easier to isolate them and study their structure and properties. Although pigment glands of cottonseed can hardly be considered subcellular organelles, their recognition as the locus of gossypol and their isolation provided the basis for the study of gossypol. Gossypol is a minor component of cottonseed but is 50 percent of the weight of pigment glands.

And there is the challenge to create new forms of proteins which will be interesting and to improve the quality of some naturally occurring proteins. In the preceding chapter, we have discussed the question of form. Let us discuss here the question of upgrading protein quality. The animal does it: it ingests low-quality proteins or even simple sources of nitrogen and converts them into its own protein of higher grade. In so doing there is a selective utilization of the amino acids of the ingested proteins. Those amino acids which are excessive to the requirements for protein synthesis are metabolized so that the final aminogram of the animal protein contains a different pattern of amino acids from the food. This pattern is better for fulfilling the nutritional need of humans. The question therefore arises whether the same sort of sorting of amino acids can be done chemically, selectively enough to convert any given pattern of amino acids into a more suitable pattern with the least waste and cost in amino acids. This can be done by adding missing amino acids or by removing excessive amino acids. Such activities require more information on the nature of the major proteins of foodstuffs, particularly of seeds, than is now available.

There are many new products of science which may prove advantageous in food processing. Availability of high-energy rays suggest radiation of foods as a means for destroying toxins, microorganisms, and of generally preserving without destroying essential food ingredients. On the basis of many experiments, it would seem possible to treat foodstuffs in this manner advantageously without any harm to persons who eat these foods. Indeed selected food items have already been cleared for such processing.

Of utmost importance in sophisticated food processing is to be able to measure the quality of the final product, to determine the degree of improvement or the degree of destruction in quality. Nothing would endanger more the introduction of a new foodstuff than the accident of presenting poorly processed, improperly processed, or not completely detoxified products to the public. The experience of one generation would require many more generations to be forgotten. It has always been a wonder why the soybean, for example, is more widespread in some countries than others in the same part of the world. One possible explanation might be that somewhere in antiquity there might have been a bad experience with the soybean resulting from improper usage, and this experience might have prevented further experimentation to provide usable forms.

We have mentioned earlier the excellent new techniques

for identifying chemical compounds by the various forms of chromatography and by the newer forms of physical analysis, such as nuclear magnetic resonance or activation analysis. This makes it possible to identify a minor constituent, to assess its role in the quality of the product, and perhaps to develop synthetic replacements or additives. And certainly it makes possible more careful control of ingredients in a food-processing operation.

Sometimes the harmful ingredients are of exogenous origin. Improper storage and handling of the raw materials may permit microbial proliferation which produces heat-stable toxins. Ergot is a classical example of a problem developed in the field. Toxins have been found on occasion in samples of rice, corn, and peanuts; and, no doubt, have appeared in many other products but may not have been recognized. As we increase the nutritional stresses by feeding rapidly-growing animals such as turkey poults, ducklings, or trout, more evidence for existence of such toxins will be uncovered. And as we demand more of our foodstuffs particularly freedom from components which could be suspected as promoters of human diseases such as cancer and atherosclerosis, there will be more critical scrutiny of suspected biologically-active ingredients, either endogenous or of exogenous origin.

The ultimate procedures for eliminating foreign toxins is to recognize the optimum conditions for production of these toxins and so to handle the raw materials from the very beginning that the opportunity for microbial growth of the type needed to produce toxins will not develop. But in addition, there must be simple methods of screening which will allow for regular checks of the products.

Sophisticated food processing also becomes an alternative and competitor to selective breeding. Sometimes it may be advantageous to accomplish the improvement by genetic evolution. But often it may be more rapid to accomplish the same end by a new processing step. This is the situation in cottonseed, where selective breeding and improved processing are vying to be first to arrive with improved sources of protein for man and animals. Perhaps the two approaches may even be combined to produce a superior protein concentrate.

## Synthesis

From time to time there have been spurts of interest in synthetic foods, particularly during periods of wartime shortages. There have been some successes in synthesizing fats from petroleum and in breaking down cellulose and nonedible carbohydrates into edible forms. This need not be done entirely by chemical means; it can equally well be done wholly or in part by microbiological or biological means using raw materials which have been modified chemically. It is natural when faced with shortages of nutrients from agricultural production to consider the possibilities of synthesis. McPherson points out that the history of civilization contains example after example of chemical synthesis of natural materials. Among the best are the synthesis of textiles and rubbers; dyes and other complicated chemicals have been synthesized and produced more cheaply than the natural product. Why then cannot foodstuffs be synthesized as well?

It is natural that most people who concern themselves with the problems of foods prefer to rely on the traditional methods based on photosynthesis and modification of the photosynthetic product. They contend that until we have exhausted every possibility for fullest use of these products, there is no need to consider synthesis. Moreover, this is by far a more expensive operation than a system which derives its energy from the sun. The record, however, indicates that synthetic products have already become an established part of the human dietary; there is no reason why they cannot make a more substantial contribution. McPherson points out that, in 1953, production in the United States of vitamins amounted to 2.1 million kilograms at an average price of $36.80 per kilogram, while five years later the production was 4.4 million kilograms at a price of only $17.83 per kilogram. Hence, production doubled while the price per unit quantity was cut in half. Synthetic vitamins are already an established article of the human dietary. Their micro requirements make it possible to incorporate them into diets even though they are individually expensive. Fox calculates that the cost per person per year of the common vitamins is 55 cents. (This does not include the costs of packaging, transport, and other operations leading to the retail level.)

No protein has as yet been synthesized, but amino acids have been. Although there are synthetic routes for production of most amino acids, there are critical shortages and hence a need for only a few of them. Lysine is the critical amino acid in cereal grains and methionine is the one in short supply in legumes. Tryptophan may be considered a third amino acid, often limiting. DL-Methionine or its hydroxy analogue, which seems to serve equally as well, is being incorporated regularly into diets for animals and could well be an ingredient of the human dietary. L-Lysine made either by chemical synthesis or by fermentation has been incorporated experimentally into human diets with good results. It is all a matter of cost. L-Lysine was selling for about $10 a pound at the end of 1960 and for about $7 per pound in 1961; there are predictions that the cost could be below $1–2 per pound in mass production. Methionine is already close to $1 per pound and could go down in price; L-tryptophan is still much more expensive. We have previously pointed out the dangers of indiscriminate supplementation with amino acids. But certainly this synthetic pathway for improving the quality of proteins which increases in effect their quantity will not be neglected in the overall pattern of increasing protein supplies.

There may be some nutritional advantage to supplementing with amino acids in peptide chains, as in proteins, rather than with the free acids. The caloric requirements with proteins were shown by Rose to be less than for the corresponding free amino acids. And it may be possible by providing amino acids in a peptide chain to overcome the danger and fear of excessive supplementation with certain amino acids. Polyamino acids of precise composition have been synthesized by Katchalski and his associates; these would probably be too expensive for food utilization. Fox has produced polyamino acids by simultaneous thermal polymerization of many amino acids and considers this potentially an economic process.

We have concentrated on the essential amino acids, assuming that there will always be a plenty of the so-called nonessential ones. It has been found that urea, which can be made entirely synthetically, and some of the simple amino acids such as glycine can serve as partial sources of nonessential amino acids for humans. There are diet situations where these are limiting. We thus have synthetic pathways both to the critical essential amino acids and to general resources of nitrogen to replace nonessential amino acids.

Oparin divided the history of our planet in terms of living things into two epochs. The first which occupied approximately two to three billion years was one in which the atmosphere of the earth was in a chemically reduced state. Under these conditions there occurred on the surface the abiogenic formation of first simple and then complicated organic compounds. It was a slow process, and inefficient. Then there arose the new and far more efficient method of synthesis of organic materials, photosynthesis, which has only been in existence for 700 to 800 million years.

It is Oparin's belief that the current developments of science justify the contention that we may be on the threshold of a third epoch: the controlled application of nuclear energy to synthesize organic substances directly from carbon dioxide at any place or time, independent of season, weather, or area of the earth's surface. To quote

Oparin, "Certainly this is only a dream, but it is already a dream with a scientific foundation and it shows what tremendous vistas of a cosmic nature are opening out before mankind as a result of a wise and progressive use of the achievements of science."

## General Sophistication

Our discussion of sophistication was confined to matters relating to food supply and, particularly, to protein supply. This, of course, is but one aspect of the total problem—the one we have chosen to deal with. But we cannot put on the agriculturalist and food scientist the burden of feeding a world in which there is unrestrained population increase. It would be a cruel hoax indeed to advance in techniques of food production and to gain the competency of finally abolishing hunger only to be frustrated by an even more rapidly increasing population. And the social climate will have to be conducive to most efficient production and distribution of food supplies so that hand-in-hand with improvements in technology, society will also manage to maneuver itself into a position to take the most advantage of these developments.

## Conclusion

We have endeavored to place protein procurement in the stream of cultural evolution alongside developments in power, medicine, transportation, housing, textiles, communication, and other products of modern science and technology. We have shown in one section that the understanding of proteins themselves has flowered and kept pace with other developments. Actually the advances in protein chemistry have been the cornerstone for much of progress in modern biochemistry. Protein nutrition was shown to have risen from a concept of some needed material containing nitrogen to an apprecitaion of essential and nonessential amino acids, finally to a science which puts in quantitative terms the requirements for protein components of different types of animals and of humans at various stages of development. It now remains to be determined whether our concepts of the trends in protein supply remain reasonable extrapolations. Time will tell whether or not this is so.

## SELECTED BIBLIOGRAPHY

GENERAL

Brown, H., J. Bonner, and J. Weir. *The Next Hundred Years.* New York: Viking, 1957.
Cuthbertson, D. P. "The World Food Situation as Related to Knowledge of Science and Its Application," in *World Food Forum Proceedings,* May 15-17, 1963. Washington, D. C.: U. S. Dept. of Agriculture, 1963, p. 111.
Dorn, H. F. "World Population Growth: An International Dilemma," *Science,* vol. 135 (1962), p. 283.

FOOD HABITS

Burgess, Anne, and R. F. A. Dean (eds.). *Malnutrition and Food Habits.* New York: Macmillan, 1962.
Cassel, J. "Social and Cultural Implications of Food and Food Habits," *Am. J. Public Health,* vol. 47 (1957), p. 732.
Clark, F. Le Gros. "History of the Human Diet," in *Tradition, Science, and Practice of Dietetics.* Proceedings of the Third International Congress of Dietetics. Bradford, England: Wm. Byles and Sons, 1961, p. 13.
Harper, E. B. "Cultural Factors in Food Consumption," *Econ. Botany,* vol. 15 (1961), p. 289.
Harper, R. "Psychological Aspects of Food Acceptance with Special Reference to Feeding the Underprivileged," *Advan. Sci.,* vol. 17 (1961), p. 568.
Lee, Dorothy. "Cultural Factors in Dietary Choice," in *Symposium on Nutrition and Behavior.* Nutrition Symposium Series No. 14. New York: The National Vitamin Foundation, 1957, p. 64.
Lepkovsky, S. "The Physiological Basis of Voluntary Food Intake," *Advan. Food Res.,* vol. 1. (1948), p. 106.
"The Problem of Changing Food Habits," *Bull. Nat. Res. Council,* No. 108, Washington, D. C., October 1943.
Yudkin, J. "Man's Choice of Food," *Lancet,* No. 6924 (May 12, 1956), p. 645.

PHOTOSYNTHESIS

Ames, O. "The Significance of the Angiosperm Seed," in *Economic Annuals and Human Cultures.* Cambridge, Mass.: Botanical Museum of Harvard University, 1939; see also *Econ. Botany*, vol. 17 (1963), p. 3.

Black, W. A. P. "The Algae," in A. M. Altschul (ed.), *Processed Plant Protein Foodstuffs.* New York: Academic, 1958, p. 805.

Bonner, J. "The Upper Limits of Crop Yield," *Science*, vol. 137 (1962), p. 11.

Casey, R. P., and J. A. Lubitz. "Algae as Food for Space Travel," *Food Technol.*, vol. 17, no. 11 (1963), p. 48 (1386).

Champagnat, A., C. Vernet, B. Laine, and J. Filosa. "Biosynthesis of Protein – Vitamin Concentrates from Petroleum," *Nature*, vol. 197 (1963), p. 13.

Dean, R. F. A. "Use of Processed Plant Proteins as Human Food," in A. M. Altschul (ed.), *Processed Plant Protein Foodstuffs.* New York: Academic, 1958, p. 223.

"Evaluation of Algae as a Food for Human Diets," *Nutr. Rev.*, vol. 21 (1963), p. 7.

Helbaek, H. "Domestication of Food Plants in the Old World," *Science*, vol. 130 (1959), p. 365.

Mangelsdorf, P. C. "Biology, Food, and People," *Econ. Botany*, vol. 15 (1961), p. 279.

Nielsen, E. S. "Productivity of the Oceans," *Ann. Rev. of Plant Physiol.*, vol. 11 (1960), p. 341.

Oswald, W. J. "The Coming Industry of Controlled Photosynthesis"; B. S. Cook, "The Nutritive Value of Waste-Grown Algae"; R. C. Cooper, "Some Public Health Aspects of Algal-Bacterial Nutrient Recovery Systems," *Am. J. Public Health*, vol. 52, no. 2 (1962), p. 235.

Pettersson, M. "Increase of Settlement Size and Population since the Inception of Agriculture," *Nature*, vol. 186 (1960), p. 870.


PROCESSING

Altschul, A. M. "Seed Proteins," in H. W. Schultz and A. F. Anglemier (eds.), *Symposium on Foods: Proteins and Their Reactions.* Westport, Conn.: Avi, 1964.

Anson, M. L., and A. M. Altschul, "Introduction," in A. M. Altschul (ed.), *Processed Plant Protein Foodstuffs.* New York: Academic, 1958, p. 1.

Byers, M. "Extraction of Protein from the Leaves of Some Plants Growing in Ghana," *J. Sci. Food Agr.*, vol. 12 (1961), p. 20.

Dieckert, J. W., J. E. Snowden, Jr., A. T. Moore, D. C. Heinzelman, and A. M. Altschul, "Composition of Some Subcellular Fractions from Seeds of *Arachis hypogaea*," *J. Food Sci.*, vol. 27 (1962), p. 321.

Morrison, J. E., and N. W. Pirie. "The Large-Scale Production of Protein from Leaf Extracts," *J. Sci. Food Agr.*, vol. 12 (1961), p. 1.

"Mycotoxicoses – Food-Borne Fungal Diseases," *Nutr. Rev.*, vol. 20 (1962), p. 337.

Duckworth, J., and A. A. Woodham, "Leaf Protein Concentrates. I: Effect of Source of Raw Material and Method of Drying on Protein Value for Chicks and Rats," *J. Sci. Food Agr.*, vol. 12 (1961), p. 5.

Pirie, N. W. "Progress in Biochemical Engineering Broadens Our Choice of Crop Plants," *Econ. Botany*, vol. 15 (1961), p. 302.

Pirie, N. W. "Future Sources of Food Supply: Scientific Problems," *J. Roy. Statist. Soc.*, vol. 125, part 3, series A (1962), p. 399.

SYNTHETIC FOODS

Fox, S. W. "The Outlook for Synthetic Foods," *Food Technol.*, vol. 17, no. 4 (1963), p. 22 (388).

Howe, E. E. "Summary of Progress on the Use of Purified Amino Acids in Foods," in *Progress in Meeting Protein Needs of Infants and Preschool Children*. Publication 843. Washington, D. C.: National Academy of Sciences-National Research Council, 1961.

Jansen, G. R. "Lysine in Human Nutrition," *J. Nutr.*, suppl. 1, part II, vol. 76, no. 2 (1962).

Katchalski, E., and M. Sela. "Synthesis and Chemical Properties of Poly Amino Acids," *Advan. Protein Chem.*, vol. 13 (1958), p. 244.

McPherson, A. T. "The Synthesis of Food," *Food Technol.*, vol. 16, no. 11 (1962), p. 34.

Oparin, A. I. *The Origin of Life on the Earth*. Translated by Ann Synge. 3rd ed. New York: Academic, 1957, p. 143.

# Index